AF785012

PIPE FITTINGS

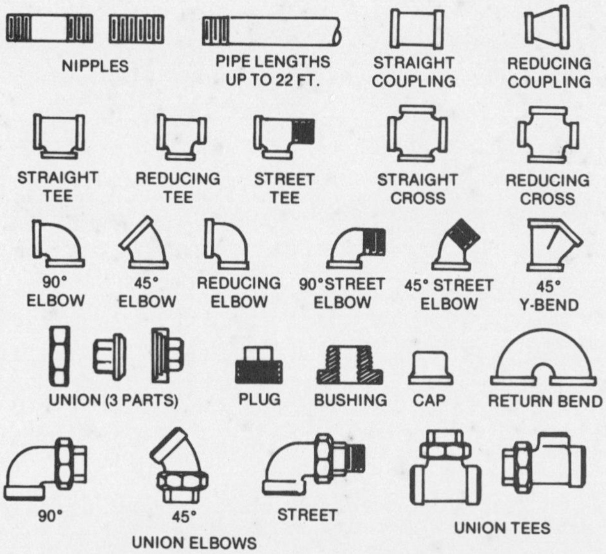

Here are the common steel pipe fittings. Nipples are simply short lengths of pipe threaded on both ends. Reducing fittings join two different sizes of pipe.

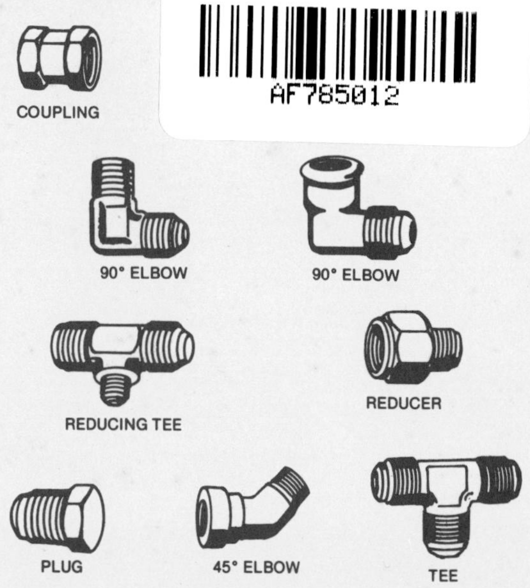

Compression fittings of the flared-tube type are the easiest for the novice to handle when working with copper tubing.

STANDARD STEEL PIPE (All Dimensions in Inches)					
Nominal Size	Outside Diameter	Inside Diameter	Nominal Size	Outside Diameter	Inside Diameter
1/8	0.405	0.269	1	1.315	1.049
1/4	0.540	0.364	1 1/4	1.660	1.380
3/8	0.675	0.493	1 1/2	1.900	1.610
1/2	0.840	0.622	2	2.375	2.067
3/4	1.050	0.824	2 1/2	2.875	2.469

SQUARE MEASURE

144 sq in = 1 sq ft
9 sq ft = 1 sq yd
272.25 sq ft = 1 sq rod
160 sq rods = 1 acre

VOLUME MEASURE

1728 cu in = 1 cu ft
27 cu ft = 1 cu yd

MEASURES OF CAPACITY

1 cup = 8 fl oz
2 cups = 1 pint
2 pints = 1 quart
4 quarts = 1 gallon
2 gallons = 1 peck
4 pecks = 1 bushel

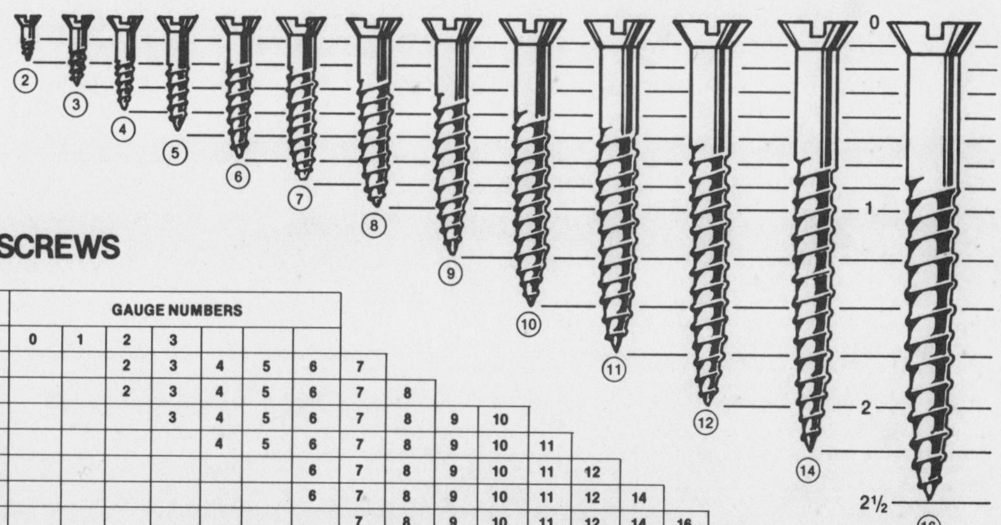

WOOD SCREWS

LENGTH	GAUGE NUMBERS																
1/4 INCH	0	1	2	3													
3/8 INCH			2	3	4	5	6	7									
1/2 INCH			2	3	4	5	6	7	8								
5/8 INCH				3	4	5	6	7	8	9	10						
3/4 INCH					4	5	6	7	8	9	10	11					
7/8 INCH							6	7	8	9	10	11	12				
1 INCH							6	7	8	9	10	11	12	14			
1 1/4 INCH								7	8	9	10	11	12	14	16		
1 1/2 INCH							6	7	8	9	10	11	12	14	16	18	
1 3/4 INCH									8	9	10	11	12	14	16	18	20
2 INCH									8	9	10	11	12	14	16	18	20
2 1/4 INCH										9	10	11	12	14	16	18	20
2 1/2 INCH													12	14	16	18	20
2 3/4 INCH														14	16	18	20
3 INCH															16	18	20
3 1/2 INCH																18	20	24
4 INCH																18	20	24

WHEN YOU BUY SCREWS, SPECIFY (1) LENGTH, (2) GAUGE NUMBER, (3) TYPE OF HEAD—FLAT, ROUND, OR OVAL, (4) MATERIAL—STEEL, BRASS, BRONZE, ETC., (5) FINISH—BRIGHT, STEEL BLUED, CADMIUM, NICKEL, OR CHROMIUM PLATED.

THOSE RICH WALLS are made of plywood paneling, one of the easiest of all building materials to use. Transform a room overnight. See page 2056.

In this volume . . .

FOR TOP PERFORMANCE from your outboard, see the really complete 21-page article which takes you step by step through outboard servicing. It starts on page 1981.

HARDBOARD wall paneling can totally transform a room within a few hours. It is easy to install against an existing wall (right) or a brand new stud wall. It presents a finished appearance the moment it is installed. The stone pattern below is by Masonite and is called "Chapel Stone." See the article on hardboard wall paneling on page 2054.

HERE'S ANOTHER EXAMPLE of a room beautifully finished with hardboard wall paneling. It's durable and has a fascinating texture. See page 2054.

YOU MAY USE the most expensive paint, but unless you also use a brush designed for the job your work will be shoddy. Find tips on selecting the right brush on page 2048.

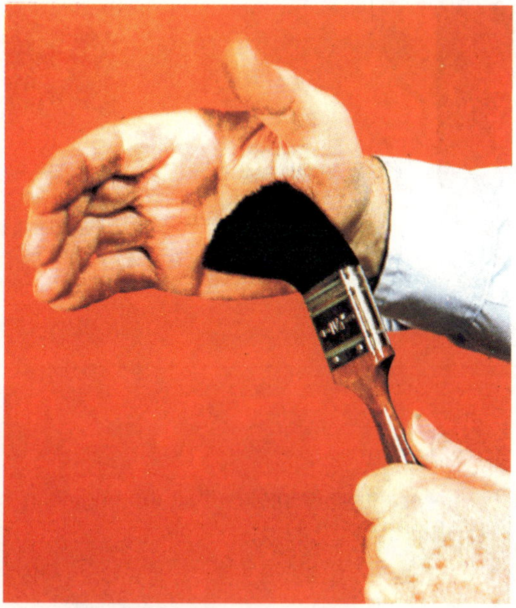

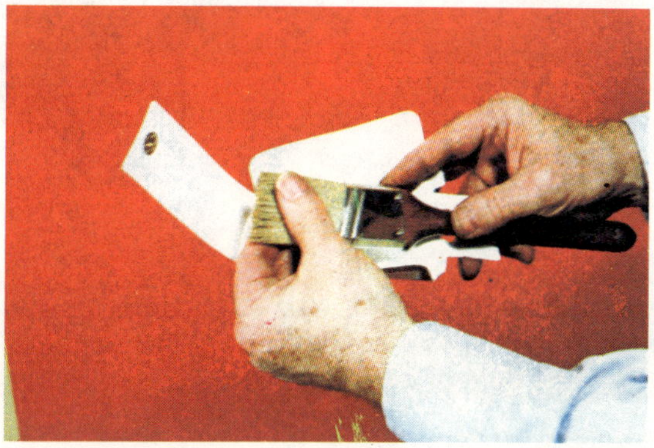

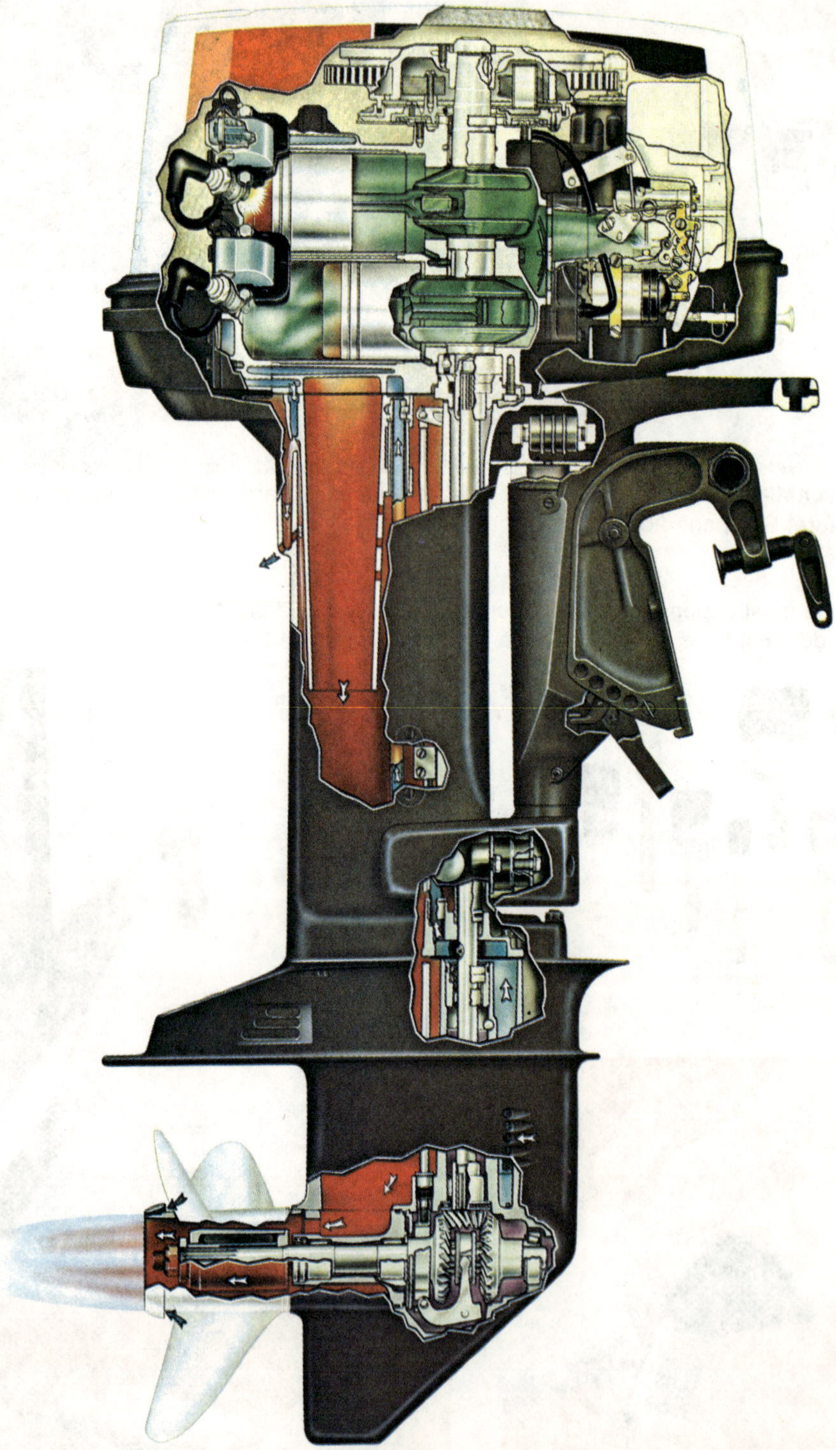

THE OUTBOARD ENGINE is an engineering triumph—in some ways more complex than the engine in your car. It requires precise servicing, too. For details, see page 1981.

Popular Mechanics

do-it-yourself encyclopedia

in 20 volumes

a complete how-to guide for the homeowner, the hobbyist—
and anyone who enjoys working with mind and hands!

All about:

home maintenance
home-improvement projects
wall paneling
burglary and fire protection
furniture projects
finishing and refinishing furniture
outdoor living
home remodeling
solutions to home problems
challenging woodworking projects
hobbies and handicrafts
model making
weekend projects
workshop shortcuts and techniques
hand-tool skills
power-tool know-how
shop-made tools
car repairs
car maintenance
appliance repair
boating
hunting
fishing
camping
photography projects
radio, TV and electronics know-how
clever hints and tips
projects just for fun

volume 13

ISBN 0-87851-078-8

Library of Congress Catalog Number 77 84920

© 1982 THE HEARST CORPORATION

All rights reserved. No part of this book may be reproduced or used in any form or by any means—graphic, electronic, or mechanical, including photocopying, recording, taping or information storage and retrieval systems—without written permission of the publishers.

The Hearst Corporation cannot assume responsibility for proper application of techniques, implementations or proper and safe functioning of any of the manufactured or reader-built items, products or projects resulting in whole or in part from all or any part of any plans, prints, projects or instructional materials published in this volume.

The Hearst Corporation cannot assume responsibility for the continuing availability of any special parts listed in articles in this volume.

MANUFACTURED IN THE UNITED STATES OF AMERICA

contents

VOLUME 13

A guide to electric motors

There are several important factors you'll want to consider when you choose a motor

WHEN YOU NEED a replacement motor for an appliance or workshop tool, ordering a new unit is easy enough—just take the necessary data from the motor's nameplate. But when you're scratch-building a worksaver like a bench saw, don't make the common mistake of selecting a motor by simply guessing.

Actually there are four factors you must consider before making a choice: horsepower rating, starting effort, shaft speed and operating voltage.

Horsepower is the primary consideration. As an indication of requirements for different jobs, the table on the opposite page lists motors of various horsepower and their typical uses. If your particular application is not listed, simply compare it to a similar job and select the next larger motor to avoid overloading.

Continual overloading of a motor above its rated power can cause it to overheat and shorten its life. For this reason, most new fan, blower, pump, compressor and conveyor motors have automatic-reset overload protection to guard against such overheating. It's important that the thermal protector automatically resets the motor in installations like a furnace blower, where you would not want the furnace to remain inoperative overnight, or on water pumps located away from the house. A manual-reset overload device, however, is recommended for motors that drive potentially dangerous tools, such as a saw, jointer or lathe.

Load moving is critical when you start a motor. Machines such as free-running saws or fans are easy to start. Others that must start under load—such as concrete mixers, conveyors, pumps and air compressors—need motors with extra turning strength, or torque, during the starting revolutions. For most home, farm and workshop uses, easy-to-start machines call for *split-phase* motors; hard-to-start machines require *capacitor-start* motors.

Split-phase motors have only moderate starting torque and are built with ratings up to 1/3 hp. Two windings, start and run, are energized at first. At about 80 percent of operating speed, a centrifugal switch cuts the start winding out of the circuit.

Capacitor-start motors, on the other hand, deliver two to three times the starting torque for the same amount of current. These are made with ratings from 1/6 to 3 hp. Since capacitor-start motors cost from 25 to 50 percent more than split-phase motors of like power, split-phase is the logical choice when the starting load is light (as on fans and blowers), or where the load is applied after the motor reaches full operating speed (drill press).

Both types use a single-phase power supply and, combined, make up about 90 percent of the motors in the U.S. Polyphase (usually three-phase) motors constitute the balance and are designed for continuous heavy-duty work. Because of the three-phase power requirement, however, polyphase motors are not often found in home workshops.

Most single-phase motors run at full load speeds of either 1725 or 3450 rpm. The faster motor is frequently the smaller of the two, and has a lower price per hp. When possible, this is the type to use since its speed can be reduced by a 6:1 belt-and-pulley combination.

With regard to voltage, a look at the motor's nameplate will tell you whether its rating corresponds to your power supply, which likely is 115 v.a.c., 60 cycle. The dual-voltage (115/230-v.), capacitor-start motors are available with ratings beginning at 1/6 hp, while split-phase motors are rated at 1/6 hp through ½ hp.

SEE ALSO

Bandsaws . . . Belt sanders . . . Bench saws . . . Jointers . . . Power-tool stands . . . Saws, bench . . . Shapers . . . Wiring, electrical . . . Wood lathes

COMMON USES FOR ELECTRIC MOTORS

APPLICATION	HORSEPOWER	SPEED	MOTOR TYPE
Belt sander, 4″	1/4	1725	Split-phase
Belt sander, 6″	1/2	1725	Capacitor-start
Belt sander, 10″	1	1725	Capacitor-start
Belt-driven blower	1/8-3/4	1725	Split-phase
Churn	1/3	1725	Split-phase
Small compressor	1/6-3/4	1725	Capacitor-start
Small concrete mixer	1/2	1725	Capacitor-start
Cream separator	1/2	1725	Capacitor-start
Drill press, 1/4″	1/3	1725	Split-phase
Drill press, 1/2″	1/2	1725	Capacitor-start
Drill press, 3/4″	3/4	1725	Capacitor-start
Belt-driven fan	1/8-3/4	1725	Split-phase
Feed mixer, 15-bushel	3/4	1725	Capacitor-start
Feed grinder	3/4	1725	Capacitor-start
Flexible shaft, 5/16″ dia. x 50′	1/3	1725	Split-phase
Flexible shaft, 1/2″ dia. x 75′	1/2	1725	Capacitor-start
Wheel grinder, 6″	1/3	1725	Split-phase
Wheel grinder, 7″	1/2	1725	Split-phase
Wheel grinder, 8″	1	1725	Capacitor-start
Jigsaw, 12 or 15″	1/4	1725	Split-phase
Jigsaw, 18 or 25″	1/3	1725	Split-phase
Jointer, 4½″	1/2	3450	Capacitor-start
Jointer, 6″	1/2	3450	Capacitor-start
Jointer, 8″	3/4	3450	Capacitor-start
Lathe (metal), 6″-swing	1/2	1725	Capacitor-start
Lathe (metal), 10″-swing	3/4	1725	Capacitor-start
Lathe (wood), 8″-swing	1/3	1725	Split-phase
Lathe (wood), 12″-swing	3/4	1725	Capacitor-start
Small meat grinder	1/4	1725	Split-phase
Oil burner	1/8-1/4	1725	Split-phase
Small paint sprayer	1/3	1725	Capacitor-start
Planer	3/4	3450	Capacitor-start
Jet pump	1/3-2	3450	Capacitor-start
Sump pump	1/3	1725	Split-phase
Pump jack	1/2	1725	Capacitor-start
Bandsaw, 8″ throat	1/3	1725	Capacitor-start
Bandsaw, 10, 12 or 14″	1/2	1725	Capacitor-start
Bench saw, 6 or 7″	1/2	3450	Capacitor-start
Bench saw, 8″	3/4	3450	Capacitor-start
Bench saw, 10″	1	3450	Capacitor-start
Spindle shaper	1/2	3450	Capacitor-start
Stoker	1/3	1725	Capacitor-start

Courtesy General Purpose Motor Dept., General Electric Co.

How to repair home workshop motors

By LEN HILTS

Very few things you own have the reliability and stamina of the typical home workshop motor. There are only a few things to go wrong and they are easy to fix

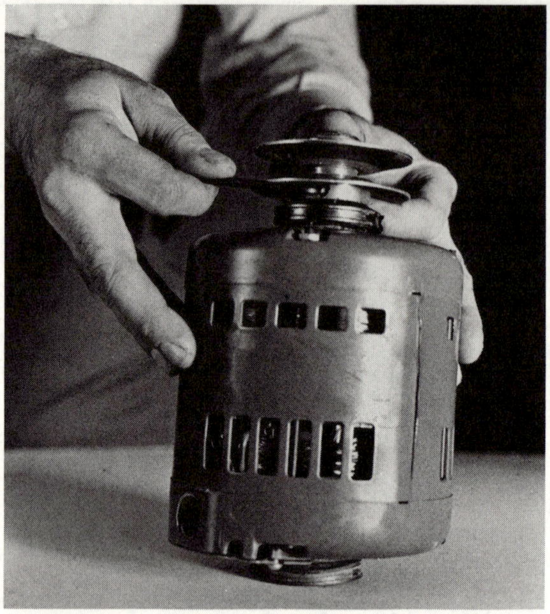

LOOK FOR a small setscrew at the base of the pulley and tighten it with an Allen wrench.

HOME WORKSHOP MOTORS, the kind you use to run table saws and drill presses, are among the most reliable machines in your home. With modest care, such motors will give years and years of trouble-free service. The care involves nothing more than a few drops of oil each month, if the motor has oil cups, and brushing dust and dirt and sawdust off of it.

If you took the case off of the typical workshop motor, you'd see an armature consisting of copper wires wound around a cylindrical rotor; and field coils of copper wire inside of which the armature turns. The armature and field coils are connected by carbon elements called brushes mounted in the commutator, an assembly of copper bars around one end of the armature shaft. One brush is positive and the other is negative. They are directly opposite each other, and are held in firm contact with the commutator by springs.

Thus the armature on its shaft is the motor's only moving part (except for the carbon brushes which push against the commutator). One reason for the great dependability of the workshop motor is the fact that it has very few moving parts.

SEE ALSO

Bandsaws . . . Belt sanders . . . Bench saws . . . Drills, portable . . . Power-tool maintenance . . . Power-tool stands . . . Wiring, electrical . . . Workbenches . . . Workshops

Here are some of the more common failures that occur in workshop motors:

1. A loose pulley. The pulley, of course, is not a part of the motor itself but is attached to the armature shaft. It is slipped over the end of the shaft and held in place by tightening a set screw. See the photograph above. If this setscrew loosens, the pulley may wobble or even work its way off the shaft. To avoid unexpected problems, check the setscrew occasionally. If it should be loose, tighten it by using an Allen wrench of the correct size. (If you don't have one, you can buy an inexpensive set of common-sized Allen wrenches at your home center.)

While you are inspecting the pulley, you should also check the drive belt. Belts are subject to wear and they may harden and crack with age. They also may stretch slightly so they're loose on the pulley. Test the belt by pressing down on it with your finger. You should be able to depress the belt about half an inch with moderate finger pressure. If it depresses more than that, the belt should be tightened. If you note cracks or badly worn places on the belt, replace it. To be sure of getting the correct replacement, take the old belt with you to the store.

2. A loose wire. If you find that your motor sometimes starts and sometimes does not, or if it emits sparks, you can suspect a loose wire. There are only a couple of wires which can be loose, and these are located, as a rule, under a

THE ACCESS PLATE on the end panel of the housing can be removed to tighten electrical connections.

WITH THE PLATE OFF, you have a clear view of any loose wires and can tighten all connections.

cover plate you will find on one end of the motor. The cover plate is held in place by two small screws. Remove these.

Before removing the cover plate, unplug or disconnect the motor from the electric power source. With the cover plate off, you can use a small wrench to tighten the connections. Then replace the plate and reconnect the motor.

3. *Bad brushes*. The brushes in a motor are small pieces of carbon held under spring tension against the turning commutator. They are subject to wear and may have to be replaced every few months in a motor which gets an exceptional amount of use, or perhaps every few years in a motor which gets only occasional use.

You can suspect worn brushes when the motor starts sluggishly or gives off sparks as it runs. Some motors have brushes contained in small housings under slotted caps. By carefully removing these caps, you can replace the brushes without disassembling the motor.

When removing these caps, turn slowly and lift away slowly, because the brushes under the caps are spring loaded. If you pull the cap away suddenly, the spring and the brush will fly out. Lift the cap slowly, allowing the spring under it to relax. Then lift the spring and brush out.

Check the spring as well as the brush, and replace both if necessary. You can buy springs and brushes at good hardware stores or at places which specialize in home power tools. To install the new brushes, simply insert them in the chamber under the cap, put the spring into the chamber, and then screw the cap into place. Always replace both brushes, positive and negative, at the same time.

In some motors, you must disassemble the motor housing to get at the brushes. Begin the disassembly by removing the pulley from the shaft. Then look for screwheads in indentations on the side of the housing. The housing is held together by long screws which extend through the motor. As a rule, there are four screws, secured by nuts at the other end. Use a screwdriver to remove these screws, being careful to hold the nuts as the screws are loosened.

With the screws removed, you should be able to lift away both ends of the motor housing. If the ends stick, place a block of wood against each of them and tap it briskly with a hammer until the component loosens.

With the ends of the motor housing removed, you should see the brush holders at the commutator end of the armature shaft. The brush holders may be held in place by small screws or clips. Remove these and lift each holder off the motor, then remove from it the brush and brush spring.

As before, check the brush and the spring and replace both as necessary. Also, replace both the positive and negative brushes. Insert the new brush and spring in the holder, then put the hold-

THE MOTOR housing is held together by long screws and nuts. Remove the screws to disassemble.

PULL THE ENDS of the motor housing apart to gain access to the brush holders on the commutator.

er back in position on the motor with the tip of the brush in contact with the commutator.

4. Frozen bearings. Fortunately, bearings don't fail very often. The usual cause is lack of lubrication. Keep in mind that there are two kinds of motors in terms of lubrication. There are those which are lubricated at the factory and sealed, and never require any additional lubrication. And there are others which have tiny oil cups built in just over the main drive shaft. These little oil cups have spring-loaded caps on them to keep them closed, keeping dirt out. If your motor has these little cups, you must add several drops of machine oil regularly. If the cups run dry and the motor continues to run, you are risking frozen, burned-out bearings.

If the bearings burn out, you face an expensive repair job, one which you shouldn't attempt to do yourself. The professional mechanic and motor specialist has special pullers for removing bearings from the end cap. Without these special tools, you can easily ruin an otherwise repairable motor. Some do-it-yourselfers try to remove the end cap with a hammer to get at the bearings. It may work, but the risk of a ruined motor is great.

You sometimes can tell that the bearings are going bad when the motor begins to run noisily. In time, the bearings will freeze: The motor will hum when you turn it on, but it will not revolve. When that happens, remove the motor from the tool and take it to a professional repairman.

Operating tips. Keep in mind that the home workshop motor is a split-phase motor and that, as such, it draws a heavy electric current as it starts and for the first 10 seconds of operation. This is the reason that the lights in your workshop may dim momentarily when you start a motorized unit.

Under normal circumstances, this overload doesn't mean anything to the average homeowner. But there are two times when it can be very important.

One time is when all the current is shut off in the house as, for example, when the power company shuts down the power for an hour or two to make repairs. When the power is turned on again, everything electrical with its switch turned on starts immediately. If several motor-powered units are on—say the furnace blower, the washer, the dryer, and the refrigerator—all of these motors will be activated at the same time. This causes a great drain of power, since all of these motors draw so heavily in the first few seconds, and the usual result is a bevy of blown fuses.

The other time the heavy power drain caused by the starting of a home workshop motor is important is when you are operating several power tools on the same electric circuit. The electric circuit in your workshop is (or should be) a 20-amp. circuit, capable of carrying 2300 watts.

It is a good idea to know the wattage of each tool and accessory in your workshop, and to keep a mental total of how many watts you are drawing at any time. This way, you can anticipate overload problems.

SECRET of the unique setup is that the large pulley (lower left) is free-running on the motor shaft.

Piggyback speed reducer

By WILLIAM WAGGONER

LIFT YOURSELF by your bootstraps?

That's what this novel piggyback speed reducer appears to do, for it cuts your 1725-rpm double-shaft motor to under 200 rpm, and with only *one* shaft.

The heart of the speed reducer is the 6-in. free-running pulley to which the drive pulley is bolted. It revolves freely and is driven through speed-reducing pulleys from the other end of the motor. To use the motor at normal speed, you just slip one belt and turn a setscrew.

To construct the piggyback, remove the top motor-housing bolts and replace the longer bolts. Sections of angle iron, shimmed out with spacers of ⅛-in. pipe, provide support for the hangers.

Many ½-in. motor shafts have a flat ground on the shaft. In this case epoxy a ½-in. bronze bushing over the shaft and use a ⅝-in. arbor pulley.

SEE ALSO
Bandsaws . . . Bench saws . . . Cutoff machines . . . Power hacksaws . . . Power-tool stands . . . Saws, bench

BRONZE BUSHING (below) is epoxied to a ½-in. motor shaft to enlarge the bearing surface for pulley.

PIGGYBACK SETUP (below right) is ideal for cramped quarters, such as making your bandsaw a metalcutter.

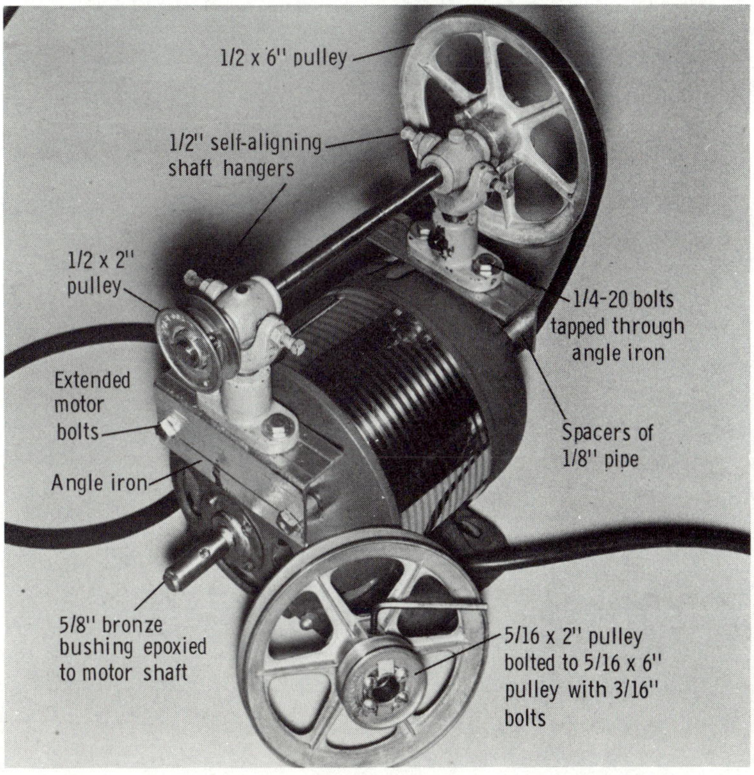

How to mount your photo prints

Show off some of your most prized photos by mounting and protecting them. You can have a professional do it, but here are some hints and methods to help you do-it-yourself

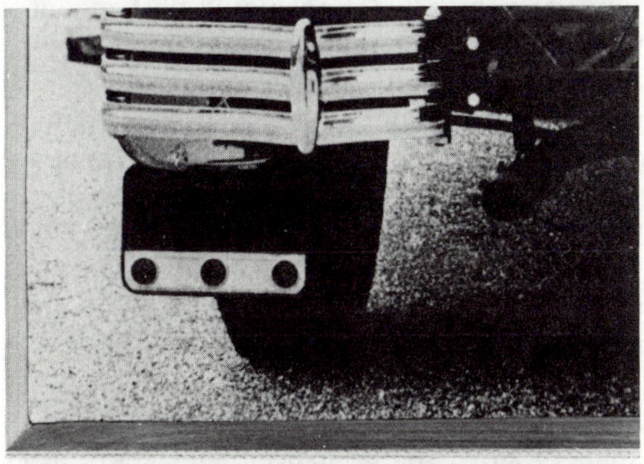

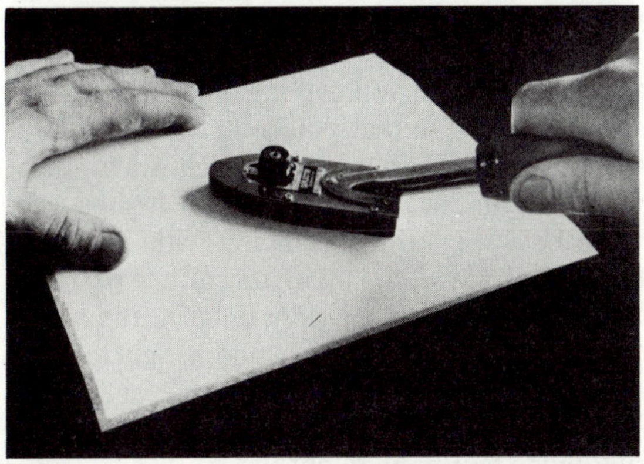

MOUNTING TRICKS include centered-flush mounting (top; note black border around full-negative image); matting (above, center); use of "tacking iron" (bottom) to hold the tissue in place while mounting.

By DAVE SAGARIN

GOOD REASONS to mount your photo prints abound: Mounting makes a print thick and keeps it flat, which protects it against curling, cracking and rough handling. But mainly, mounting makes a print special. It shows that you think a lot of the picture, and want others to see it at its best.

Of the many ways to mount prints, the best, in my opinion, is dry mounting, using a press or hand iron to bond the print to a mount board. Dry mounting is permanent, handsome and fairly cheap.

The simplest way to get a print mounted is to have it done commercially at an art supply store, framer or custom photo lab. A typical price for flush-mounting an 8x10 print on illustration board is about $1.50. But if you have a friend at an ad agency, a corporate graphics department, or an art school, you may be able to use their press.

For dry-mounting at home, the first requirement is a clear work space large enough to lay out your supplies, cut mounting boards, and set prints out to cool. Cover your work surface with cheap board.

You can't mount a print that's tightly curled.

SEE ALSO
**Christmas cards . . . Cutting boards . . .
Developing, photo . . . Dryers, photo . . .
Frames, picture . . . Montages, photo . . .
Photography . . . Prints, photo**

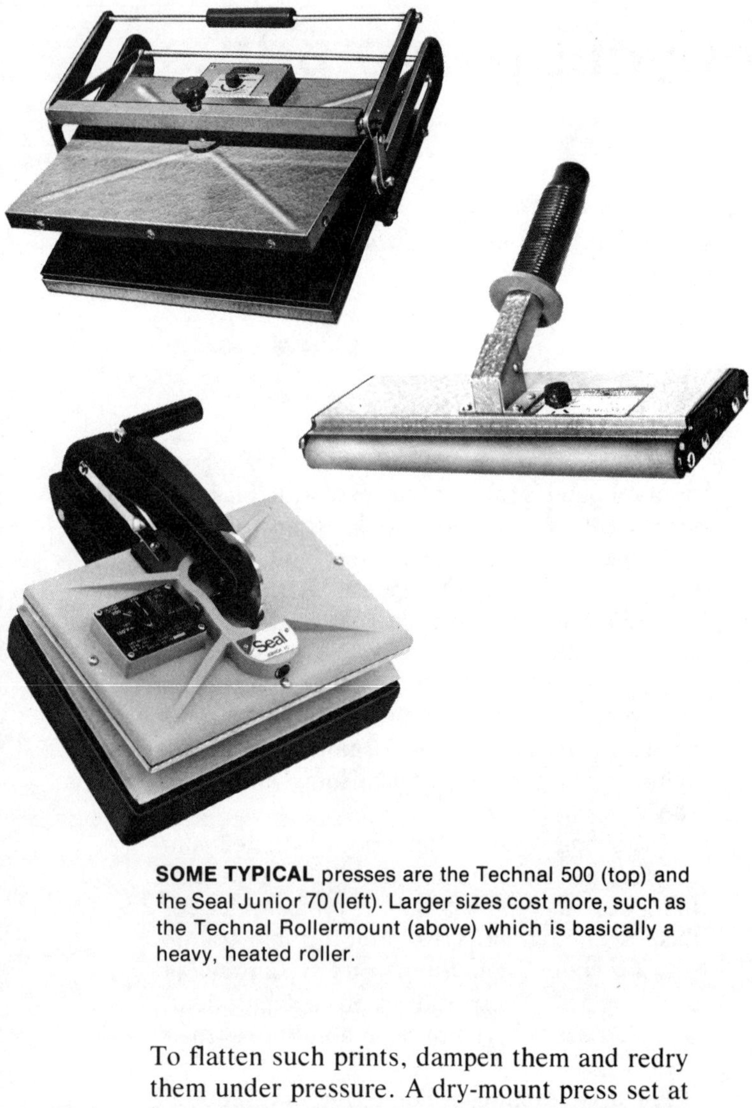

SOME TYPICAL presses are the Technal 500 (top) and the Seal Junior 70 (left). Larger sizes cost more, such as the Technal Rollermount (above) which is basically a heavy, heated roller.

To flatten such prints, dampen them and redry them under pressure. A dry-mount press set at low temperature can speed drying and provide the pressure needed. If you stack prints as you press them flat, you need only dampen one out of three or four.

Cracks, stains, fingerprints and ripples (frilling) can mess up the edge of a print. To avoid these troubles when you're making prints you know you'll mount, center the image on a larger-than-normal size piece of printing paper, leaving a generous border all around that you'll trim.

For dry-mounting you need heat, pressure and dry-mounting tissue. The tissue is impregnated, like wax paper, with a meltable adhesive.

During the time it takes for your iron or press to heat, set the print on a piece of mount board and shift it around to decide what size the final mount should be, and where the print should sit on it.

basic methods

To my mind, there are three approaches to this: *Flush* mounting carries the image to the very edge of the mount, with no border; the print image fights its environment, a good technique for journalistic or other dynamic shots. *Centered* mounting is more formal, with a border (often a raised ''mat'') surrounding the image; usually both sides and the top are the same width, and the bottom is a bit wider, but some pictures seem to look cramped if you don't widen the top border. *Centered-flush* mounting runs the printing paper to the edge of the mount, but leaves the image centered; to keep the borders white, you'll need a cropping easel, unless you're printing the whole negative. Many photographers widen their enlargers' negative carriers with a file so that light shining through the clear film borders around the image area will leave a black outline.

You can now rough-trim it to within an inch of the area to be mounted. The mounting board should be cut to the same size as the rough-trimmed print for flush or centered-flush mounting; for centered mounting, leave generous borders. If you're going to frame or mat the print, make sure the mount board size is measured in whole inches to allow the use of precut frames.

measuring and cutting

To measure, use a rigid ruler and start at the one-inch mark, remembering to subtract one inch from the result.

For cutting, lay a heavy metal straightedge (other materials can be cut into) across the mount or print so the measurement dots just peep out from under its edge; a wide strip of masking tape stuck to the bottom of the straightedge will help keep it from slipping. Arrange the work so that you're in a comfortable position, with bright, nonglaring light and so that the blade will cut into waste area if it slips.

The best way to cut prints is with a single-edged razor blade, held with its surface perpendicular to the print and its edge entering the cut at about a 30° angle. Cut with a smooth, light touch.

To cut mount board, use a mat knife or a razor blade in a holder. Change blades frequently—dull blades tear as they cut.

Put print and board in the hot press about a minute to dry them out and reduce curl. Open the press at least once to let dry air in.

Cut a piece of dry-mount tissue the same size as the rough-trimmed print. Set the print face down and make sure it's completely clean and dust free—if you don't, you'll see how large a bump a tiny piece of grit can make. Put the tissue on back of the print and tack it down with a short stroke of the iron from the center of the print toward one corner, to keep it from shifting. Don't press hard, or you may leave a ridge in the print. A tacking iron (drawn toward you, not to its point) made for this is best, but you can also use a corner of a mounting press or the tip of a clothes iron

use the right heat

Your iron should be just hot enough to tack the tissue, not hot enough to melt the tissue over the iron. Practice on waste stock, first, waiting a few minutes after each heat-setting change.

Now that they're tacked together, trim print and tissue to the exact edge of the image you want to see. Position the trimmed print on the board by eye, moving it until you like the way it looks. Then check with the ruler that the side borders are equal and the print is square to the board edge. Gently lift the untacked corner of the print, and slide the iron underneath to tack the tissue to the board: If you have a mounting press, protect the face of the print with a sheet of clean, smooth, porous paper and insert the covered print into a sandwich of mounting boards or hardboard till the sandwich is thick enough for the press to apply maximun pressure.

To set press temperature properly, start with a medium heat, insert a single-weight, nonresin-coated scrap print tacked to a two-ply mount board, close the press without locking it, count five seconds, then remove. The print should lie flat, with its edges lifted, and should peel off when the board is flexed. If it doesn't lift off, the press is too hot; if it doesn't even flatten out, it's too cold. Once you find the right temperature setting, a permanent mounting should take about 15 to 20 seconds with the press locked shut. Thicker, glossier and larger things require higher mount temperatures and longer times; RC prints and special tissues recommended for them require lower temperatures and shorter times.

If you're using a clothes iron, use it dry (no steam), set it to "synthetic" and use the low-temperature RC-type tissues. Preheat the print and mount individually by covering them and slowly ironing all over. Trim and tack as above. To mount, iron one swath at a time, heating first by ironing gently from the center toward one edge for several passes before pressing firmly. Keep the iron moving, and don't let the cover sheet shift. Check each as it is completed. Work toward each edge, then toward the corners. When mounting is finished, the print should lie perfectly flat.

Ridges and bubbles in the mounted print may be eliminated by reinserting in the press or reironing, first with gentle pressure to heat the affected area thoroughly, then with very high pressure to flatten it down.

The tissue is soft when the print comes out of the press; to reduce edge-lifting, cool it under the pressure of piles of books with newspapers protecting the print.

Mount boards come in several types from art supply stores and large stationers in a variety of sizes, finishes, colors and substances.

Illustration board, a quality paper surface on a pulp core, is the choice for most work. Thicker, four-ply board is better than two-ply for large mounts or when the print will get a lot of handling. Museum board is a premium type whose composition varies: The best is 100-percent natural cotton fiber throughout, but there are also cotton-faced pulp-core boards, and boards faced with acid-free sulphite. Your board and pictures will last longest with 100-percent cotton board.

You can also use a piece of photographic printing paper, fixed and washed and mounted back-to-back with your print.

matting

For wall-hung prints, try a mat. The mat's color and texture act as moderators between the image and the wall—you're freer to experiment with colors, here, as you can always throw the mat away.

Cutting a mat takes skill and special tools—you may prefer to have it done by a professional framer. If you do it yourself, be sure to measure precisely: First measure the image area and the exact distance from each edge of the image to the nearest edge of the mount. Sketch these on paper. Now cut the mat board to the exact size of the mount, lay it face down, and mark hole dimensions of the sketch, top to top, bottom to bottom, but reversing the sides.

After cutting the mat, if its surface is dark in color, darken the newly cut edges with a felt pen.

The print is now ready to be framed, but if you're going to hang it with clear plastic framing or edge clips, bind the mat and mount together with Mystik tape.

Add 3-D to your photo display

Simple snapshots mounted on wood blocks create an unusual wall decoration that's easy to mak

By HARVEY SHAMAN

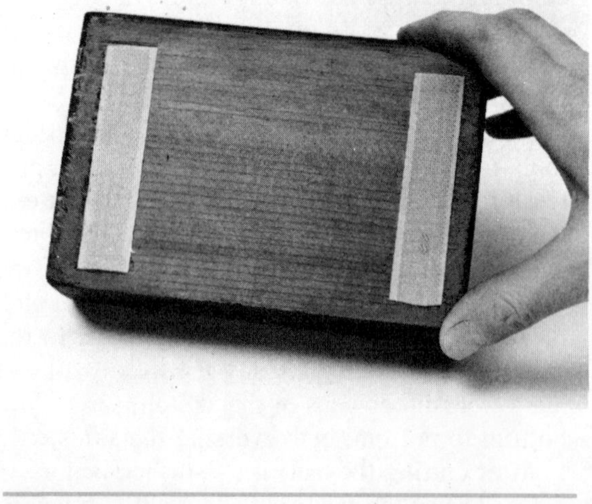

SMALL STRIPS of Velcro tape on back of each block make it easy to arrange pictures on panel covered with matching Velcro. Blocks stick firmly and can be quickly removed and rearranged.

SEE ALSO

Enlarging, photo . . . Frames, art . . .
Montages, photo . . . Photo hints . . . Photography . . .
Picture frames . . . Prints, photo . . . Trimmers, photo

ORDINARY SNAPSHOTS take on a dramatic appearance when you mount them on blocks of wood, producing a three-dimensional relief effect. By varying the size and thickness of the blocks, you can create an unusual random-pattern wall display of pictures that otherwise get stored away unseen in a bureau drawer or photo album.

The blocks are standard wood thicknesses—¼-inch, ¾-inch (1-inch nominal) and 1⅝ inch (2-inch nominal). Three basic sizes accommodate 8x10, 5x7 and 4x5 prints. You can, of course, make the blocks any other sizes you wish depending on how you want to crop your shots. Trim off the borders and mount the prints on the blocks with a white wood glue (don't use rubber cement as this will bleed through, staining the prints).

The blocks are painted flat black to give a sense of depth and contrast. After the prints are cemented on, trim their edges flush with a sharp knife or razor blade and sand them smooth with fine abrasive paper. Then touch up the paper edges with a black felt-tip marking pen so they blend in with the blocks and become invisible. Arrange the blocks on a backing panel of ¼-inch plywood or hardboard. This can be edged with picture-frame molding or 1x2 strips to create a shadow-box effect to enhance the 3-D look of the photos.

The display panel shown here incorporates an added feature that makes the blocks easy to mount and rearrange. It's based on the use of Velcro—the two-part, self-adhering material sold as a substitute for zippers and buttons on clothing. One part consists of thousands of tiny nylon loops and the other part has hook-shaped fibers that catch in the loops. When pressed together, the two stick firmly to each other, yet can easily be pulled apart.

The looped Velcro is cemented to the display panel and strips of the matching hooked material are fastened to the backs of the blocks. All you do is press the blocks onto the Velcro-covered panel and they stay by themselves. You can move them around to change the arrangement or add new blocks whenever you like.

Velcro comes in black, white, gray and various colors. The looped material is 48 inches wide and sells for about $12 a yard. Cut in half, one yard will cover two 2x3-foot panels—a handy size for wall display. The matching hooked material comes as a tape ¾ inch wide for about $1 a yard. Special cements for mounting both types are also available. Velcro supplies are sold at many department stores, sewing centers and fabric shops. They are distributed by Maharam Fabric Corp., 130 W. 46th St., New York, N.Y. 10036 or 1113 S. Los Angeles St., Los Angeles, Calif. 90015.

If you don't wish to use the Velcro, you can attach the blocks with either screws from the rear or glue. In this case, lay out the blocks on the display panel in a flat position and make sure you have a pleasing arrangement before permanently mounting them.

MATERIALS for photo display include ¼-inch panel, wood blocks of assorted sizes, self-adhering Velcro material, special Velcro adhesive, trimming knife and a small brush for spreading glue.

BLACK MARKING pen touches up edges of prints so they blend in with black-painted blocks. Run tip along the corners, slanting pen backward so that it can't slip and mar the faces of the prints.

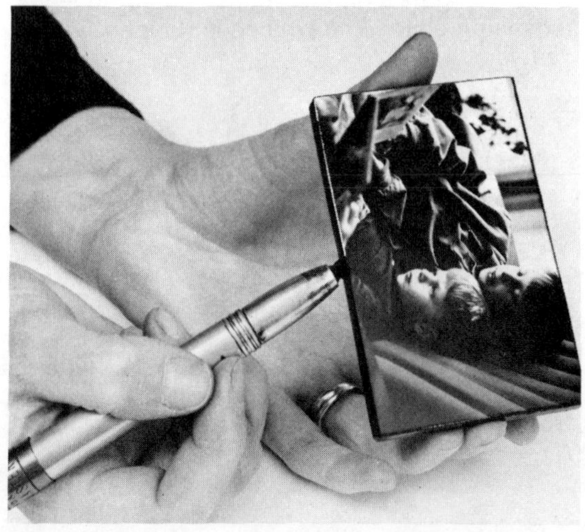

A SERVICEABLE HINGE for a box lid can be made from four or more cotter pins and a length of wire which passes through their eyes. The pins are driven tightly into pre-drilled pilot holes, and positioned so their eyes overlap like the knuckles of a regular hinge. The ends of the wire hinge pin are bent at right angles to lock it in place.—*Walter E. Burton, Akron, OH.*

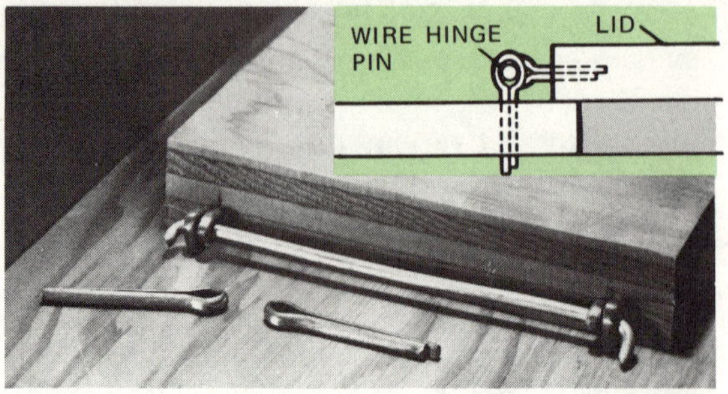

A STRONG HAND PUNCH can be improvised from Vise Grip pliers and a hollow rivet, when your regular hand punch won't do the job. Sharpen the end of the rivet with a rosehead countersink and insert it through a metal clip. Slip it over the Vise Grip jaw, with a pad of sheet lead over the opposite jaw to protect the rivet.—*Peter Legon, Malden, MA.*

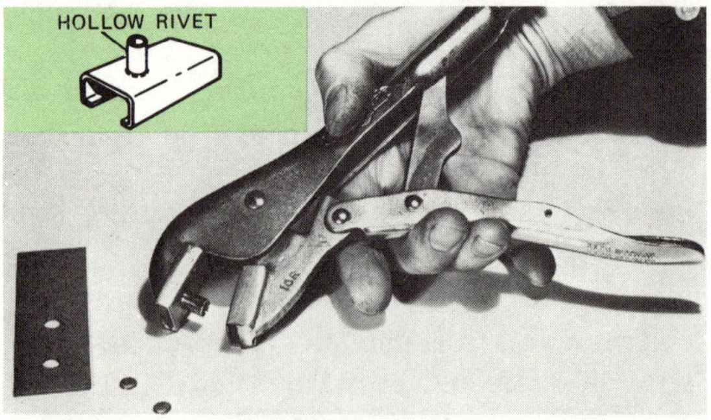

POCKET SCREWDRIVERS made from large washers are standard equipment for many mechanics. The edges of the washer are filed to leave stub blades that fit the screw slots. Rather than file the stub blade in the center of the washer as is usually done, I suggest offsetting the blades for greater leverage when you turn the screw. A tool-steel washer works well.—*B. W. Ervin, Kent, OH.*

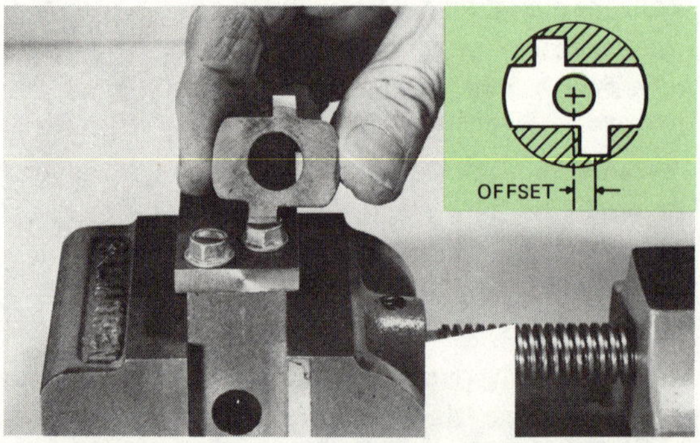

THIS MODIFIED WRENCH will provide a fast "ratcheting" action on a nut. Grind off and round one jaw of an open-end wrench as shown. The wrench will then be able to slip over corners of the nut until the continued swing of the wrench causes the jaw to grip succeeding flats on the nut as it is tightened. For a loosening action, the wrench is flopped.—*H. Miller, Vallejo, CA.*

THIS PILOT-HOLE 'AWL' is a handy homemade tool made from a double-headed scaffold nail. While drilling pilot holes for wood screws works well in hardwood, screws hold better in softwood when the fibers are forced aside. To make the awl, file the first nailhead to a point, the second head prevents the point from going too deep.—*Thomas E. Louis, Dobbs Ferry, NY.*

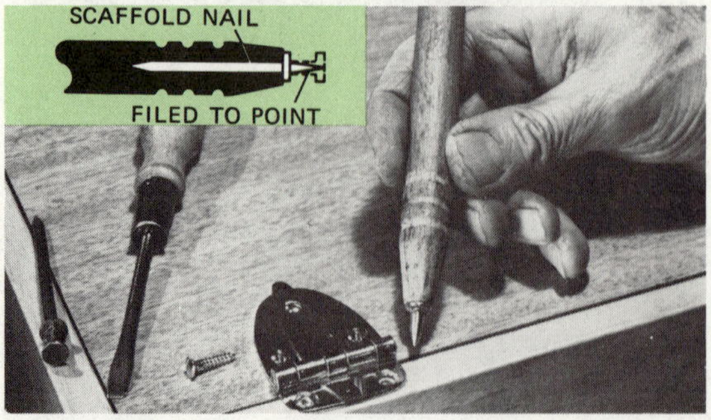

Get your power mower ready for spring

IF YOU SIMPLY PUSHED your power mower into a corner of the garage last fall after its last mowing session, it's time to be thinking about a spring-cleaning job to ready the machine for the season ahead. Overheating, hard starting, internal engine wear and other serious problems will result if dirt trapped under, on and inside your power mower isn't cleaned away. It takes some effort to have a mower that's ready for use any time: The information on these pages will make that task less troublesome because it covers the nitty-gritty of spring tune-ups.

Start inspection with the blade. A common problem is vibration caused by unbalanced blades. To check balance, remove blade and insert a screwdriver in the mounting hole. Hold the screwdriver vertically; if blade is unbalanced, blade will tip. Using a fine-grit grinding wheel, remove a little metal from the heavy end. If grinding doesn't balance the blade, replace it.

CLEAN COOLING FINS

The engine of a power mower is cooled by circulating air through fins inside the blower housing. If these fins become clogged and the airflow is blocked, the cooling process will be impeded or stopped completely. Overheating and damage to the internal parts can and will result. To clean the cooling fins, remove the blower housing and use a clean, dry paintbrush to brush dirt from between the fins. Packed-in dirt first can be loosened with a screwdriver.

If dirt is stubborn, use a commercial degreaser and a narrow, stiff-bladed scraper to clean out the fins. Fins should be cleaned periodically during the season.

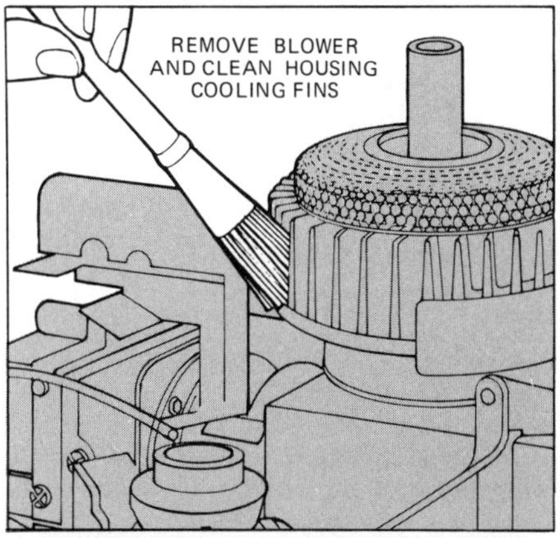

THEN CLEAN UNDERSIDE OF BLADE HOUSING

Often, because grass is moist when cut, the underside of the blade housing becomes clogged with layers of dried-on grass. If you failed to turn the mower over and clean the blade housing with a putty knife and whiskbroom after each cutting session, the task will be somewhat harder now. After each cleaning, also turn the machine right-side up and wipe the body exterior with a soft, clean cloth. A spray automotive-engine degreaser can be used to dissolve stubborn dirt and grease.

Now pay special attention to the carburetor linkage and choke-plate pivots. To clean these units, use a spray-type automotive-carburetor cleaner that's available at auto supply outlets. Then apply a drop of oil to the moving parts. Finally, remove the wheels, thoroughly clean the hubs and axles, and then coat the axles with a layer of an all-purpose grease.

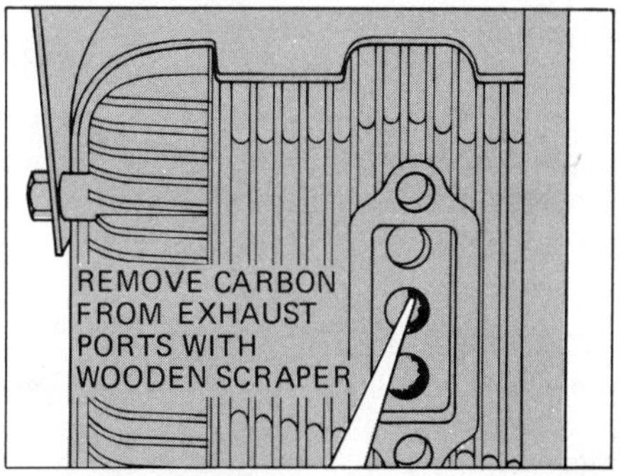

EXHAUST PORTS

Carbon is also a form of dirt, and an accumulation of it in the exhaust ports of power-mower engines (two-cycle engines, in particular) will reduce the power output appreciably. Before scraping off the carbon, exercise the precaution of first removing the sparkplug from the engine (to prevent the engine from starting). Then remove the muffler.

Next, turn the crankshaft slowly by means of the starter cord or self-starter until the lower part of the piston covers the ports. In this way, carbon will be kept out of the cylinder when its scraped loose.

SEE ALSO

Engines, small . . . Grass . . . Hand mowers . . . Landscaping . . . Lawns . . . Snowblowers . . . Snowplows . . . Tractor lifts . . . Tractor trailers . . . Trees

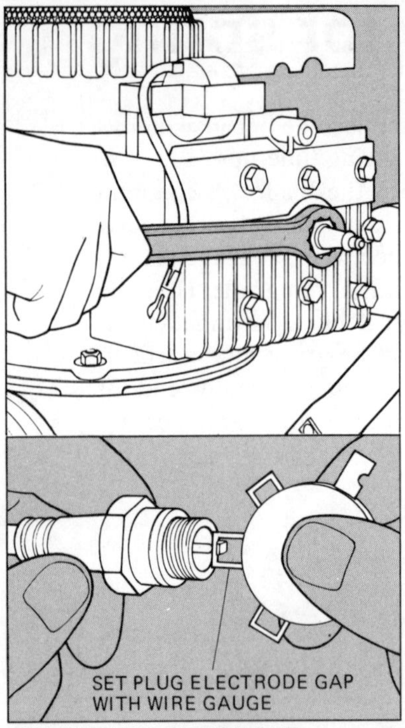

SPARKPLUG CHECKOUT

Remove the sparkplug and examine it carefully. If the electrodes are burned away or pitted, or if the porcelain is cracked, discard the plug and get a new one of the same designation. You will find the designation printed on the plug. Generally, 100 operating hours should be considered as maximum life for a plug.

If the plug looks fine, use a penknife or small wire brush to scrape dirt from around the electrodes. If you have a compressor, complete the cleaning with a blast of air. Lacking this equipment, blow out particles by mouth.

Whether the plug is new or not, set the electrode gap to the manufacturer's specification with a wire-type, sparkplug gauge like the one shown above. If you've lost the owner's manual and don't know the gap specification, for two-cycle engines gap is set at .028 to .033 in.; for four-cycle, it's .025 to .028. Insert plug and finger-tighten. Then, give an additional half turn with a wrench.

Inspect the sparkplug lead wire. If it is not too badly frayed or damaged, you might be able to patch it with insulating tape. Otherwise, you will have to get at the coil to replace it; in some machines, this means removal of the flywheel—a job best left to a professional. Sometimes, the lead wire is connector-fastened to the coil so that it can be replaced with the coil left in place.

In other mowers, the wire is molded to the coil: To make the change, both wire and coil must be replaced.

FUEL-OIL MIXTURE

If your power-mower engine is four-cycle, warm it up, then shut it off. Remove the oil drain plug and drain the dirty oil into a waste pan. Replace the drain plug and fill the crankcase through the oil filler to the level mark. Use the type and weight of oil specified in your owner's manual.

In two-cycle engines, a mixture of oil and gasoline is used in the fuel tank. Improper fuel-oil mixture is the main cause of operational problems with two-cycle engines, so check the owner's manual for the correct ratio. (The correct mixture is usually ½ pint to 1 gallon gasoline.) The oil should be of the type and weight specified in the owner's manual or of the type made especially for two-cycle engines.

Insufficient oil in the mixture means that engine parts will be improperly lubricated, resulting in overheating and seizure. Too much oil causes engine smoking, loss of power and sparkplug clogging. So take the time to mix the fuel properly.

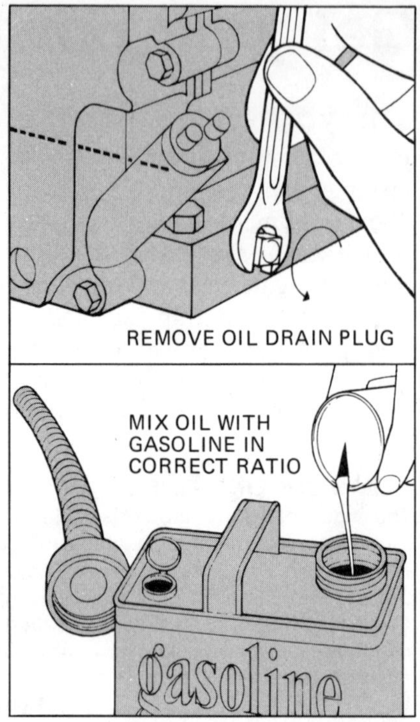

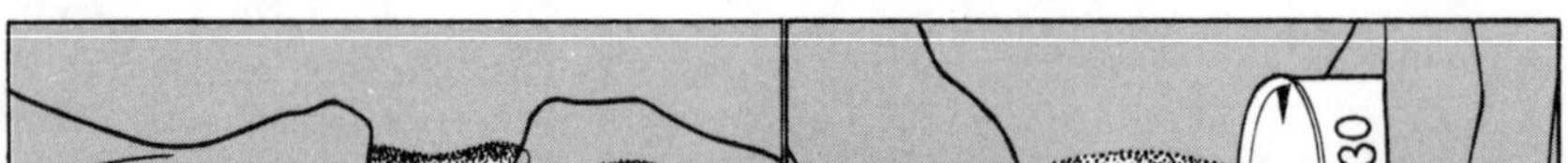

POLYURETHANE-SPONGE AIR CLEANER

An air cleaner is the primary protection a power mower has from dust particles that can get inside to clog moving parts. One common type of air cleaner has a polyurethane-sponge element as shown in the drawings above. To clean it, (1) wash element in liquid detergent and warm water, (2) wrap in a cloth and squeeze dry, (3) saturate with SAE 30 engine oil and (4) squeeze to remove excess oil. Clean the container that holds the element, replace the element and cover lightly.

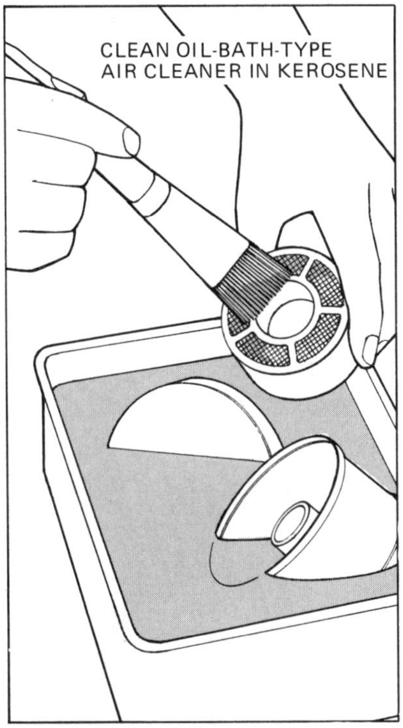

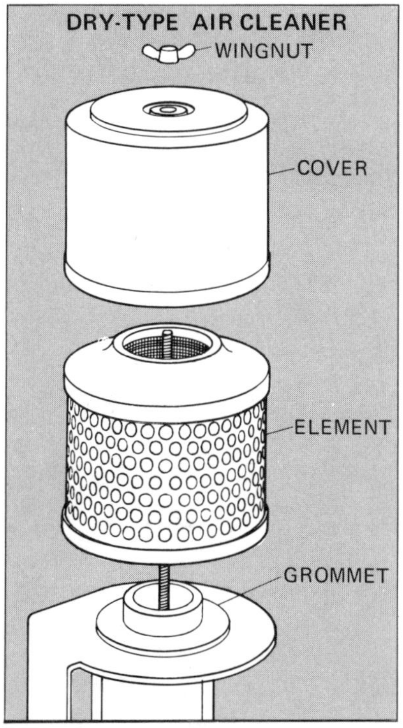

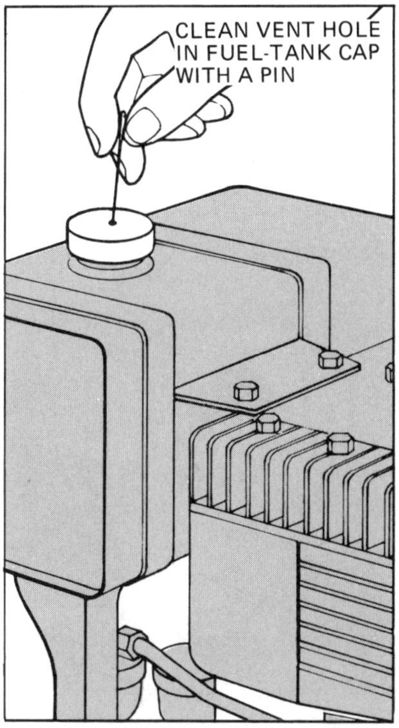

OIL-BATH CLEANER

This type of air cleaner comes with a container that uses a layer of oil to trap dirt and dust particles.

To clean it, remove air cleaner from the engine and disassemble. Dump out the dirty oil and wash all the parts thoroughly in a solvent such as kerosene. Let these parts air-dry; then reassemble them and fill the cleaner to the level mark with a clean SAE engine oil.

DRY-TYPE AIR CLEANER

With this type of air cleaner, unscrew the cover as shown above, take out and examine the filter element. If the element is paper, replace it. If it is metallic, carefully tap it on a flat surface to loosen dust and dirt. Then wash it thoroughly. Finally flush the element (from the inside out) with water until the water that comes out of the sides of the element looks clean. Allow the element to dry.

FUEL-TANK CAP

Some fuel-tank caps have a small vent hole. If it becomes plugged, a vacuum is created that will stop the flow of fuel and the engine will stall. Remove cap and clean out dirt in the hole with a pin. *Take care not to enlarge hole.* In addition, be sure that only proper fuel is poured into the fuel tank (pure gasoline or a correct mixture of oil and gasoline).

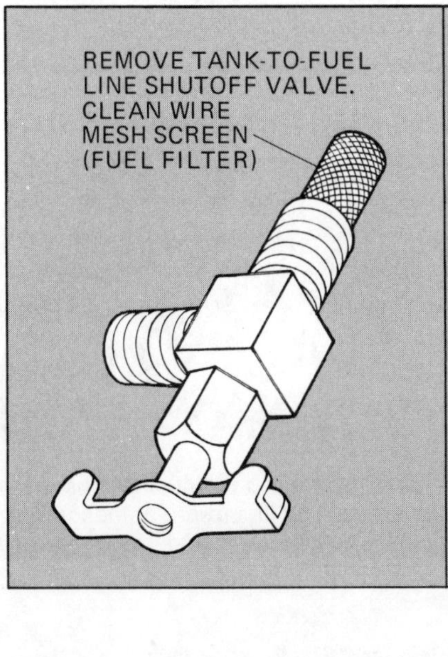

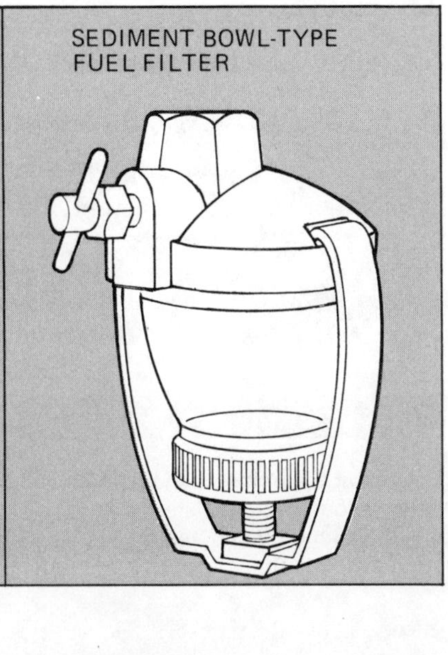

FUEL FILTER

Remove the fuel filter from your power mower and wash it thoroughly in kerosene, or let it soak in engine degreaser. The filter in many small engines is located in the tank-to-fuel-line shutoff valve. Remove the valve to get at the filter (far left).

Other engines have a sediment-bowl-type fuel filter that houses a ceramic element. Remove the bowl. If there is gasoline in the tank, be sure to first turn off the shutoff valve. Disassemble the filter and wash the parts in kerosene. If you're using engine degreaser, soak all parts for an hour or two; then wash in water and dry with an air-pressure hose which also blows away dirt.

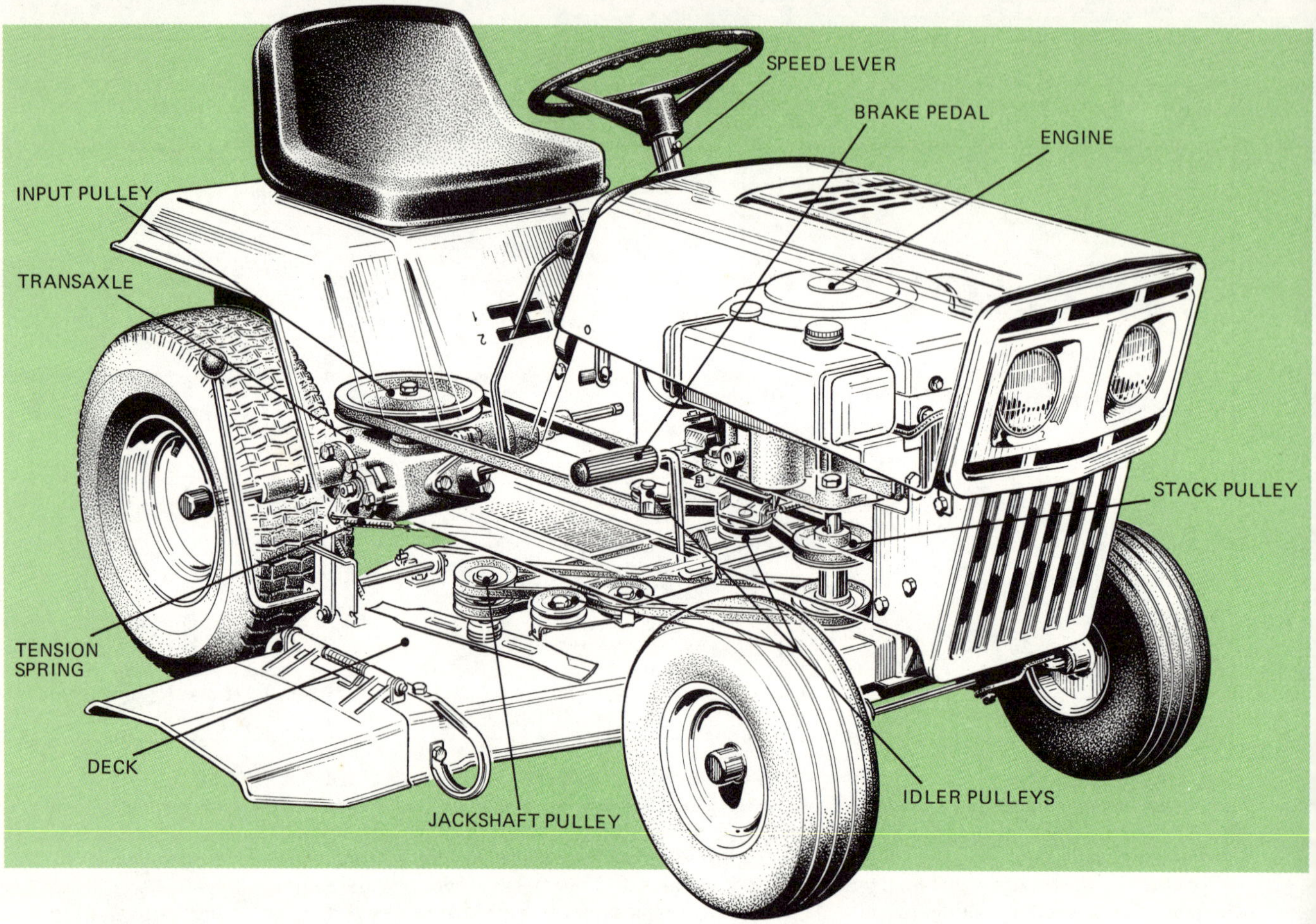

How to choose a riding mower

By GLENN S. HENSLEY

SEE ALSO

Engines, small . . . Grass . . . Hand mowers . . . Landscaping . . . Lawns . . . Tractor lifts . . . Tractor trailers . . . Trees

THIS SPRING many homeowners will be getting ready to shell out cash or sign a credit card slip in return for a lawn tractor or rear-engine riding mower. Both machines are becoming increasingly popular—especially those in the 8- to 11-hp category.

There are relatively inexpensive lines of

12 SHOPPING TIPS FOR SELECTING A MOWER

1 Since all engines need some service, lift the hood and check access to the sparkplug, air filter, oil filter and oil drain. Hood should lock securely.

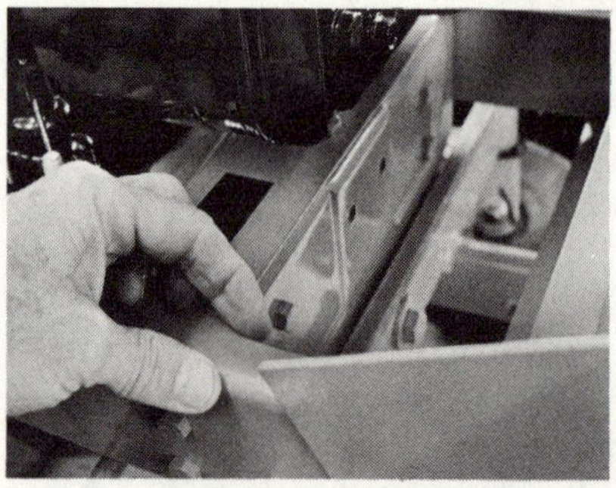

2 Look at the frame. It should be heavy, welded or bolted steel with a rugged, stamped frame and engine support combined. These frames are sturdy.

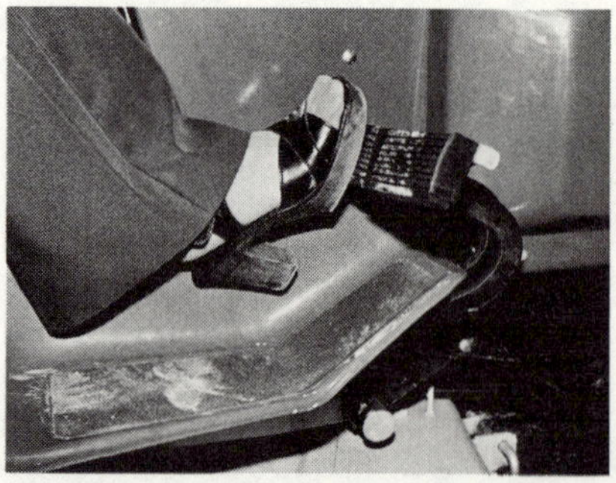

3 The unit you select should have footrests that tilt upward at the forward end. The larger the step, the greater the protection for the operator.

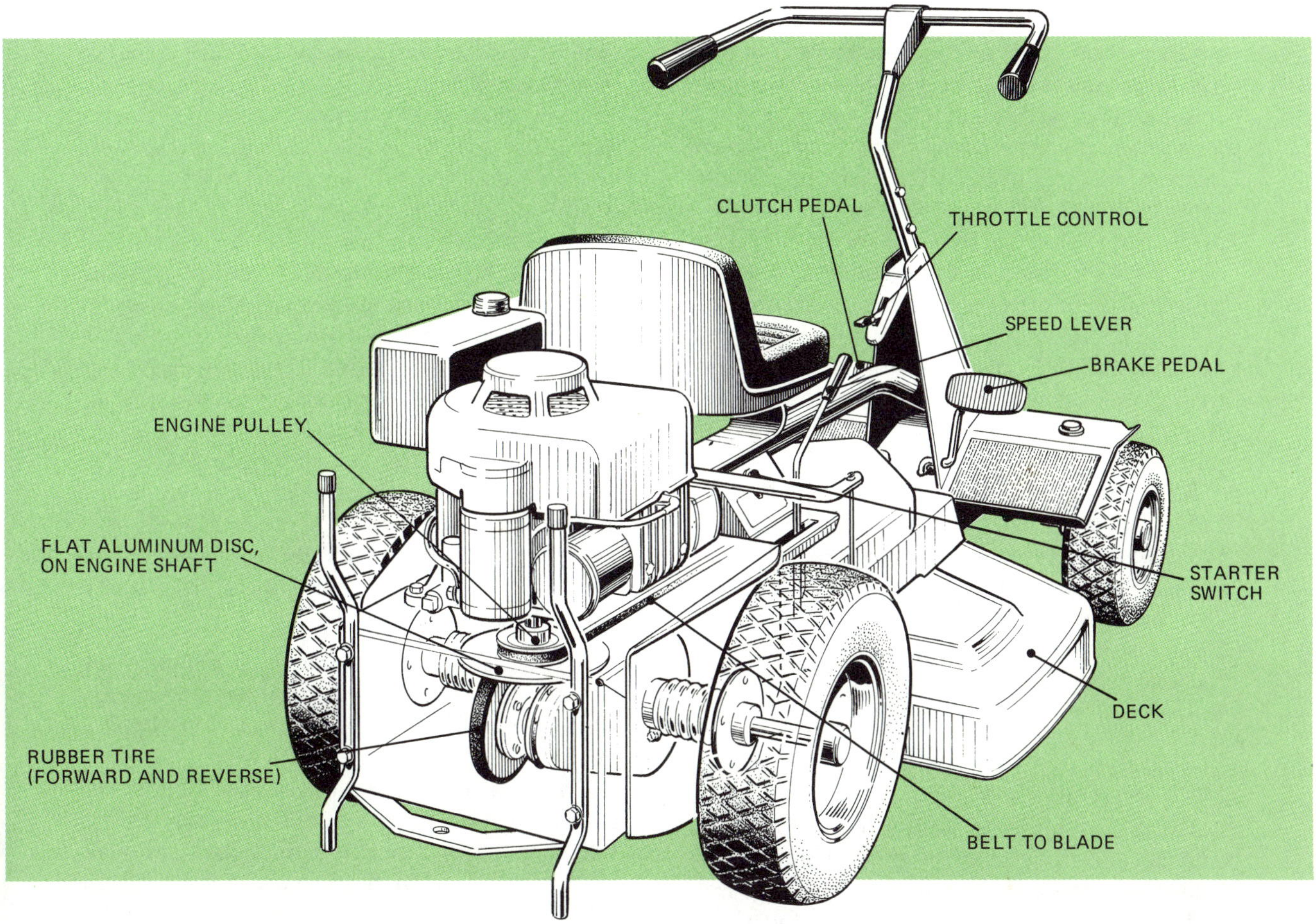

mowers that won't stand up to rugged, long-term use. Then there are the better engineered units, built for years of service, that are, naturally, priced higher.

For example, a high-quality lawn tractor, good for many seasons of use and purchased from a reliable servicing dealer, will probably require an investment of more than $1100. With such a machine, however, you'll be able to count on a dealer's service shop and parts department—absolute essentials in the purchase of anything mechanical.

The width of strip a mower can cut (also called swath) ranges from about 30 in. on the 8-hp machines to 42 in. on the 11-hp models. When you make comparisons, remember that a 42-in. mower will cut your yard in half the time needed by a 30-in. unit, providing you maintain a 2-in.

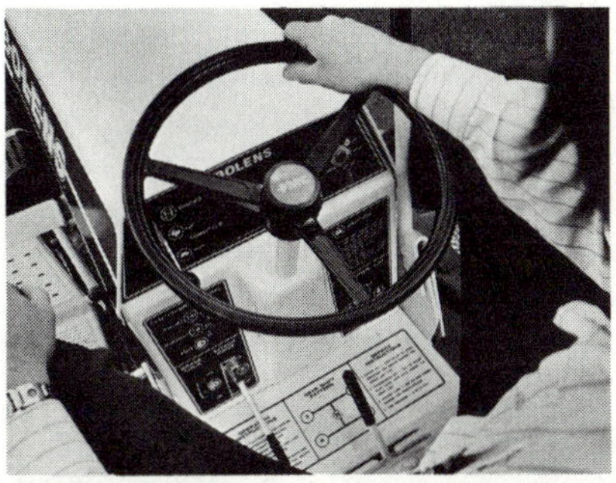

4 Sit at the wheel. You should be positioned comfortably with controls convenient. Instruction labeling should be understandable at a glance.

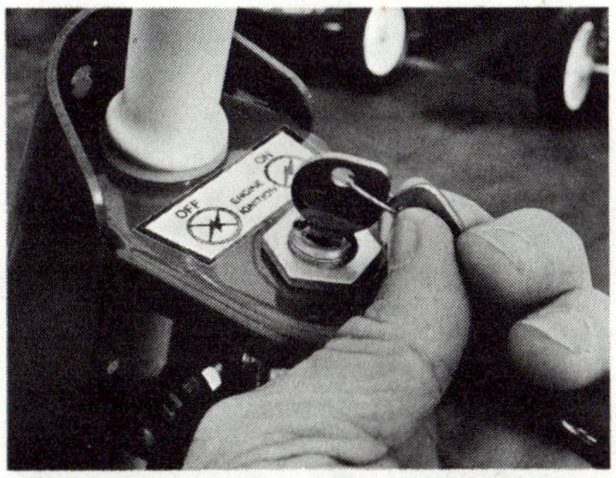

5 Keyed ignitions give you control of the mower use. When the key is out, the mower shouldn't start. This extra protection is worthwhile.

6 Seat backs that are as deep as the spread of a hand provide good, basic support and keep you from accidentally sliding off over rough ground.

swath overlap. Also, a 36-in. mower will do the job 25 percent faster than one with a 30-in. cut.

Some lawn tractors and rear engine riders have much more precise steering than others. Geared steering, with provision for wear take-up, usually provides less than 1 in. of steering-wheel movement (play) before the front wheels move. This is considered precision steering—with it you can easily maintain a 2-in. cutting swath overlap.

Units that have more steering-wheel play will probably force you to allow about 3 in. of swath overlap to keep from leaving stray strips of grass. Naturally, more overlap means extra time on the job.

Before buying, determine a mower's turning radius either firsthand or by asking. The tighter the radius, the less hand trimming you'll have to do around trees and plantings. Direct comparisons between two mowers of equal cut width, horsepower and ground speeds have shown that the one with the tightest turning radius saves from 5 to 10 percent of total job time.

check the mower blade

The mower blade tip (and shield) should extend beyond the wheels by about 2 in. This is convenient when trimming along flower beds and curbs. The less overhang, the more hand trimming you'll do. Some units accomplish trim overhang by offsetting a narrow mower to the side opposite the discharge chute. Overhang is automatic if the blade tip circle is wider than the tractor wheels.

Authorities say that no more than one-third of the standing height of grass should be removed in one mowing or there can be plant damage. If a spinning blade bounces off the ground, it not only scalps the lawn below proper cutting height, but becomes dull.

Mowers mounted so they tilt with the vehicle's front axle greatly reduce scalping. If the front wheels follow ground contours so will the mower blades.

Scissors hitch-type mountings rely on the rear wheels to adjust the mower's vertical position. They are more prone to scalping on irregular lawn surfaces, since they are guided by terrain already passed over. Look for antiscalp rollers or wheels mounted on the front of the mower. They also greatly reduce the scalping tendency. The wider the ground-contact surfaces of those rollers, the more accurately they will guide the mower over bumps and slumps. Mowers suspended entirely from the vehicle and without antiscalping rollers, work well only on level lawns.

side vs. rear-discharge mowers

Side discharge mowers fan grass clippings over a wider area than do rear discharge machines, which are designed to leave a swath or clipping behind them.

If the rear discharge mowers have a chute between the vehicle's rear wheels, they will leave a relatively narrow swath of clippings and will keep you and the mower cleaner and safer from flying objects. A towed sweeper picks up all debris in one pass. Side discharge mowers with special bagging attachments can do a good job collecting clippings, but the lowest cost and fastest way to remove cuttings is to use a pull-behind sweeper. This lets you dump the clippings from the tractor seat.

front vs. rear engine

You'll get a greater feeling of security with a front rather than a rear engine. The front-engine

12 SHOPPING TIPS FOR SELECTING A MOWER, CONTINUED

7 Look for mufflers that direct exhaust away from the driving position and are shielded against possible contact that could cause nasty burns.

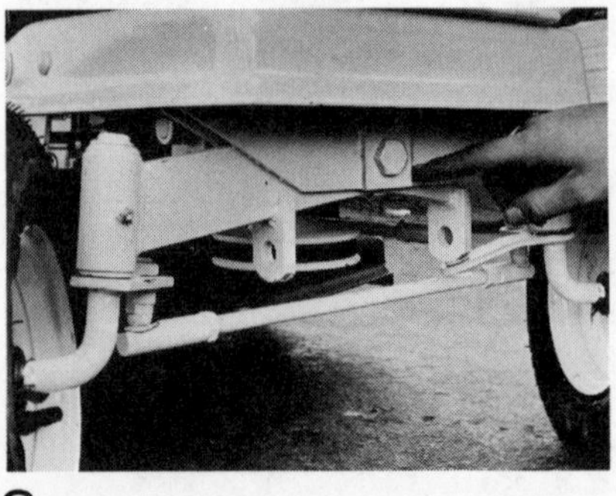

8 Front axles must be rugged to take constant pounding. They should be pivoted with a sturdy bolt under the front part of the frame.

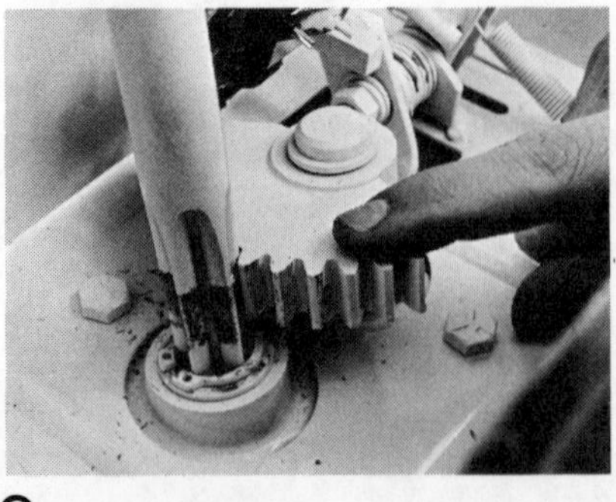

9 Geared, automotive-type steering allows more precise guidance than the "bent rod" type. Ask to see the steering in model you want.

TWO GOOD IDEAS IN LAWNMOWER DESIGN

SIMPLE PIECE of curved pipe on Simplicity tractor engines lets you drain oil without the black, greasy stuff drowning other tractor components. Just remove the cap and let the oil run into a container.

BOLENS puts a garden-hose fitting on top of its mower decks to aid cleanup. Twist a hose into the fitting, turn on the water and start the mower. The blades wash clippings out.

TWO DESIGN FEATURES THAT ARE QUESTIONABLE

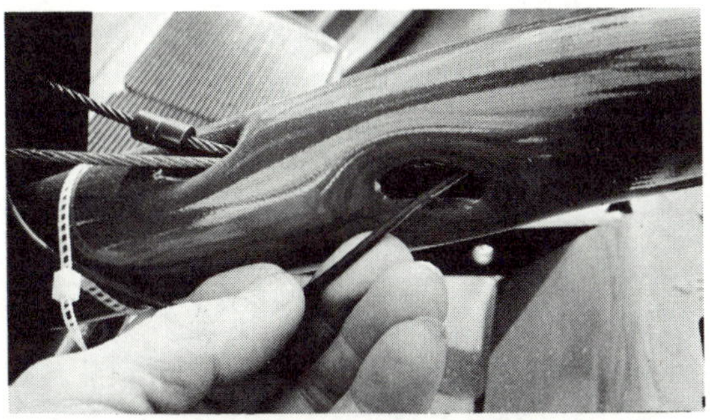

SHARP, METAL EDGES aided by vibration will soon chew through soft insulation around electrical wiring. If the line feeds into such an opening, it should be protected with a soft rubber grommet.

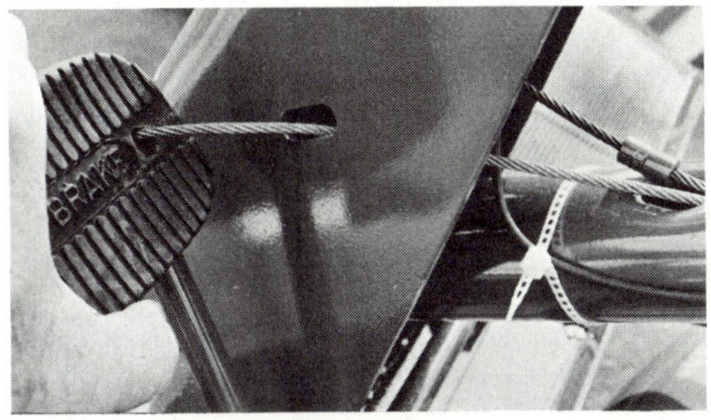

CABLE that abrades against rough-punched metal hole edges will fray. This weakens the cable. Also, sharp ends of frayed wire can catch clothing. Better alignment can eliminate this problem.

units actually do give greater uphill stability and are better at climbing steep grades. Engine weight placed forward reduces any tendency to tip over backward. As power is applied, leverage action causes a weight transfer which increases rear-wheel traction—especially important when you use a rear-mounted grass catcher. Vibration is reduced, too, since the engine is physically located farther away from operating position.

Rear-engine units, in turn, give greater forward visibility, are easier to get on and off and usually have less complicated traction-drive belting. You'll be wise to select a machine using belts with the fewest number of turns and twists.

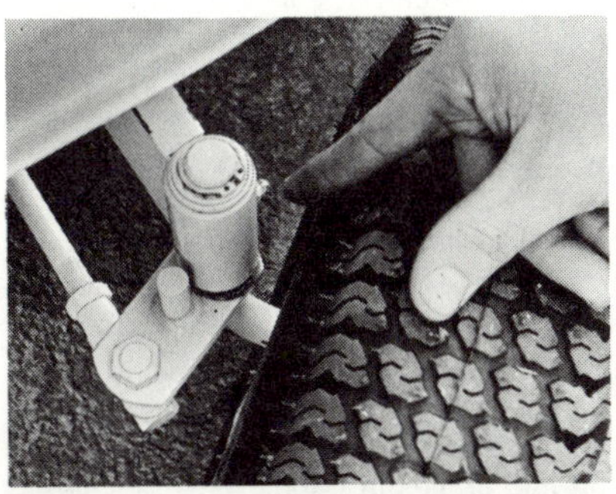

10 Standard grease fittings make maintenance servicing easier. Check to see that points needing regular lubrication are equipped with nipples.

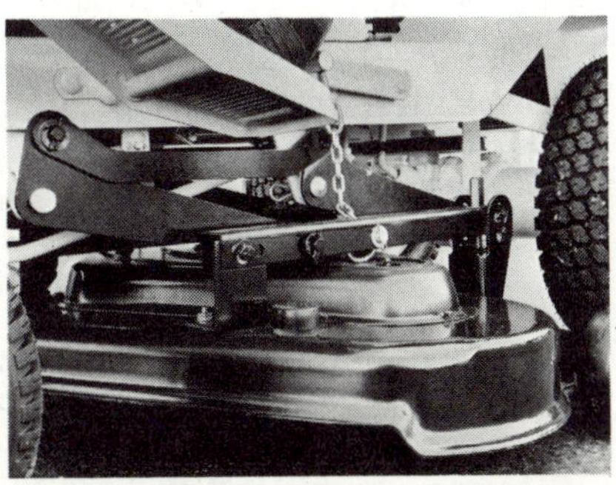

11 The mower mount should be of a heavy steel, pivoting on large-diameter pins and giving evidence of careful design, construction and finish.

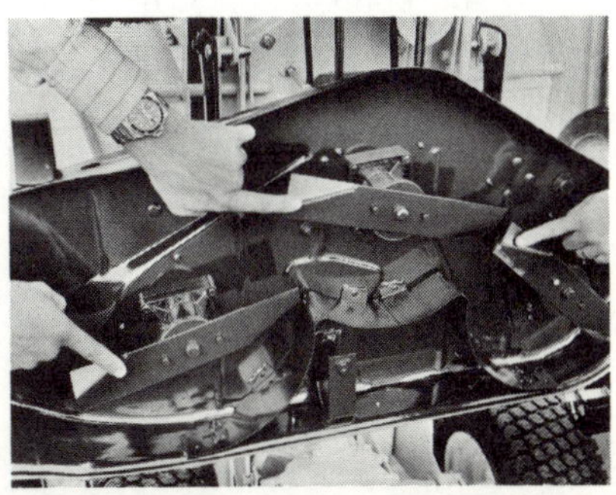

12 Finally, ask to look under the mower shroud. Check bearings, welds, blades, finish and baffles. This is the "working" part of your lawnmower.

Keep your power mower purring

A series of simple checks locates any problems. Then this sensible sequence makes diagnosis and repair of your power mower or yard tractor an easy, straightforward matter

FAILURE TO START, hard starting and stalling are common mid-season problems that strike gasoline-powered lawnmowers and tractors. The most common causes include lack of compression, lack of or too much fuel in the cylinder, and no spark.

But a major reason for trouble can often be averted by knowing the difference between four and two-cycle engines: In four-cycle engines, ignition occurs with every fourth stroke of the piston. Four-cycle engines burn straight gasoline and possess a separate lubrication (oiling) system. It is imperative that gas and oil *not* be mixed.

In two-cycle engines, ignition occurs every second stroke of the piston. The engine runs on a mixture of oil and gasoline, and failure to mix the correct proportions of gas and oil *properly* is the single greatest cause of trouble (other than sparkplug failure). If yours is a two-cycle engine, consult the owner's manual to determine correct proportions and what kind of gas and oil is recommended. Gas and oil should be thoroughly mixed in a clean container *before* you pour it into the fuel tank.

SEE ALSO

Engines, small . . . Grass . . . Landscaping . . . Lawns . . . Snowblowers . . . Snowplows . . . Tractor lifts . . . Tractor trailers . . . Trees

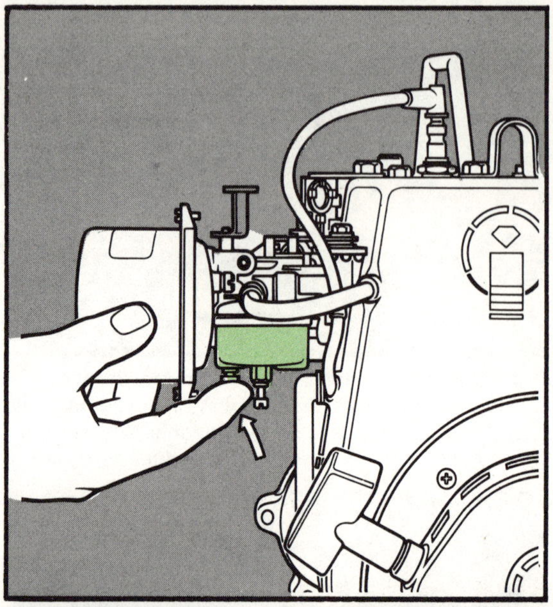

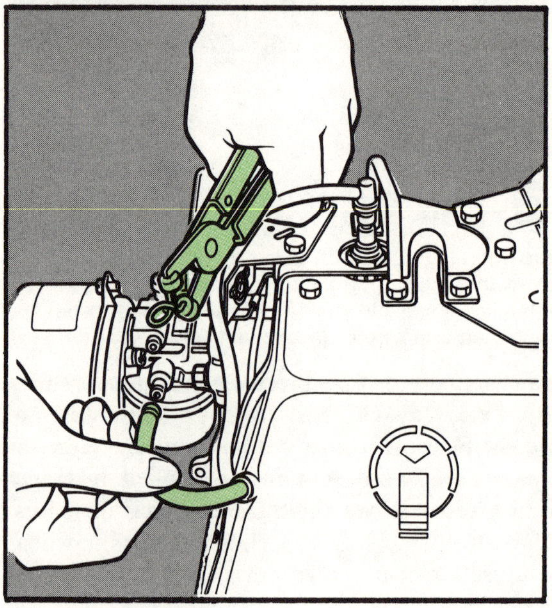

Engine won't start

An engine won't start or will stall if fuel isn't getting to the carburetor, and from the carburetor to the cylinder. First, remove the sparkplug and inject two or three squirts of fuel into the cylinder using a clean oil can. Reinsert the plug and crank the engine. If it doesn't start, the cause of the trouble is elsewhere, but if the engine does start, runs for a few seconds and then stops, the problem will be found in the fuel system.

See if there's a drain valve in the base of the carburetor bowl. Press it (top). If no fuel leaks, there's an obstruction in the fuel line or fuel tank. If fuel leaks, there's probably an obstruction in the carburetor. If there is no drain valve, disconnect the fuel line at the bowl (bottom). If no fuel comes out, look for a blocked fuel line or obstruction in the fuel tank. If fuel leaks, a fouled carburetor is probably the cause.

Blocked fuel line

If the fuel line is blocked, the first step is to check for contaminated fuel. Let some fuel drop into your hand; if water and dirt remain after the gas evaporates, dump all fuel and wash the fuel tank thoroughly with kerosene. It may also be necessary to clean the fuel line and carburetor.

To trouble shoot when fuel isn't getting to the carburetor:

- Replace a bent or clogged fuel line.
- Tighten all carburetor bolts, fuel-line connections and fuel-pump housing (if present) because air leaks destroy the vacuum necessary to pull fuel to the carburetor.
- Clean choke linkage and choke-plate pivots; repair damaged choke parts. Lack of choking action will make the engine hard to start; a choke stuck in the closed position will flood the engine and prevent starts.
- Clean or replace a dirty fuel filter. One kind is a wire-mesh screen in the fuel line shutoff adapter; other engines have filter bowls.
- Replace the fuel-pump diaphragm if it has any holes.
- Clean clogged screens of fuel pipes that extend from the carburetor into the fuel tank of diaphragm-type carburetors (those without separate fuel pump).

If fuel is not getting from carburetor to engine:

- Clean the air cleaner to reduce flooding.
- Lightly tap the bowl of a float-type carburetor with a screwdriver to loosen a stuck needle valve.
- Adjust the carburetor. Back out the idle-mix screw one turn from finger-tight. Turn the speed screw *in* one turn from where it first touches the throttle lever.
- Last, strip and clean the carburetor thoroughly.

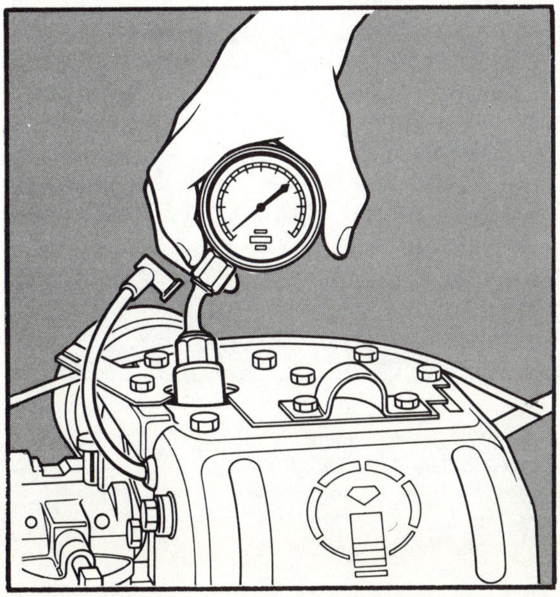

Inadequate compression

Stated simply, compression is the ability of the piston to compress the fuel/air mixture. Inadequate compression leads to hard starting and loss of power. Poor compression results when a cylinder is scored, piston rings stick or wear, valves stick or wear, or the crankshaft oil seal is damaged. The pressure loss reduces compression, which makes ignition more difficult.

One obvious sign that there is compression loss is a sloppy manual starting cord. If the cord offers little resistance and doesn't snap back, then sufficient compression is questionable.

An accurate check can be made with a compression gauge. Remove the sparkplug, insert the gauge fitting firmly, and crank the engine until the gauge reaches its maximum reading. The *minimum* compression of two-cycle engines is 60 psi; of four-cycles of 4½ hp or less, 65 psi; and of four-cycles above 4½ hp, 70 psi.

Compression loss may be caused by a loose sparkplug. Seat the plug by hand and give it one-half turn with a socket wrench.

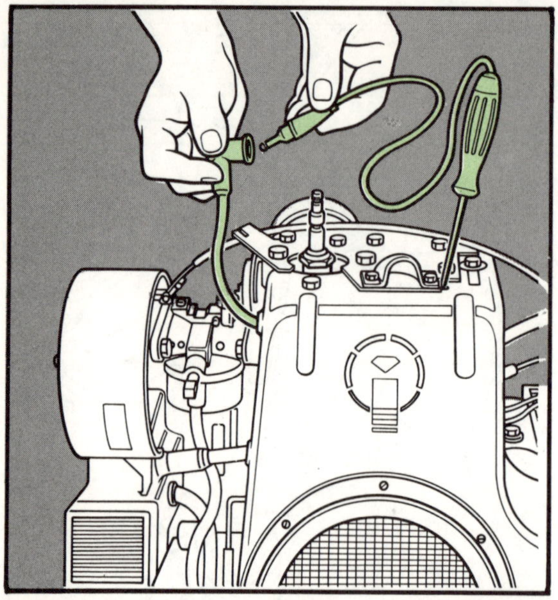

Garden tractors

Garden tractors with high-horsepower engines usually have transformer-coil ignition systems that are like those in cars, but must powermowers use a magneto system. Magnetos make their own electricity by a magnet-equipped flywheel that revolves around stationary field coils.

You can test a magneto system by gapping either a 14-mm or an 18-mm sparkplug to 5/32-3/16-in. Attach it to the sparkplug lead and ground it against the cylinder head as you crank the engine. A blue spark should jump the electrode gap.

The same test can be made of a transformer-coil ignition system, but use the engine's sparkplug at its normal gap.

Use a spark-intensity tester for checking breakerless systems (left). Disconnect the lead from the sparkplug and attach the tester to the lead's metal terminal. Touch the test instrument's probe to a ground as you crank the engine. The test light will flash if the system is operating properly.

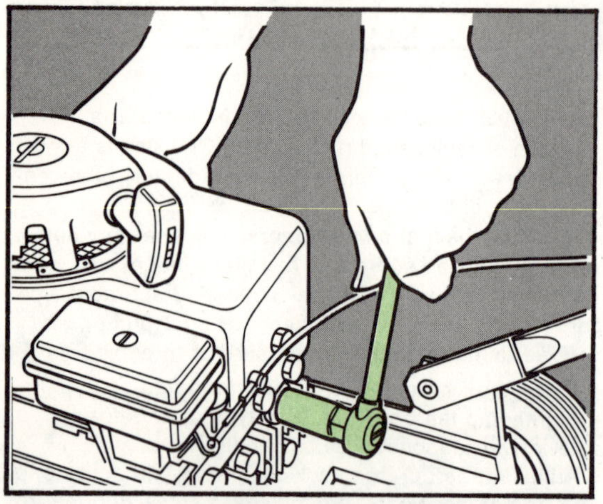

About sparkplugs

The sparkplug is one of the biggest single causes of engine problems. First, check the owner's manual to make sure you're using the right one. Then make certain the plug lead is connected tightly to the plug terminal, and to the magneto or coil output. If the lead's insulation is cracked, replace the lead. Buy a new sparkplug if the insulator is damaged or if electrodes are worn, burned or heavily coated with carbon or oil. Carbon on a plug usually means an engine is operating on an overly rich fuel mixture or that the ignition output is below par; oil on electrodes usually means that piston rings or valve stems (four-cycle engine) are worn; burned electrodes indicate that the engine is probably overheating.

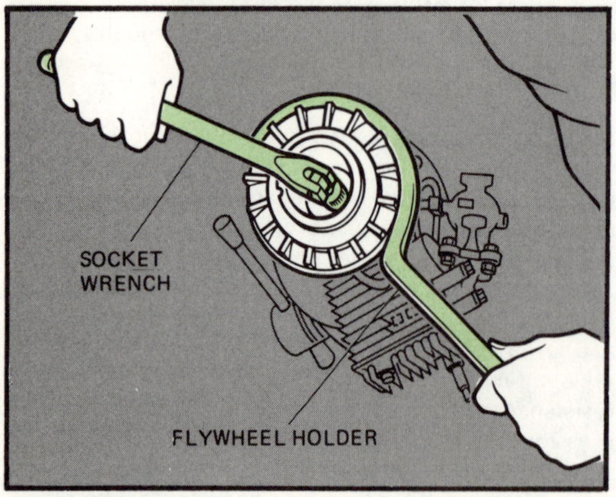

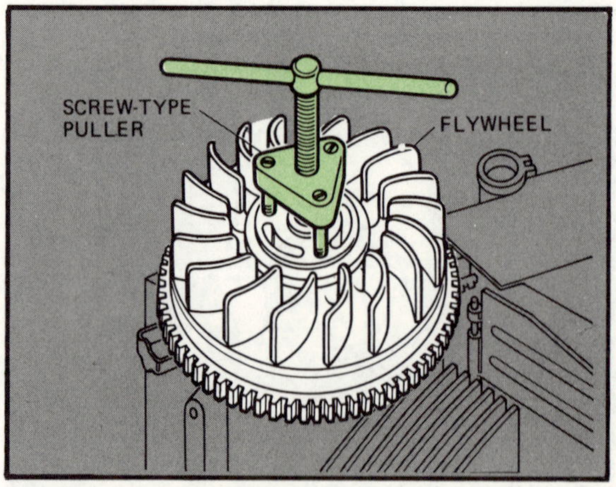

Magneto repair

To repair a magneto ignition you have to remove the flywheel. On most two-cycle engines, first remove the flywheel nut. Some of these nuts have a right-hand thread; others, left-hand. If the flywheel moves as you turn the nut, hold it fast with a flywheel holder. With the nut off, it can usually be removed. On most four-cycle engines, hold the flywheel with a flywheel holder as the flywheel nut is removed. Install a knockout puller, hold the flywheel firmly, and rap the puller with a hammer to jar the flywheel loose.

Varnish with the shakes

I was told never to shake varnish before use, but I have not been told why. What happens when you do?—H.P., Miss.

Replacing the lid on an opened can may trap air inside, producing bubbles in the varnish if you shake the can. Your brush will pick up these bubbles and lay them on the surface being finished. When the varnish is drying, the bubbles will form tiny flecks that you can feel on the surface. Always stir—never shake—varnish.

Faucet washers wear out

I have to replace washers in bath and kitchen faucets every six months or so. The seats seem to be in good condition, yet the old washers have rather deep grooves when examined closely. What's wrong, or what am I doing wrong?—Frank J. Hall, Bergenfield, N.J.

You may be using washers of the wrong size or type, or you may need to resurface the washer seats with a resurfacing tool made for the purpose. Usually this special tool is available from a local rental service at a nominal charge. Be sure that the washers you're using are of the correct size.

'Blooming' finish

I've just removed a chest of drawers and a vanity from the basement where they had been stored, covered with newspapers to protect against dust. Now the finish seems to have turned a milky white that doesn't come off readily. Is there any way to correct this damage, or must I refinish?—Nancy Holston, Louisville, Ky.

The "milky white" you see is referred to as "blooming" of the finish and removal is no easy task. First try rubbing with a half-and-half mixture of boiled linseed oil and turpentine kept warm in a pan of warm water. Use a clean, lintless cloth in a rub-on and rub-off motion. There's a chance that this will clean up the milky color and restore the finish. If not, then complete refinishing of the furniture is the only sure cure.

Changeable wood joints

I cured a problem with "sweating" windows by covering the crawlspace with roofing paper. Now I notice that joints in trim, wall cabinets and floorboards contract in winter and expand in summer, leaving unsightly gaps. Will this cause any problems, damage? Also, should crawlspace vents be open during winter, summer?—Robert J. Pfaff, Richmond, Va.

You might have done better to have covered the crawlspace with a plastic membrane, sealed at overlapped joints and carried up foundation walls a foot or more. However, since the roofing accomplishes the desired result, a change is hardly worthwhile now. Opening and closing of trim joints seasonally is usually due to a rather high moisture content of the wood when installed. In time this generally corrects itself without serious damage.

As a rule, crawlspace vents should be left open winter and summer.

Vulnerable veneer

I applied birch veneer over ¾-in. plywood and had to leave the job partially finished. Now, two months later, the veneer has a quite uniform ridged and rippled appearance. Apparently it loosened from the plywood. Am I finished or is there some hope of salvaging it?—Pat Percival, Bay Village, Ohio.

You may have used too much glue. I'm afraid you'll have to do the job over; but first you might try several methods of fixing it. First, place a piece of aluminum foil on the veneer to protect it, then go over it with a medium-hot iron to melt the glue. Next roll the veneer firmly to squeeze out excess glue and weight down the veneer overnight.

If that doesn't work, make slits in the veneer ripples in the direction of the grain, using a sharp modeler's knife. Put glue in slits with a syringe-type glue injector and press the veneer overnight.

Smoky oil-burning furnace

Occasionally there is a puff and flow of smoke from the warm-air heating ducts, and a heavy odor of oil is present in the rooms. The furnace has been checked over by our local heating service but the trouble still persists. Can you suggest a cause and remedy?—Mrs. Robert Ermer, Hawkins, Wis.

If, as you say, the installation has been checked but no operational defects have been discovered, then it would seem, judging from your description of performance, that a possible cause of a smoke and fume leak is a crack or break in the furnace. If the break is small, it usually is possible to repair with refractory furnace cement. This can be determined with certainty only by an on-the-spot check of the fire chamber. I have to assume that the burner has been properly adjusted and that all other routine checks have been carried out.

Super-simple cabinets organize mud-room clutter or stow a convertible dishwasher out of the way

Hideaways for kitchen and laundry

By WAYNE C. LECKEY

A MUD ROOM need not look like a mud room. It can be the gay and colorful entry you see here. With shelves standing by to corral boots, lunch boxes, jump ropes and baseball gear, the family back-door entry takes on anything but the look of a corner catch-all. When the shelves are painted lively colors to tie in with matching colors on the entry door itself, the overall effect adds a touch of excitement.

There's nothing to making such a shelf unit. For maximum simplicity, the whole thing, except for the back, is made from stock 1 x 10 boards which you just saw to length. If rabbets pose a problem to cut, forget them and let the plywood back lap the rear edges. The jigsawed letters can be the youngsters' initials.

When a convertible dishwasher can join in and be a part of a cooking/serving center, it's almost better than having a built-in unit, even when

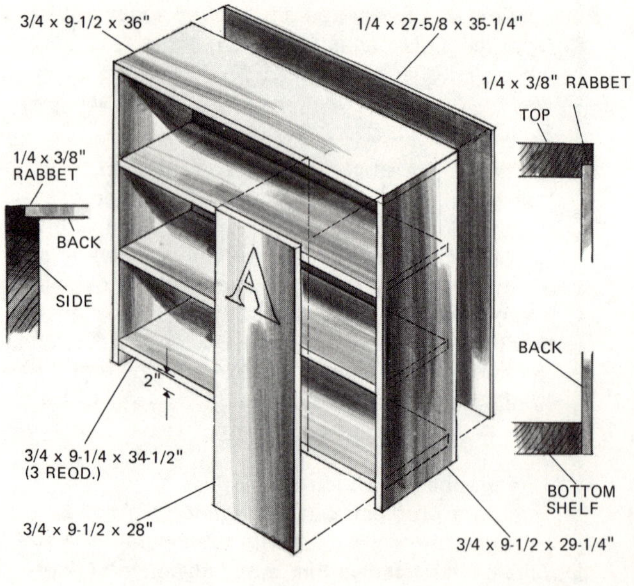

SEE ALSO

Cabinets, kitchen . . . Clothes dryers . . . Dishwashers . . . Drawers . . . Kitchen accessories . . . Washing machines

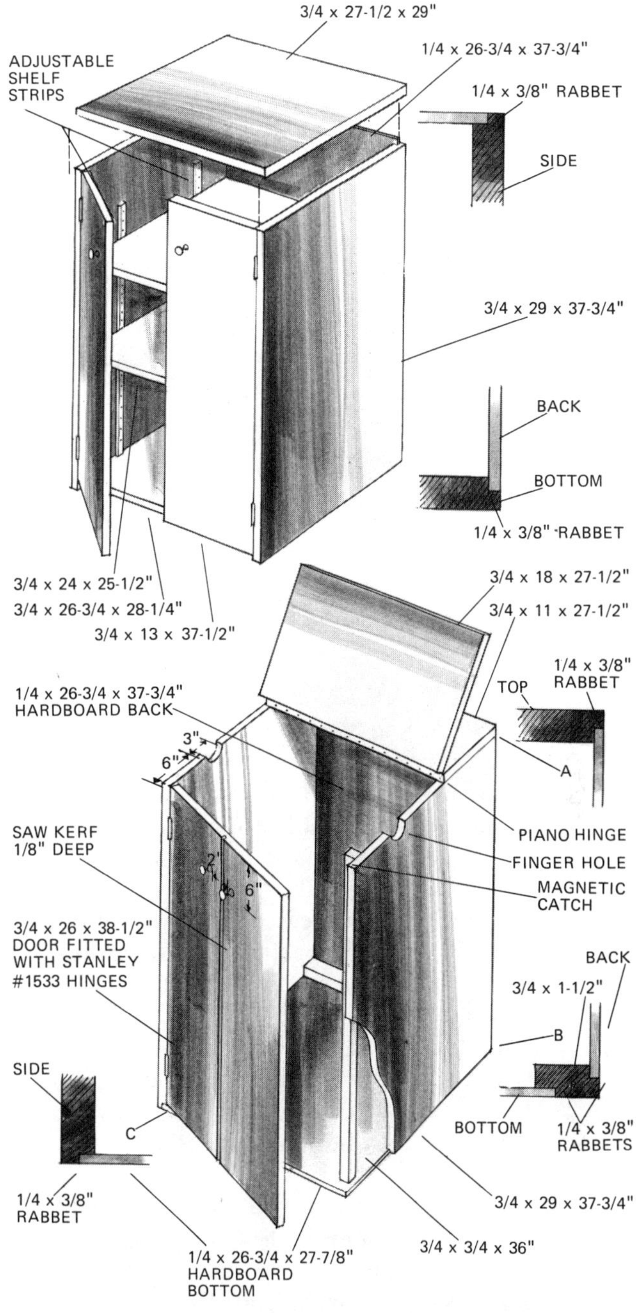

there is room for one. In this case there wasn't, but there was still the question of where to park a convertible out of sight when not in use. The answer was the clever side-by-side storage unit, shown above, which provides not only the perfect hideaway for a convertible dishwasher but also lots of storage for small appliances and bulky serving dishes as well. What's more, the top of the hideaway lifts up to reveal a handy wood cutting block perched on top of the dishwasher. When it's completely closed, no one would ever guess there's a dishwasher parked inside.

The twin cabinets have wipe-clean plastic-laminate tops and sides covered with natural grass-cloth vinyl accented with screen molding painted bright orange to match countertops.

Both boxlike cabinets are identical in overall size, the washer cabinet being dimensioned to accept a Maytag convertible. Except for the ¼-in.-hardboard bottom of the washer cabinet and the backs of both, ¾-in. plywood is used throughout. The joinery can be simplified where the work is being done primarily with hammer and saw. Rabbet joints add to overall sturdiness and offer no problem when you have a table saw. However, the backs can be merely lapped and nailed. The washer cabinet has a single door made to look like double doors by running a saw kerf down the middle.

By JOE KELLEHER

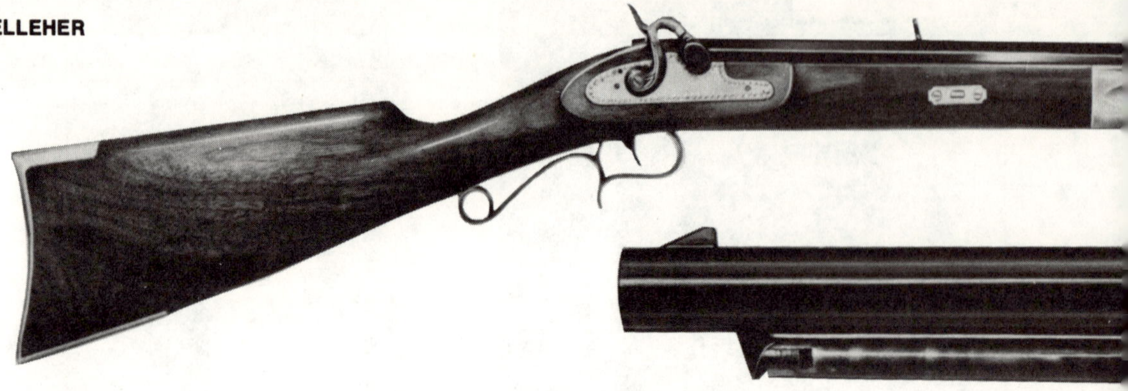

The old art of muzzleloading

IN THE 100 YEARS after the founding of the United States, the black powder muzzleloading rifle was the principal weapon of the military and an essential tool for settlers moving west. These rifles put meat on the table for generations of Americans, held off the Indians and knocked down marauding grizzlies. The old charcoal burners finally got pushed aside by the introduction of the metallic cartridge, but recently they've been making a smoky comeback to the shooting scene.

Until a few years ago, shooters had to rely on a dwindling supply of original models if they got bit by the muzzleloading bug. These original guns have not only become increasingly expensive, but neglect and lack of replacement parts have made many of them much less than reliable. Today, however, some of the finest flintlock and percussion rifles ever made—plus a full line of accessories—are being produced again. You can have your pick from a range of target models, with adjustable sights, to authentic copies of famous military and hunting rifles.

SEE ALSO
Gun cabinets . . . Gun racks . . . Hunting . . . Marksmanship . . . Shooting . . . Shotguns

One of the most popular muzzleloaders sold today is a Hawken, produced by Thompson/Center Arms Co. The original of this rifle was made, starting in 1822, by the Hawken brothers in Saint Louis for fur traders and explorers pushing westward. This half-stocked rifle, weighing 8½ pounds, has a 28-inch octagon barrel with 12 lands and grooves.

Available in .45 or .50 cal., the model has polished brass trim on the butt plate, fore-end cap, ramrod fittings, patch box and trigger guard. Open hunting sights are micrometer-adjustable to simplify sighting in. Double-set triggers enable the shooter to squeeze off consistent 1½-inch, five-shot groups at 50 yards. A caplock and a flintlock version are being made. With either model, Thompson/Center offers an accessory pack with bullet mold, package of patches, powder measure, short bullet starter, powder solvent, extra nipple and nipple wrench—all for one low price which is well worth it for the beginner.

Hawken rifles are also produced by the Navy

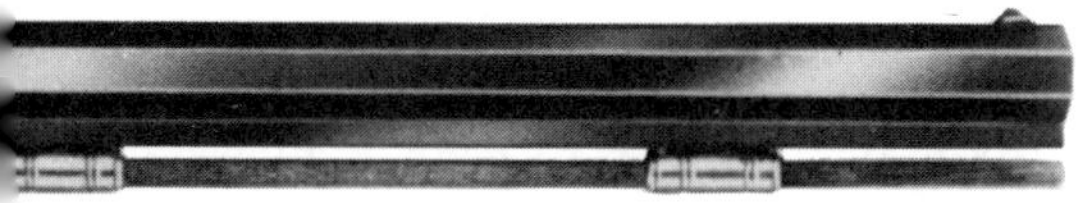

HAWKEN HURRICANE, in .45 or .50 cal., and the Hawken Hunter in .58 cal. with a magnum ignition system and micrometer-adjustable open hunting sights are both modeled after the Hawken brothers' fur-trader rifles of the 1820s. They are now made by Navy Arms who claim you will get four-inch groups at 100 yards from benchrest.

1860 PERCUSSION ARMY revolver from the Reloading Products Div. of Lyman has eight-inch barrel and fires a .451 round ball or Lyman hollow-base conical ball. It comes with a single-cavity .451 round ball mold with handles, precut patches, six spare nipples, nipple wrench, Hodgen's Spit Ball and a Lyman manual.

Arms Co. whose Hawken Hurricane comes in .45 and .50 cal., while their new Hawken Hunter is an elephant gun magnum in .58 cal. that has been tested on African safari.

For the military buff, Lyman offers the .58-cal. 1863 Zouave of Civil War fame. A natural for those interested in the War Between the States, the Zouave was claimed to be the most accurate military rifle of its day. With careful loading and practice, it can produce surprisingly tight groups or knock down the heaviest U.S. game. It's from Lyman, and a small additional cost will bring you a kit with .58 Minié-ball mold, spare nipple, nipple wrench, bullet lube and Lyman's Black Powder Manual.

REVOLUTIONARY LAND PATTERN "Brown Bess" musket is a ready-to-shoot 42-inch 10½-pound replica from Lyman Products for Shooters. The gun is .75 cal. Graduated Powder Measure of solid brass (at right) adjusts to hold up to 120 grains of black powder in 10-grain increments. It is manufactured by Michaels of Oregon.

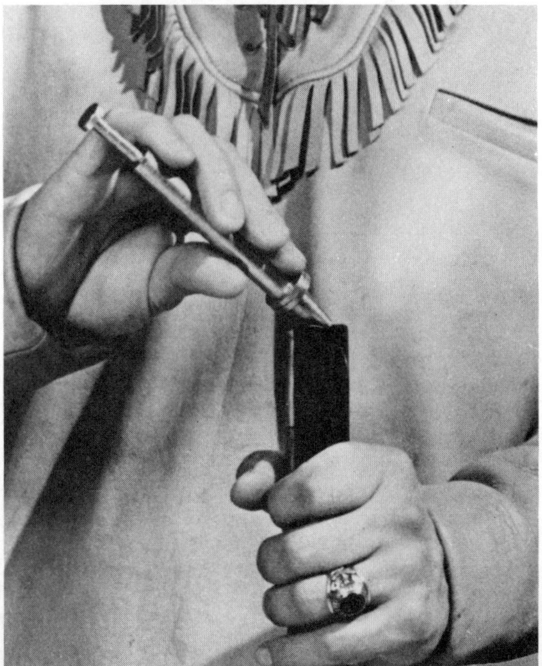

The Kentucky long rifle, often called a squirrel gun, was a favorite of famous frontiersmen. Hopkins & Allen has reproduced a fine model called the Minuteman. Available in flintlock or percussion, the full-stocked 55-inch rifle has a 39-inch octagonal barrel bored for .36 or .45-cal. balls. The 9½-pound Minuteman is ready to fire, or comes as a kit. All metal parts in the Hopkins & Allen kits are ready to be fitted. Only a rasp and sandpaper are needed to finish the stock, which is machine inletted, drilled and fully formed.

Building your muzzleloader is fun, but the real challenge is shooting. Each shot fired from a charcoal burner is a test of your skill as a loader as well as marksman. Accuracy with either flint or percussion rifles depends on careful fitting of the patched ball to the bore, and then carefully ramming the ball down onto the measured charge of black powder in one smooth stroke. For smaller bore rifles of .45 cal. and under, the patched ball is best. But the big-bore weapons, .50 cal. and up, can produce accurate results with hollow base bullets called Minié balls. Loaded without a patch, the lubricated Minié has a cavity in the base that expands to engage the rifling in the bore.

Loading technique starts with drying the bore with a clean patch and snapping off a percussion cap or two to clear the nipple. Set the butt on the ground with the muzzle pointed away from you and pour a measured amount of powder down the barrel. Lubricate a precut patch with saliva and lay it over the muzzle. Place the lead ball in the bore with the sprue pointing up. Using a short ramrod called a ball starter, push the ball into the bore until it is flush with the muzzle. Trim off any excess patch with a sharp knife and push the ball into the bore using the starter. Then switch to your ramrod and seat the ball on the powder with one smooth, uninterrupted stroke. Banging or tamping the ball can result in a de-

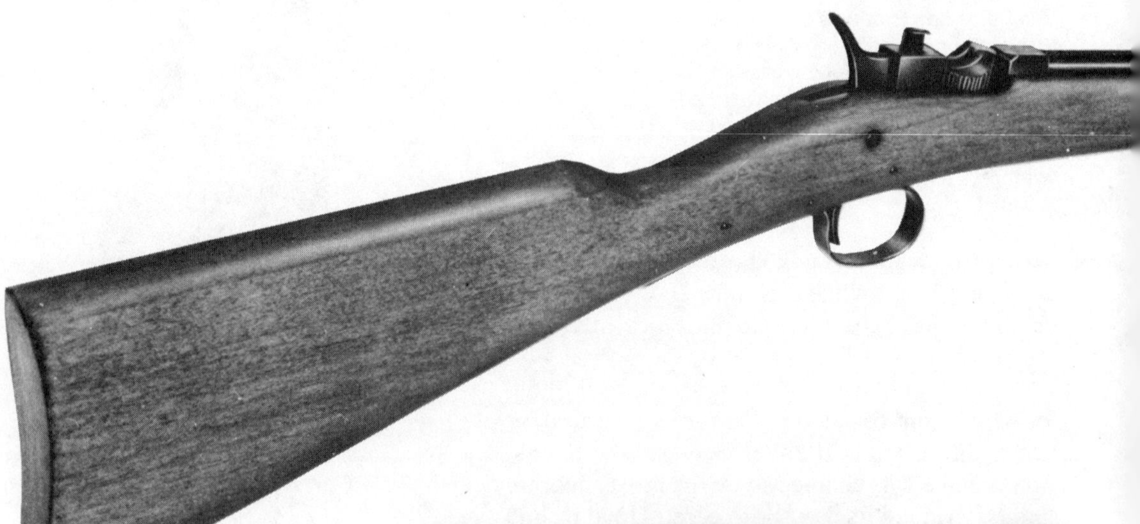

A .22-CAL. model for boys and beginning shooters, the RMAC breech loader makes a single-shot first rifle that can fire up to 250 shots for about $1. Breech turret holds ball and only the correct safe load of powder and cap. Sear safety blocks hammer until turret locks close. Traditional black powder rifle is by Rocky Mountain Arms. Old English muskets, arranged for antique auction at right, are valuable but more dangerous to fire than modern replicas.

formed ball, a compressed powder charge or an air space between the ball and the charge. Deformed balls are inaccurate, compressed powder often misfires and an airspace can cause a bulged or split barrel.

Now with the charge and ball seated, put the hammer on full-cock and press a cap on the nipple. You're set to take aim and fire.

If a Minié ball is used, the procedure is simplified. After the charge is poured down the barrel, the Minié is pushed into the barrel by hand and seated with the ramrod. Add a cap and fire. After firing, leave the cap on the nipple to smother any sparks from the preceding shot. Whether you use a patched ball or a Minié, accuracy depends on perfecting your loading technique. Don't hurry, stick to a set routine, and you'll find that speed comes with practice.

Black powder shooting is not for the white-suited fastidious marksman, however. After a dozen or more shots, the shooter and his gun will be liberally covered with soot. While the soot scrubs off the shooter's skin easily, his gun is a lot harder to clean. Black powder soot is very hygroscopic—which means it tends to soak up moisture from the air. Within hours, depending on humidity, an uncleaned black powder gun can start to rust, so precautions must be taken as soon as a shooting session is over.

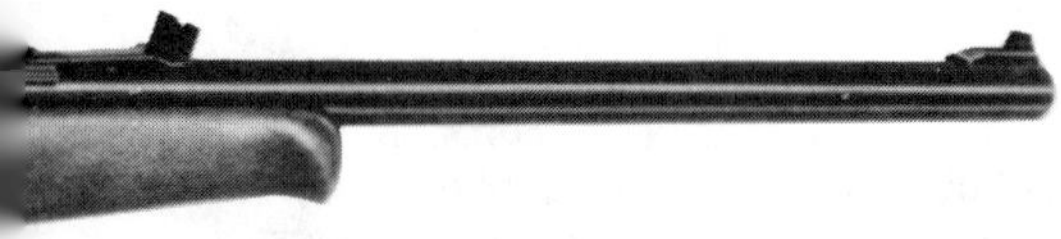

BLACK POWDER ready-to-fire replicas are shown in the photo below. They are from top to bottom, an 1855 Buffalo Hunter; 1841 Mississippi Rifle; 1864 Remington Zouave Rifle; 1797 Kentucky Percussion; 1797 Kentucky Flintlock Carbine. They are all manufactured and available from the Navy Arms Co., Ridgefield, NJ.

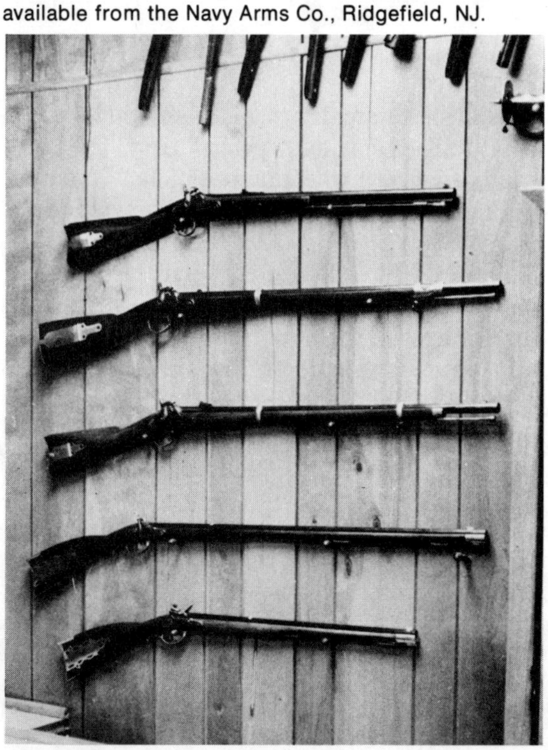

Several good black powder solvents are available to soften up the soot and speed cleaning, but to really clean a black-powder muzzleloader there is no substitute for hot water, soap and lots of elbow grease. Start by putting a piece of rubber over the nipple and letting the hammer down to hold it in place. This seals the barrel which can then be filled with really hot, soapy water. A plastic or aluminum funnel in the muzzle will help get the hot water into the barrel rather than on the shooter. Let the hot water soak for about 15 minutes to soften up the powder fouling.

Then dump the water and run soapy patches through the bore until they come out clean. Next fill the barrel with clean hot water to flush out the soap. After flushing several times with hot water, the barrel should be quite hot. Run patches through the hot barrel until they come out absolutely clean and dry.

oil before reassembling

Next step is to clean the breech area with a damp cloth. A toothbrush is ideal to get into those crevices and crannies around the nipple and tang. If you intend not to shoot the gun for some time, remove the nipple and clean it thoroughly. While the gun is still warm from the hot water, apply oil to all metal parts and reassemble. Check your gun for the next few days to make sure you have removed all the fouling and no rust is commencing. The bore should be swabbed with a clean patch and reoiled. Your muzzleloader will last for generations if cleaned thoroughly after firing and kept well oiled and cared for as outlined here.

For a beginner thinking about getting started and the experienced shooter as well, Lyman's 26-page booklet, *Black Powder Basics,* is one of the best guides for accurate muzzleload-shooting sport. The booklet provides clear and simple how-to information on loading flint and caplock rifles, bullet casting, patched and Minié balls, accuracy tips, loads and cleaning. And with nearly 75 models of rifles, shotguns and pistols now produced for the sport, a muzzleloader can look forward to endless collecting and shooting fun.

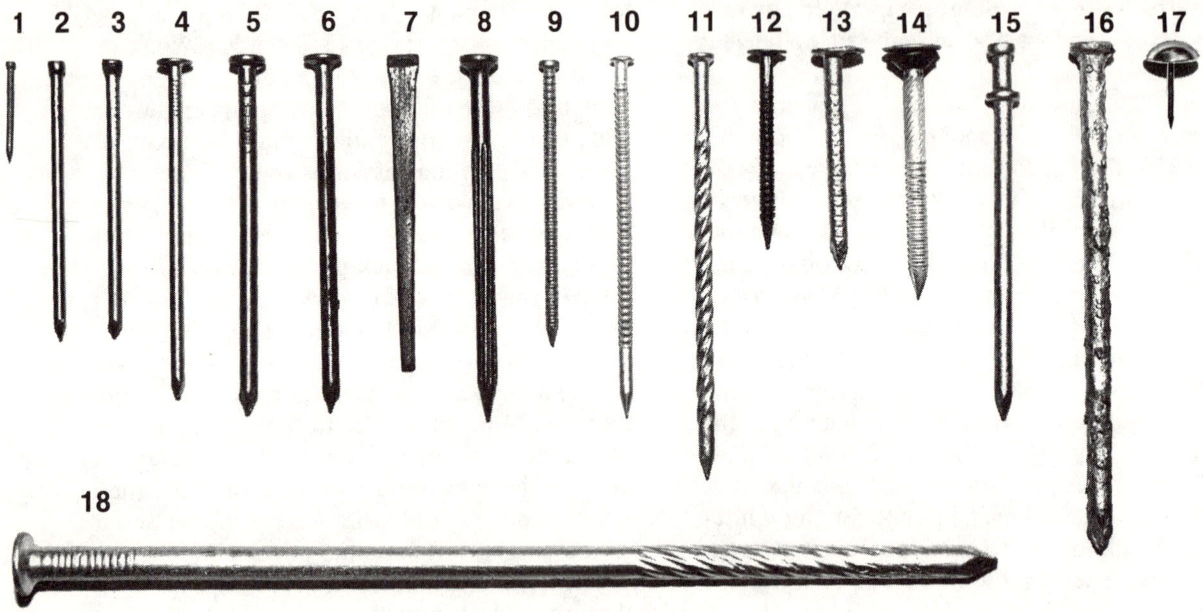

A LINEUP of useful nails: (1) brad; (2) finishing; (3) casing; (4) box; (5) common; (6) cement-coated box; (7) cut flooring; (8) fluted masonry; (9) wood shingle; (10) asbestos shingle; (11) exterior hardboard; (12) drywall; (13) barbed roofing; (14) neoprene-seal roofing; (15) double head; (16) hot-dipped galvanized; (17) upholstery; (18) gutter spike (also comes with chisel point).

Drive the right nail

By ROSARIO CAPOTOSTO

■ NAILS PROVIDE one of the simplest and easiest ways to fasten things. But all nails are not the same. So in order to do a job properly and most effectively, you should know some basics about the variety of nails that are available. The following guidelines—prepared with the help of the nail-producing people at Armco's Western Steel Div.—will enable you to match the nail properly to the job.

Nails differ according to size, shape, material and finish. In various combinations, these factors have a direct bearing on the intended use of the nail.

SEE ALSO

Bolts . . . Fasteners . . . Hardboard . . . Lumber . . . Measurements . . . Roofs . . . Screws . . . Sheathing . . . Shingles . . . Siding . . . Upholstery

Nail lengths are designated (somewhat confusingly) in both inch and "penny" sizes. The latter is indicated by a whole number followed with a small "d," which is an ancient abbreviation for penny (See *History of Penny-sizing,* page 1955). Generally, as the length of a nail increases, so does its diameter or gauge. Nail gauge refers to the diameter of the wire from which it is made. No. 1 gauge is the largest; 20 gauge, the smallest.

Shapes of nailheads, shanks and points vary considerably. Nail finishes can be bright, cement-coated or galvanized.

For use around the home and shop, nails may be grouped in two categories: general-purpose and special-purpose. General-purpose nails are available in four types—box, common, casing and finishing.

Common nails have a large, flat head, smooth shank and diamond point. They are used for all types of general construction and rough carpentry where appearance is not of primary importance.

Box nails are similar to common nails with one important difference: The box nail has a larger-diameter head in relation to shank diameter. The large heads of both nails hold the nailed member securely by spreading the load or grip over a broad area. When nailing thin stock—which has a tendency to split with a thick-shank common nail—the thin-shank box nail is used instead. The alternative is to predrill holes in the top member, which is tedious and time-consuming.

Casing and finishing nails have very small heads and are the choice for cabinet work, molding, window and door trim, and wherever a finished appearance is important. Both are available with either a cupped or flat brad head.

Cupped versions have a slight indentation in the head to accommodate a nail-setting tool. A nailset is used to sink the nailhead slightly below the surface. The hole is filled and sanded for total concealment.

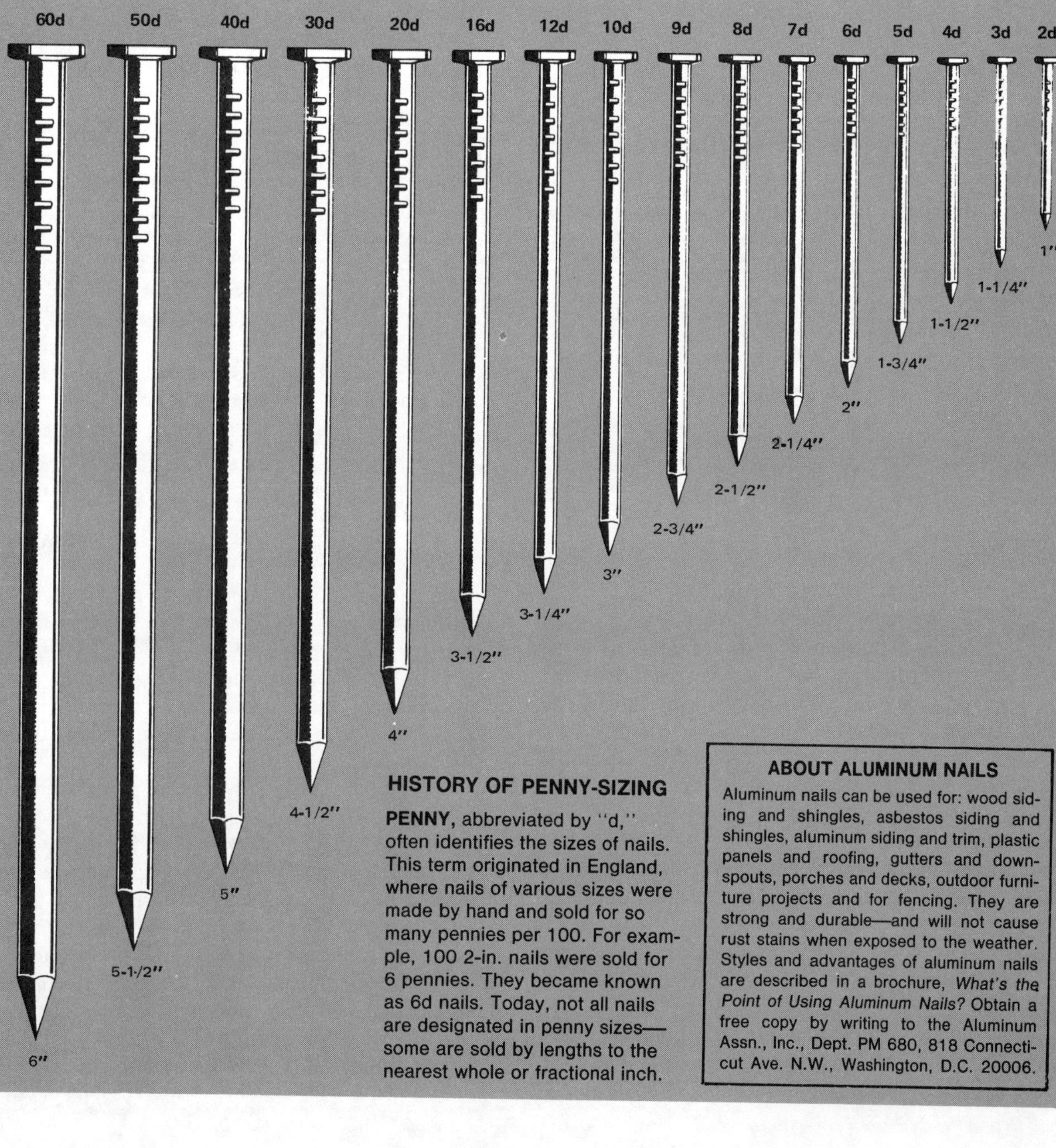

HISTORY OF PENNY-SIZING

PENNY, abbreviated by "d," often identifies the sizes of nails. This term originated in England, where nails of various sizes were made by hand and sold for so many pennies per 100. For example, 100 2-in. nails were sold for 6 pennies. They became known as 6d nails. Today, not all nails are designated in penny sizes—some are sold by lengths to the nearest whole or fractional inch.

ABOUT ALUMINUM NAILS

Aluminum nails can be used for: wood siding and shingles, asbestos siding and shingles, aluminum siding and trim, plastic panels and roofing, gutters and downspouts, porches and decks, outdoor furniture projects and for fencing. They are strong and durable—and will not cause rust stains when exposed to the weather. Styles and advantages of aluminum nails are described in a brochure, *What's the Point of Using Aluminum Nails?* Obtain a free copy by writing to the Aluminum Assn., Inc., Dept. PM 680, 818 Connecticut Ave. N.W., Washington, D.C. 20006.

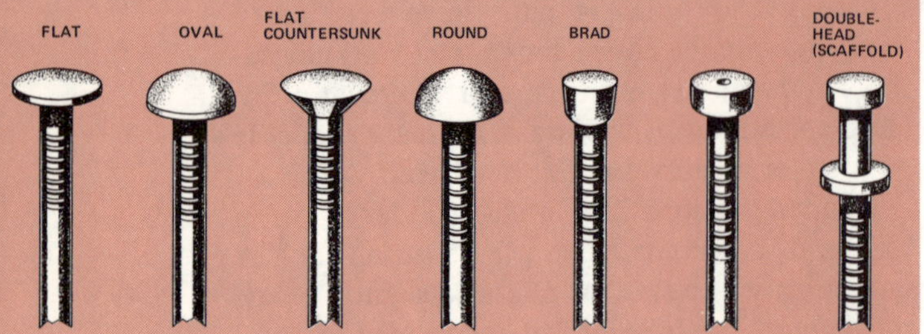

NAILHEADS PROVIDE a striking surface and help keep the joint from pulling apart. The head shape is usually determined by the desired finished appearance.

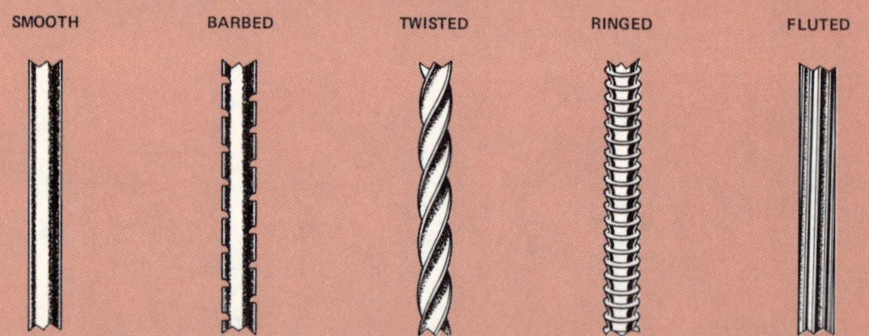

NAIL SHANKS are responsible for how effectively a nail grips material into which it is driven. Hold, due to friction, is improved by barbs, twisted ridges and rings.

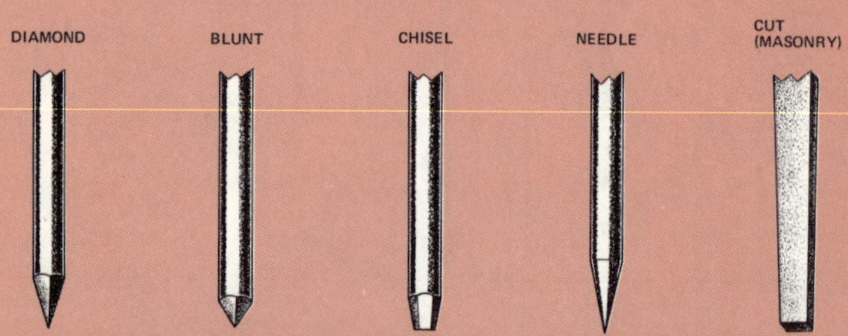

POINT OF A NAIL facilitates penetration into material being nailed. A blunted point sacrifices some ease of penetration in order to minimize splitting.

Nails with flat brad heads are intended to be driven flush to the surface. They cannot be set properly because the nailset tends to slide off the smooth surface.

The difference between the casing and finishing nail is similar to the difference between the common and box nail—a casing nail is thicker than a finishing nail of equal length. Brads are small finishing nails sized from ⅜ to 1 in. They're designated by inch length and gauge rather than penny size.

In general, the proper nail size is dictated by the thickness of the surface board being nailed: The nail should penetrate two times the thickness of the top board to gain sufficient holding power. For example, when nailing through nominal 1-in. stock (¾ in. actual), the nail should be at least 2¼ in. long (7d or 8d). Of course, there are exceptions to this rule. It won't hold when fastening 1/32-in. sheet metal, for instance.

nails for special jobs

The above-mentioned nails will do fine for average nailing requirements, but they won't do when you need extra holding power or rust resistance, or when you want to attach plasterboard, hardwood flooring, roofing or wood to masonry. For these jobs, a variety of special-purpose nails have been developed with distinct advantages for particular applications.

Most special-purpose nails are named to signify their specific use, such as for roofing, drywall, underlayment and masonry. Others are named for significant characteristics, such as ringed, cement-coated, galvanized and double-head.

Different physical characteristics bring about the improvements in special nails. Extra holding power is achieved by special shank shapes, such as barbed, twisted, fluted and ringed. When an ordinary nail is driven into wood, the squeeze of the displaced fibers against the nail serves to hold it in place. However, a smooth-surfaced nail will have a tendency to withdraw slightly if the joint remains under stress for a period of time. In addition, as the wood ages, the wood fibers often lose moisture and shrink, thereby enlarging the nail hole and, in effect, shortening the nail depth. This results in loosened nails or protruding nailheads. A common example of this is a "popped" drywall nail—one that has been pushed from its hole by green lumber that has dried and shrunk. Use of the newer drywall nails with ringed shanks helps to eliminate this. Other irregular-surfaced shanks are designed to prevent loosening.

Cement-coated nails have a resin coating that also provides more friction and greater holding power. However, they are not more effective than nails with shaped shanks.

To protect nails against atmospheric corrosion, a coating of zinc (galvanizing) is applied to the surface. When applied by an electrolytic process, the coating is smooth and thin and the nails are termed electrogalvanized. This treatment offers only moderate protection. For maximum resistance to rust, hot-dipped and tumbler-galvanized nails are recommended. Due to their very coarse surface of zinc flakes, these nails also possess remarkable holding power. They are, however, somewhat harder to drive than smooth nails.

Most nails have standard diamond points, but

some special-purpose nails are characterized by blunt, needle and chisel points. Hardwood flooring nails come with blunt diamond points. These reduce the possibility of splitting because the point shears through the fibers instead of slicing through, as would occur with a regular diamond point. The slicing action spreads the fibers, resulting in a split.

Softwood fibers are more resilient so that a regular diamond point can penetrate without causing a split. A good trick when splitting occurs while driving ordinary pointed nails is to blunt the point with a light hammer blow.

Chisel points are found on heavy-gauge gutter spikes and heavy hinge nails. The shape of this point allows these extra heavy gauge nails to be driven into heavy timbers with relative ease.

Needle points are usually found on nails used on insulated building board and fiberboard. The sharp point makes penetration easier and reduces the chances of deforming the material.

12 popular, special nails

1. *Cement-coated:* Box, casing, common and finishing nails, as well as most other types, are available with optional cement coating.

2. *Concrete and masonry:* Several types of masonry nails are available for fastening wood or other materials to masonry walls and floors. They come with smooth and round, square and fluted shanks. The last two provide maximum holding power. All are hardened. Hardened nails are particularly susceptible to chipping at the head when struck with an erratic hammer blow. Therefore, wear safety goggles when driving hardened nails to protect your eyes, and use a heavier hammer or hand sledge to do the driving. Masonry nails have very little tensile strength (resistance to pullout), but do have good lateral strength (resistance to shear).

3. *Drywall:* This is the nail to use for attaching plasterboard sheets to interior wall studs, joists and rafters. The newest type has rings for superior holding power, a countersunk head that drives flush to the wallboard without cutting the paper, a depression in the head that ties in the joint cement, and a sharp point for easy nail starting. This type is far superior to the conventional drywall nail.

4. *Double head:* Intended for temporary lumber construction such as concrete forms and scaffolding, this nail is simply driven to the lower head for a solid assembly. The projecting upper head assures fast and easy withdrawal when dismantling is desired.

5. *Flooring:* There are several types of flooring nails, the oldest version being the cut nail. This has a rectangular cross section and a flat, blunt tip that is capable of penetrating hardwood flooring edges without causing splits. A more widely used type has a twisted shank and blunt diamond point. Also available are smooth-finish and cement-coated types. Some are made of stiff steel to resist bending.

6. *Gutter spikes:* There are long nails used for attaching and supporting rain-gutter systems. They are available galvanized with flat or oval heads and diamond or chisel points.

7. *Heavy hinge:* This is a smooth-shank nail with a chisel point used for fastening hinges on heavy doors. It's available with an oval, or flat, countersunk head.

8. *Lath:* A thin-gauge nail with a flat head used for attaching wood lath to studs.

9. *Roofing:* There are two types of roofing nails made for residential applications. The most common is the large, galvanized flathead nail with a barbed shank that is used for nailing asphalt shingles, roll roofing and felt.

The other is a sealing roofing nail. It has a neoprene washer under the large head and is used to secure metal and fiberglass roofing and siding sheets. The washer effectively seals the nail holes against rain and wind. Its ringed shank provides good holding power. Roofing nails are usually galvanized.

10. *Siding:* Siding nails are available for simulated masonry, wood and hardboard siding. Heads are flat except for the hardboard nail, which has a countersunk head. This nail is made of a stiff grade of steel to resist bending. All siding nails are galvanized.

11. *Underlayment:* This is a ringed nail with a small, flat, countersunk head and a diamond point. It's used to install plywood or untempered hardboard subflooring to joists.

12. *Upholstery:* Upholstery nails have a large, round or decorative head and are used to fasten upholstery. They are usually colored or plated so that they have an attractive appearance.

choice of metals

All the nails described above are made of steel, but other metals are also used for making some types of nails, including aluminum, brass and copper.

It is important for you to match the nail to the metal you are working with. This prevents the problem of galvanic corrosion that results when dissimilar metals are brought into close contact.

Build a quartet of nesting tables

Made from exotic woods such as satinwood, tulipwood and ebony for trim, these replicas of Thomas Sheraton's tables are beautiful. The current antique value of the originals exceeds $1000, but these copies will cost far less to make yourself.

By DAVID WARREN

DATING BACK to mid-17th century, Thomas Sheraton's quartetto tables were among his most popular designs. Today, antique satinwood tables of this caliber command prices exceeding $1000. Reproductions cost half that. My cost was under $100.

I scaled down Sheraton's traditional 28-in. height to a modern 26¼ in. If you decide to build a trio and eliminate the largest table, it will lower the overall height further to 25½ in. and, of course, cut your material costs one-fourth.

Satinwood, tulipwood and ebony are available from fine hardwood suppliers. I obtained the ¾-in.-thick satinwood I needed from Albert Constantine & Son.

Start construction by sawing the curved former for the stretchers from a 2x6 scrap. Bending the stretchers to the former is easy if you cut the satinwood pieces about 2 in. longer than required. Choose straight-grain satinwood without knots or a fancy figure to prevent failure of the wood fibers either by compression or tension, and sand every ripple and sawmark smooth. Cut the 1/16-in.-deep grooves for the inlay with a 1/16-in. router bit.

Before laminating the stretchers, prebend the eight ⅛-in. pieces by soaking them in hot water for a few hours. Clamp the pieces to the 2x6 former so the inlay grooves for each set face outward. Keep the wood clamped for a week while it dries. When you unclamp the pieces, the amount of springback may vary. Team up each pair with strips of close-matching curvature.

Then laminate each set with plastic-resin glue and reclamp the four stretchers to the former. Put wax paper next to the former and between each stretcher so they won't stick together. Keep the stretchers clamped to the former for a few days. Cut the stretchers to finish length later—when you fit them into the legs.

SEE ALSO
Barbecue tables . . . Bridge tables . . .
Butler's tables . . . Coffee tables . . .
Legs, furniture . . . Party tables . . .
Snack tables . . . Trays, folding . . . Wood finishes

LAMINATE two-piece stretchers with plastic-resin glue. Slip wax paper between the four stretchers to keep them from sticking to each other.

USE A VENEER knife to slice the veneer 60° to the grain. Arrange the veneer pieces on a strip of veneer tape, then glue them to the table edges.

PRESS ROUTER guide firmly against the edge of the top when routing blind dadoes on the underside for rabbeted end rails—an important step.

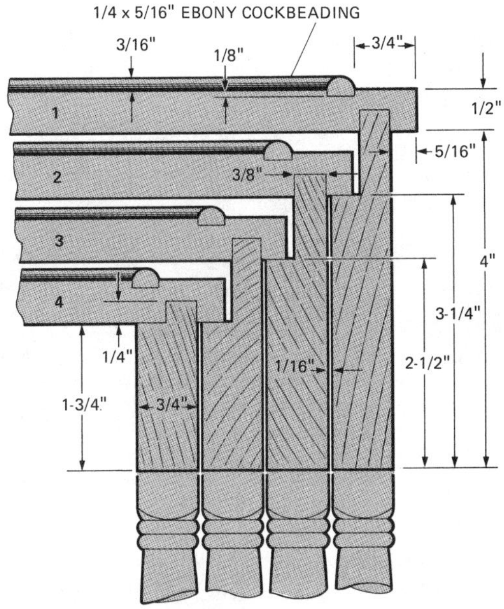

Usually there is considerable variation in grain and in color among satinwood boards. To get the top pieces to match, cut the two or three pieces of satinwood needed to make a 15-in.-wide top from the same board. Then, to minimize warping, arrange the top pieces so the annular growth rings curve alternately (they're visible in the ends). When you rout the grooves for the mating splines, hold the router edge guide against the top surface of each piece so they will join flush. Join the boards with plastic-resin glue. When dry, sand each top smooth and cut to finish size.

Veneer the edges of the tops next. Slice the striped, tulipwood veneer so it's oversize (⅝-in.-wide strips) and so the angle of the strips is 60°. Mark the center points on all four sides of each top. Cut a strip of veneer tape 1½ in. longer than the side you're veneering and make a fold line in the middle. Wet the tape and stick the veneer pieces in position, arranging them so the angle of the strips diverges at the middle fold.

Similarly, prepare the veneer feather-banding for the opposite edge. Apply plastic-resin glue to the opposite edges of the top. Align the fold mark in the tape with the center mark on the top and, using two 16-in.-long 1x2s as protection, clamp the tape-backed feather-banding in place. When the glue has set, veneer the two remaining sides. Feather-band the other three tops. When the glue has dried, soften the tape with a wet cloth and peel it off. When the veneer redries, sand the

CLAMP TABLETOP securely to the workbench when routing the groove for ebony cock beading. Square the corners carefully with a wood chisel.

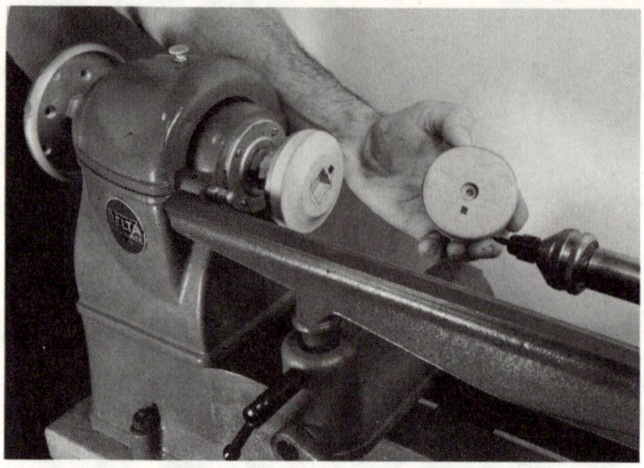

MAKE WOODEN lathe chucks for the head and tailstock to automatically center and hold each leg blank. The chucks will help prevent splitting.

MARK LOCATION of the shoulders on each leg blank with a soft pencil. The mark will show when the leg spins in the lathe. Cut with heel of skew.

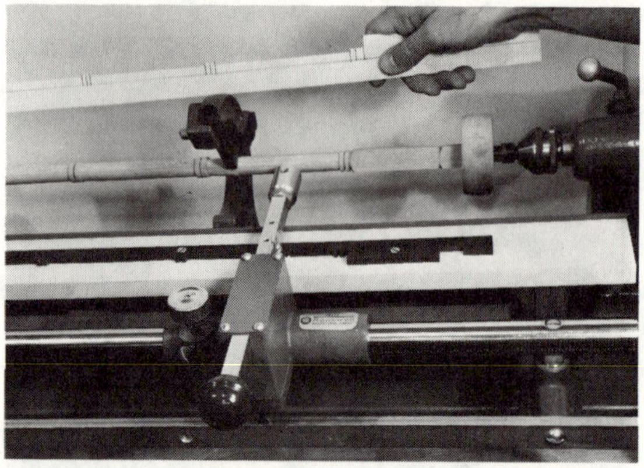

LATHE DUPLICATOR makes quick work of turning 16 identical legs and saves costly mistakes. This requires making a template master of the leg.

projecting veneer flush. If you sand inward toward the tabletop, the veneer won't splinter.

Saw rails to size, cut the rabbets and sand. Mark the location of the rails on the underside of the smallest top. Rout the stopped dadoes. Fit the rails and glue them into place, being sure they are clamped perpendicular to the top. When the epoxy glue has set, use the top to verify the location of the stopped dado in the next larger top. Each tabletop should slide into the next larger one with a 1/16-in. clearance on both sides, as well as between the tops.

Cut grooves for the ebony cock beading with a 1/4-in. straight router bit. Then square the corners with a chisel. Shape the ebony cock beading with a router and miter each stick to length. Epoxy glue ebony into place.

Experts concede that a beautiful hand-rubbed oil finish is among the most durable and repairable. Its disadvantage is the length of time it takes to build up. After sanding and wiping the tops, I began scrubbing them with a pad dipped

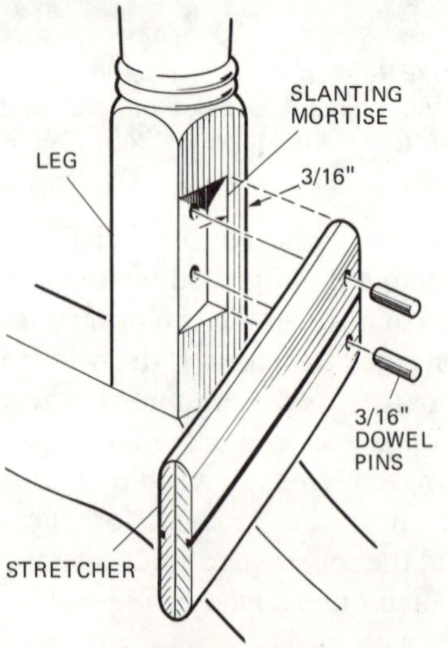

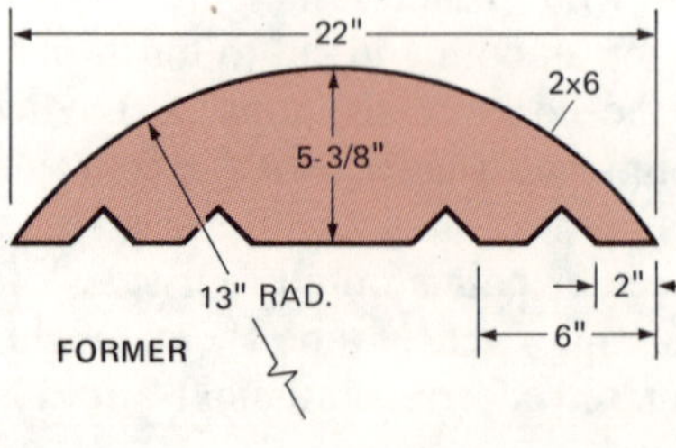

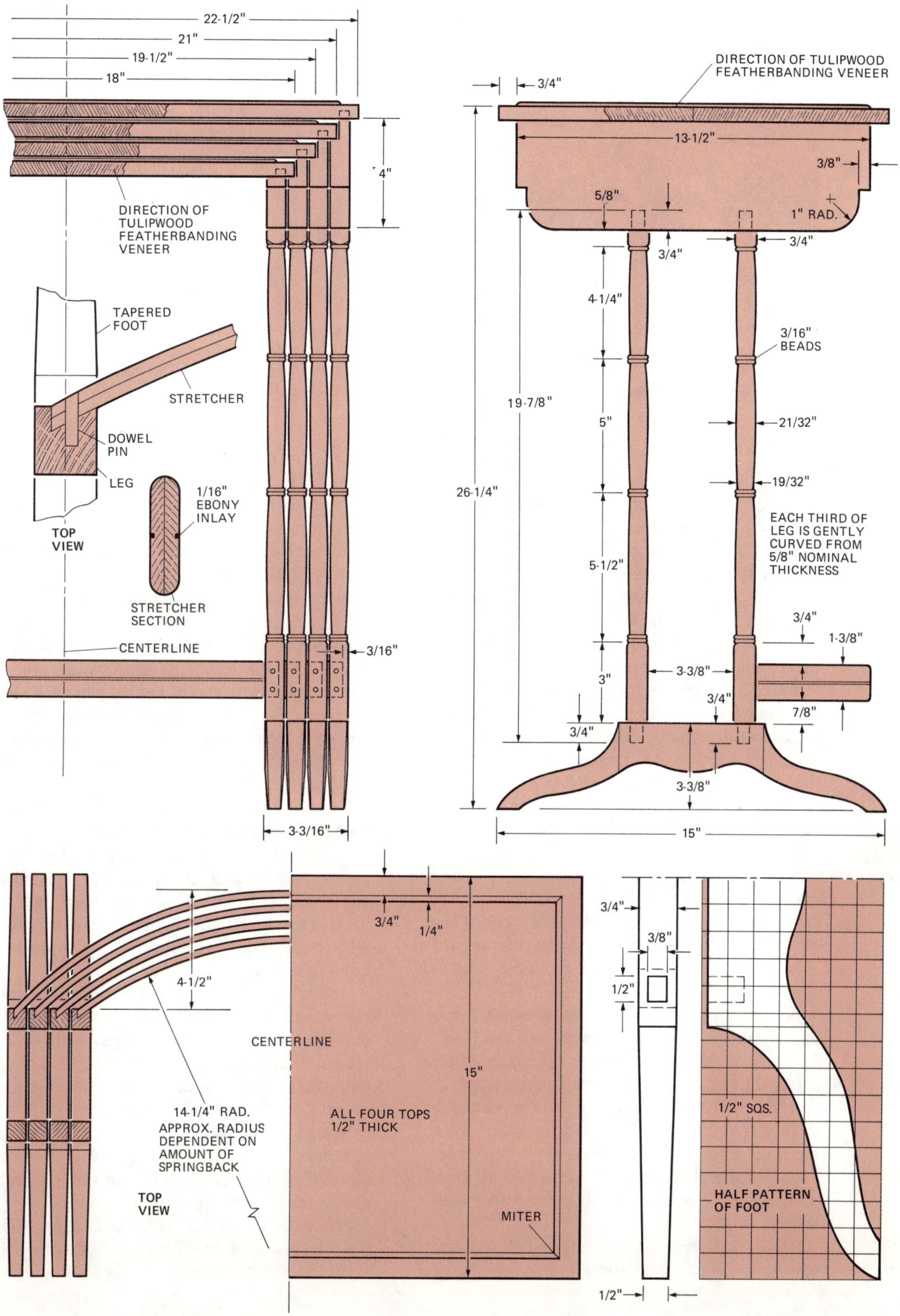

22-1/2"
21"
19-1/2"
18"
4"
DIRECTION OF TULIPWOOD FEATHERBANDING VENEER
TAPERED FOOT
STRETCHER
DOWEL PIN
LEG
1/16" EBONY INLAY
TOP VIEW
STRETCHER SECTION
CENTERLINE
3/16"
3-3/16"
3/4"
DIRECTION OF TULIPWOOD FEATHERBANDING VENEER
13-1/2"
3/8"
5/8"
1" RAD.
3/4"
3/4"
4-1/4"
3/16" BEADS
19-7/8"
5"
21/32"
19/32"
26-1/4"
EACH THIRD OF LEG IS GENTLY CURVED FROM 5/8" NOMINAL THICKNESS
5-1/2"
3/4"
1-3/8"
3-3/8"
3"
3/4"
7/8"
3/4"
3-3/8"
15"
3/4"
1/4"
4-1/2"
CENTERLINE
15"
14-1/4" RAD.
APPROX. RADIUS DEPENDENT ON AMOUNT OF SPRINGBACK
ALL FOUR TOPS 1/2" THICK
TOP VIEW
MITER
3/4"
3/8"
1/2"
1/2"
1/2" SQS.
HALF PATTERN OF FOOT

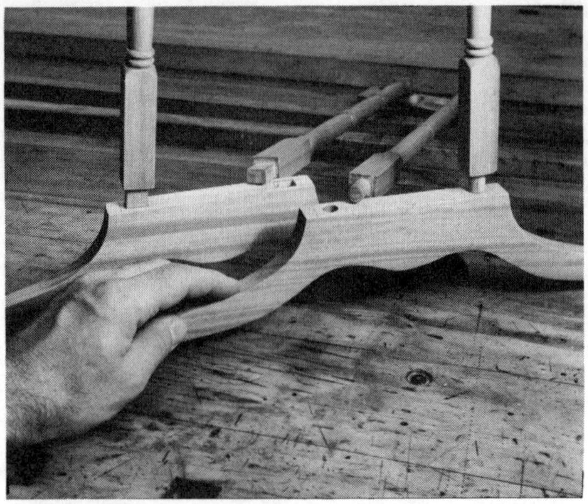

LEG TENONS can be cut to fit square mortises or turned to fit bored holes. You can cut the mortise by squaring up the hole with a wood chisel.

USE 3/16-in. dowels to pin stretchers to slanting leg mortises. Angle-cut ends of stretchers for an accurate fit and glue them with epoxy.

in boiled linseed oil thinned 10 percent with turpentine. As I proceeded to make the table trestles, I took a few minutes every few days to vigorously rub another coat of warm linseed oil into the tops. The last few coats took several days to dry. By the time the tables were assembled, the tops had acquired that beautiful sheen you get only from oil on satinwood.

Rip the leg stock and cut the square blanks to 21-in. lengths. A few preliminaries simplify their turning. Dress the leg blanks so they are smooth and square. Clamp the 16 blanks together and simultaneously mark the limits of the square shoulders. Dark pencil lines on just one side of the blank will be visible when it is revolving.

I made the two 3-in.-diameter maple chucks to center the leg blanks automatically and keep the ends from splitting.

To make the chucks, screw a 1⅛-in. piece of maple to a faceplate and turn it round. While it's on the lathe, bore a ¾-in. hole ½ in. deep. Then remove the faceplate from the lathe (keeping the chuck attached) and square the hole with a chisel.

For the tailstock, lay out a 3-in. diameter circle on a second piece of 1⅛-in. maple and saw it out. Bore a ⅛-in. lead hole through the center of the chuck. Then bore a hole big enough to accept the cup center and deep enough to get a good bite in it. On the reverse side form a ¾-in.-square mortise ½ in. deep. Extend the point of the cup center about ½ in. so it fits deeply into the ⅛-in.-diameter lead hole. I completed this setup with a ball-bearing center.

Put a black spot on one edge of the square mortises on both chucks and a spot on one side of each leg blank; then, by inserting the leg so the spots on the leg and chucks are adjacent, you'll be able to remove and reinsert the legs in the same position in the chuck each time. After you go through all the steps on one leg, mass-produce each step on the remaining 15 blanks.

Begin turning a leg by nicking the shoulders. Point the heel of the skew away from the square shoulder. Turn the cylinder next. Mark off the location of the beads on the cylinder and cut them. Then turn gently convex shafts between the beads. Originals had square tenons, but modern glues now make round tenons practical. If you intend to use round leg tenons, cut them at this time, too. Sand the legs thoroughly.

I finished the legs by burnishing them with a 50/50 mixture of linseed oil and shellac as the leg spun in the lathe. When a leg would take no more polish, I removed it to dry. Later, I applied two additional coats with a 4/0 steel-wool pad. I let the legs dry thoroughly between coats and finally reinserted them in the chucks and applied carnuba paste wax with a soft cloth.

Conserve wood by using a cardboard template to nest the outline of the feet on the board. Cut out the feet and sand the edges with a drum sander. Mark the taper on the feet, then cut the taper with a disc sander, spoke shave or block plane. Cut the leg mortises next.

Round the upper and lower edges of the stretchers, cut the inlay to length and glue it into place. Cut the sloping notches in the legs and fit the dowel-pinned stretchers into place.

Assemble the tables with epoxy glue. Finish the feet, rails and stretchers with the same polish you rubbed into the legs.

MARINA AT NIGHT, made at 1/8th second, and f:4 on Tri-X, is much more dramatic than the same scene in daylight. The slight blur is caused by boats bobbing in the water during exposure, but it isn't objectionable.

How to shoot in the dark

By JIM SLATER

Double your photography pleasure by trying for the spectacular shots waiting for you at night wherever you look

■ TO INTRODUCE a new kind of excitement into your photography, become a night person. Put aside your flash gun, because flash is a substitute for the sun and turns night into day. Instead, take pictures of the night as it really is—moonlit scenes, flashing billboards, streets that sparkle with neon stars, amusement parks with whirling, twisting lights, marinas or sandy beaches touched by light—a different world of picture possibilities.

You learn one thing quickly when you get into night photography. In daylight, you shoot pictures of lighted objects, and you are concerned about the way the light falls on your subject. At night, however, you photograph *the lights themselves*. Keep this in mind as you begin your night photography adventure and you are off to a good start.

Generally at night you shoot for the light that is available. To get this light, you use fast films which are extremely sensitive to light. Put away your light meter because it can't tell you much about these low-light situations. Instead, you experiment with different exposures at widely different times. You learn to shoot sequences of

SEE ALSO
Bird photography . . . Boat photography . . . Montages, photo . . . Outdoor photography . . . Panorama photos . . . Photography . . . Underwater photography

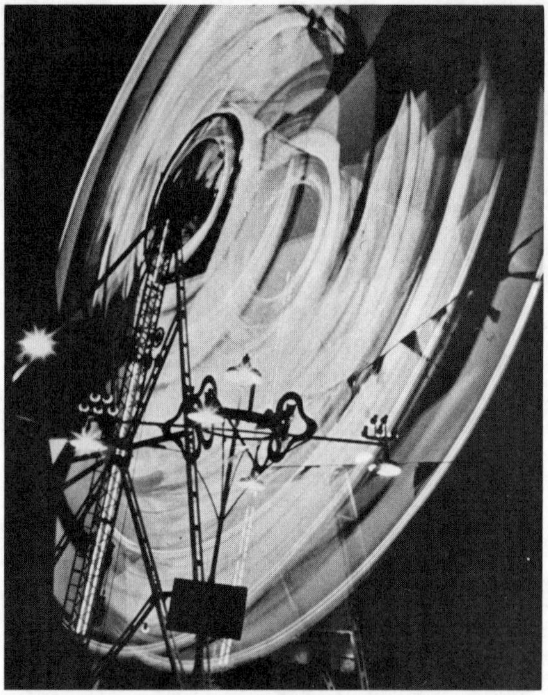

WHIRLING WHEEL OF LIGHT is an amusement-park ride shot at a long exposure—8 seconds at f:11 on Ektachrome 200. Striking effects like this photo, shot by Eastman, can't be made in daytime.

perhaps half a dozen different shots of the same picture. You learn to bracket every exposure; and you learn to use long, long exposures. And finally, you learn to use a tripod and a cable release for most of your shots.

First, the film: For black-and-white night photography, there is the old reliable Eastman Tri-X, with an ASA rating of 400. It has the speed and the latitude for any kind of a night situation.

COUNTRY CHURCH in the snow makes a picturesque night scene. To get enough illumination, this was shot at dusk—a trick you can use when full darkness would make shooting this scene impossible.

LIGHTNING IS EASIER to shoot than you'd think because it provides light to take its own picture. Use the bulb setting to open the shutter, hold it open until the lightning flashes, then close it.

RIBBONS OF LIGHT are traced by automobile headlights blurred through a time exposure of several seconds. Always use a tripod or other firm support to keep the camera steady during such exposures.

Or if you want, there are faster films available, up to as high as 1600 ASA. These, however, tend to be pretty grainy.

Color shots once were restricted to bright sunny days. Then came such films as Eastman's Highspeed Ektachrome, now rated at 200 ASA (and which can be push-processed to 400 ASA), and color entered the field of night photography. Now both Eastman and Fuji have films for making color prints rated at 400 ASA—which means you can take on any challenge the night has to offer and get spectacular pictures.

Techniques: Most of your exposures will be long, which means that you should always support your camera on a tripod. It is almost impossible to get good, sharp pictures when hand-holding a camera set at speeds slower than 1/60 of a second. It also is wise to use a cable release instead of pressing the shutter release, again to eliminate any source of vibration which might blur the photo.

All cameras have time-exposure capabilities and also "bulb" settings, which you use to hold the shutter open as long as you need it. If yours is one of the newer electronic cameras, you may have automatic timing of time exposures up to 8 or even 10 minutes, a great help for night work. Check your camera manual for details.

Bracketing and sequencing of exposures are the most important techniques in night photography. To bracket in daylight photography, you shoot one picture at the setting indicated on your light meter, then shoot a second at the next lower f-stop, and a third at the next higher f-stop. This is a good way to be sure of getting one perfect exposure.

Night bracketing is a little different. You want as much depth of field in your picture as possible, so you try to shoot at the smallest possible aperture. The pictures on these pages were shot at f:4, but might have been taken at f:8, or f:11 for greater depth. The smaller the f-stop, of course, the longer the exposure, and you should plan to get the best balance between time and aperture opening.

When bracketing at night, you change the *time* and not the f-stop. Thus you might shoot your first shot at f:8 at an exposure of 2 minutes. Then, to bracket, you would change the time, and shoot the second shot at 4 minutes and the

LONELY VIGIL of a policeman on a deserted, snowy street corner is captured in this photo shot from the window of a nearby building. Such shots create strong moods and attractive salon prints.

REFLECTIONS ON WATER, here from buildings along a river, are spectacular at night because of the shimmering lights. Wet lamplighted streets after a rain also produce eye-catching night effects.

LIGHTED FIREHOUSE is a good example of a subject that takes on new interest at night. In this case, the flash was fired during a time exposure to give a slight added illumination. The close-up of the firehouse door at the right creates an interesting light pattern.

third at 1 minute. Note that you shoot successive shots at double or half the previous shot. Thus, if you shoot one at 3 minutes, then the second would be at 6 minutes, and the third at 1½ minutes.

Sequencing of exposures is simply the shooting of the same scene at a series of settings. You might do shots at 1, 2, 4 and 8 minutes, and also at 1/250, 1/125, 1/60, 1/30, etc. The result of shooting such a sequence may surprise you. First, you'll note that you end up with a number of excellent photos. In the long exposures, you will find that an additional 4 seconds may have made very little difference.

The pictures you get will be different in subtle ways, and each will have its own mood. The longer exposures will have more over-all illumination, and light sources will be burned in and appear as diffused hot spots. On the shorter exposures, the light sources will be sharper and better defined. It is possible to get two or three prize winners in one such sequence.

TYPICAL EXPOSURE TIMES FOR NIGHT SCENES

(All times are for an opening of f/4. Adjust one stop shorter or longer for each stop of increase or decrease in opening.)

TYPE OF FILM	TYPE OF SCENE		
	NEON SIGNS	STREET SCENES	FLOOD-LIGHTED BUILDINGS
EKTACHROME 64 KODACHROME 64	1/30	1/15	2 sec
KODACOLOR II	1/30	1/30	1 sec
EKTACHROME 200	1/60	1/30	1 sec
KODACOLOR 400 TRI-X 400	1/250	1/125	1/4

Special effects: Look for opportunities to achieve special lighting effects in your night shots. For example, shoot on rainy nights and take advantage of the reflection of existing lights in the wet street surfaces. Or shoot with a river, lake, or pond in the foreground for reflections on water. Night lights on snow provide another beautiful effect. Also, shoot the same scene on a dry night, a wet night, and a snowy night. You'll have a lovely set of photos to mount side by side.

You can use your flash at night to fill in some scenes. The firehouse shot shown here was made with flash fill. To make this shot, the shutter was set at f:4 and then opened. While it was open, the flash was fired manually. Then the shutter was closed. Don't use the camera's built-in flash synchronization for a shot like this, because you don't want a flash picture.

Fireworks can provide an interesting night shot. One way to do it is to set the camera on the tripod so that it is pointed at the area of the sky where the fireworks will explode. Lock the shutter open and cover the opening with your hand or a card. When the burst lights the sky, pull the card away. Cover the lens again when the burst has died down. You can do this four or five times to make one picture of bursting fireworks.

Shots which take advantage of the fact that long exposures cause moving lights to blur into streaks are always interesting. Set your camera on a bridge over a freeway, for example, or shoot from the window of a building which looks into a lighted downtown street. The lights of the moving cars will appear as solid streaks in your picture.

Ten car noises you can't stand

A rattle here and there isn't always too serious, but there are some clangs, buzzes, hums, hisses, squeals, howls, thumps, thuds, knocks, clicks, grinds and growls you'd better take care of—and fast! Don't put them off until it's too late

By ROSS R. OLNEY

■ YOU'RE CRUISING along one of the most deserted roads in the United States, Interstate 5 through mid-California. Five is, or was until recently, notorious among drivers and truckers for having almost no service facilities for several hundred miles. You're hauling a 20-foot travel trailer. You have plenty of gas and the car is equipped to haul a load with a trans cooler, an engine oil cooler, extra brakes, leveling hitch, the works.

Then it happens.

Without warning, a loud roar fills the car. Instantly you back off as your mind races over possible causes. The trailer isn't swaying, the car seems steady, the steering is solid, you tap the brake slightly and you can feel them.

Nothing at all, yet the roar is quite evident.

Okay, you have a moment to breathe. Engine heat is within range, oil pressure is good, alternator is charging correctly, everything seems normal as you slow gradually and pull off onto a wide, safe shoulder.

You switch off.

Yeah, something like this was sure to happen eventually. You step out, look for miles in both directions, and see that the road is deserted.

a nonemergency noise

Then it hits you and you sigh with relief. You are glad you learned to talk to your car and listen when it has something to say. You know there are sounds a car can make that demand attention and others that only indicate a problem you can handle at a more convenient time.

This sound, as serious as it might appear, is one of the latter. Grinning to yourself, you walk around front, raise the hood, and reach for the fan. You're doing exactly what a shady service-station kid did some time back when your wife was driving, only he tried to sell her a new water pump because "the bearing is shot on this one . . . see, the fan turns freely even though the engine is off."

Sure it does, you explained later (after she wisely declined the water pump in favor of asking you, the expert). You told her about the fan and how it free-wheels when the engine is off because of its clutch actuated by temperature.

Out there on Interstate 5 you grab the blade and sure enough it won't turn. Maybe you can force it a bit, but it is almost solid. The fan clutch has failed, freezing tight.

You crawl back in, start her up and drive on. The roar is still there, but you know that it is only because the fan is being driven by the engine at

SEE ALSO

**Body care, auto . . . Leaks, auto . . .
Lubrication, auto . . . Misfiring, auto . . .
Noises, auto engine . . . Power-train noise, auto . . .
Tune-up, auto**

higher speeds. Normally the clutch would have disengaged and the fan would have coasted silently, windmilling by the air coming through the radiator. It'll need fixing, but not until you get where you are going.

This was a car noise you could ignore. Others cannot be ignored, not for long. Here they are, the 10 car noises you should learn to identify and then be prepared to correct as quickly as possible.

One thing, in fact, can be said with absolute certainty. If you are driving down the road and your car suddenly says, "Clang . . . buzz . . . hum . . . hiss . . . squeal . . . howl . . . thump . . . thud . . . knock . . . click . . . rattle . . . grind . . . growl," you have a definite problem. The trouble is, if it says *any one* of these things, you may still have a serious situation on your hands.

1. clang from underneath

There is no question that a universal joint can seem to go on forever, but once it begins to clang and buzz it needs attention. And attention to a U-joint ordinarily means replacement, or at least repair by replacement of the bearing units in the joint.

The U-joint is the connection at each end of the driveshaft and sometimes in the middle as well. No matter how it is bent, the universal joint transfers the torque of the transmission to the driveshaft, then to the differential (and to the rear axle).

You will normally hear the click or clang of a failing universal joint as you accelerate or as you back off. The bearing shafts are bouncing around inside the joint, first one way then the other. In operation under these conditions, they often buzz as well.

It is possible to drive the car until the bearing fails completely, but more can happen than simply being stalled alongside the road. The driveshaft can drop free if a U-joint fails. It can whip about until the car is stopped, damaging everything in sight. Certainly the expensive driveshaft will be ruined if it breaks free.

Take the car to your own service station or garage or, if you can raise the car, install the new ones yourself.

But before you do anything, a buzz can also be caused by a glob of road tar or undercoat on the driveshaft. Check it out.

2. hum from the rear

You've probably heard this expression: "That sound is typical of this model year."

Translation: I can't seem to find the real reason for this sound from this car.

A hum from the rear *can* be a difficult sound to pin down. Still, it is one of the 10 noises you must do something about.

Let's go at it in this order; but first, you have snow tires on, right? They'll hum and there isn't much you can do about it until next spring. Go ahead and drive, and don't worry.

Check the lubricant level in the differential. If a bit of oil dribbles out when you remove the oil fill plug or even if you can reach the level of the oil inside with your finger through the hole, replace the plug. There's enough oil inside.

The wheels should be pulled next and the bearings carefully inspected. The mechanic will probably insist that the pinion in the differential is too far from the drive gear, or that the end play in the bearings is wrong (and he could be right if the hum is louder when you are coasting), or that the end play in the axles is wrong, but check the bearings first.

Bearings should show no sign of chipping, burning (a brownish cast) or scoring. Nor should they make any grinding noise when they are turned by hand. The problem here is that you will have to press off the old rear-wheel bearings and press on the new ones if you find them worn. This can be done at home (try using a socket head the same size as the bearing as a pressing tool), but a service station or garage will do it for little more than the cost of the parts.

One other advantage of their doing it: Oil seals in the rear axles can be tricky. If they install the axle, they seal the hole. They should fix it if oil later leaks out on the brakes or tires.

Finally, when all else fails, go to the complicated measurements. First, axle end play (easy to adjust), then the end play measurements in the differential (not so easy). But before you drive yourself up the wall, refer to the next section. Also remember that a hum *could* be starting out as a buzz in a U-joint that is being modified and softened as it travels through the driveshaft, differential, and out the rear axle.

Or the "hum" could really be your car's way of trying to say "whirrrr," which sometimes even precedes clang and buzz to indicate a failing U-joint.

3. hiss from the front

A "hiss" or a "hiss-hiss-hiss" from under the hood generally indicates one of several minor, easy-to-correct problems. The sound can, however, be serious, so find its origin.

A hiss can come from a loose sparkplug (tighten), a loose or burned heat-riser tube (attach or replace), a leaking tire (repair, or change the valve if you can increase the hiss by wiggling it), a leak in the vacuum system (locate and reattach or replace the rubber hose), a leak or broken tube in certain power systems (repair by replacing the offending tube), or from blow-by.

The last can be easily determined, but indicates a more serious problem. A great deal of pressure is created in the combustion chambers of the engine. Each piston has rings to seal it in its cylinder and to aid in lubrication of the cylinder walls.

If these rings are worn or loose, too much of the pressure from the combustion chamber can leak down and around the piston into the crankcase. This is called "blow-by" and it must escape somewhere. When it escapes, you can hear it.

Blow-by generally can escape from two places, depending on the age of the engine.

Watch the oil-fill hole, the place where oil is added to the engine. Also watch the breather pipe (the crankcase vent tube) out of the bottom, if the engine is pre-1962. If smoke seems to be coming from either place, usually with a hiss, you could have worn rings and if you plan to keep the car you should get estimates on replacing them. They are costing you in mileage, oil consumption and power. On modern engines, blow-by gases are routed through the PCV system, fouling the PCV valve and increasing oil consumption as the gases break up oil into minute droplets to be carried by the system to the intake manifold to be burned.

A constantly fouled PCV valve is the hint here.

4. a squeal from anywhere

A squeal can mean something as unimportant as a slipping fan, alternator or airconditioner belt (dress and/or adjust, or replace), a clutch or brake pedal scraping against the floor panel (adjust), window linkages or anything else that simply needs grease (lubricate), or, if you are making a hard right or a hard left turn, a loose power-steering belt (adjust or, if worn, replace).

A squeal can indicate something a little more serious, like a low tire or a worn alternator or generator brush.

Or a squeal can indicate something very serious that needs your immediate attention, depending on where it is coming from.

Can you pin it down to the front end of the engine? Then look for water dropping or dribbling from the water-pump housing. If the bearing is failing, it will usually leak a little, and it will almost always complain with a squeal.

What if it fails? Then it will stop moving water, the engine will overheat, and finally it will stop. They'll change the water pump while you wait and it isn't a big job, but they'll charge you at least $50 depending on your make and model car. Sometimes they have to remove the radiator and that costs more.

The other squeal you might hear demanding your attention will come from one or more of the wheels when you apply the brakes. A squeal indicates that they have already stopped working as they should and may soon fail completely.

The reason brakes squeal is that the shoes, an asbestos-based material, have worn down until metal is contacting metal inside the brake drums, or pads of the same material have worn in a disc brake system and metal is contacting the metal rotors.

Either condition needs your attention. You can change the shoes and pads at home (refer to any good manual on the process and there are dozens available) or have the job done by a pro. But *not* by a bargain dealer. Brakes are important. If you are going to have the job done, pay for it and have it done correctly, with an *ironclad* guarantee.

5. howl from the transmission

Watch it! You could have a very serious problem and almost certainly you are going to need the help of an expert. There isn't much most of us can do but look around for the best deal. But there is a *lot* we can do on *that* score. Beware of the quick-buck trans shops that promise free estimates, then charge you for the teardown if you don't go for the job.

The truth is, most good transmission men can tell you *almost exactly* what's wrong and *what it will cost* to fix it, *without* tearing the trans apart.

So get some estimates, preferably from a mechanic you know. One trick: Get your local mechanic to handle the job, to farm it out if he doesn't do that work himself. You may pay a few dollars more (you'll probably pay an arm and a leg anyhow, unless it happens to be something like a simple adjustment of bands) but he, not some guy downtown you don't know, will be responsible for the guarantee and any follow-up necessary.

6. thump or thud anywhere

One driver bought a used car in excellent condition and he really loved it . . . but for one small problem. Every time he started out, the car said "thump" very softly. He searched for the source of the sound, his mechanic searched, the agency searched, and his friends searched. Nothing.

His first flat tire was in one way a stroke of good luck. When he went for the spare he found it loose—and the cause of the annoying noise.

His thump was inexpensive. Another thumper of no immediate consequence can be caused by a cold tire. It'll warm up and the thump will stop. Out-of-round or flat-spotted tires are more worrisome, but of no immediate concern.

A bulging or blistered tire, however, is a thumper that must be corrected now. Nor is there any way to repair it. Shop for a new tire. Do it today. And if you must drive, do it *slowly.*

A thump or thud from the engine compartment can mean anything from a loose battery to a slipping throw-out bearing in a manual transmission . . . or worse. Check the battery first, then test by applying and releasing the clutch to see if the sound is affected. If not, the matter often comes down to excessive end play in the crankshaft, an unpleasant, rather expensive matter.

A hint: Check the motor mounts if you hear a thump or thud. A broken mount, not a very expensive repair, can possibly cause such a sound, especially at acceleration. It's worth a look.

7. knock from the engine

Yes, this is another serious sound. Still, very rarely does a car give up on the spot, without warning. Even if it begins to knock, you probably have time to get it to a hospital. Chances are you'll need an expert.

A softer "knock" instead of a loud KNOCK! can indicate a loose piston pin, with the sound coming every time that cylinder fires. Remove the sparkplug wire from that cylinder. If the knock stops with the engine running, you've probably found the expensive problem.

A light metallic "knock" which reduces with the car coasting and out of gear often indicates a worn connecting-rod bearing. If the engine seems to struggle and emit a heavy, thudding knock, suspect the crankshaft main bearings.

Or you could be lucky. An out-of-time engine tends to knock. Start there and work toward the worst possible causes.

8. clicking from the wheels

Wheel bearing? Wait a minute. More likely it's the hubcap. Reinstall it or hammer it on a little more firmly, then drive again. A pebble caught in the tread of a tire can cause an annoying click-click-click when you drive. They should check these things when they lube the car, but usually they don't. Flip out pebbles with a screwdriver, rolling the car a few feet so you can reach all areas.

Or the clicking could be coming from a wheel bearing and this needs your attention now. Especially if the clicking is gradually changing to a humming sound. Check the bearing, or have it looked at by a mechanic.

9. rattling from anywhere

Usually nothing to worry about, rattles are a language an older car uses when it simply wants to complain about something loose here or wearing out there. A rattle can, however, be serious.

If you hear a rattling coming from up front, pull in and have the car lifted. Spin the front wheels one by one, for this is still another way a wheel bearing in the front announces its coming demise.

Another rattle for immediate attention is a shock absorber which has come adrift. It isn't uncommon for a shock to come loose at one end or the other and you can imagine what that does to the handling of the car. Yet it is an easy and inexpensive matter to correct.

10. grind or growl anywhere

It is possible, if the grinding or growling is coming from the area of a manual transmission, to try lubricating the throw-out bearing to extend its life. Chances are that could be the problem.

If there is grinding or growling from the transmission itself (manual or automatic), refer to No. 5, a howl from the transmission.

Occasionally a U-joint will complain with a grind or a growl. Drive *carefully* to your home or garage.

A grind or growl can also indicate bearing problems in the wheels (see No. 2 or No. 8) or occasionally a problem in the expensive differential. Remember, always beware of the mechanic who wants to proceed directly to the big stuff without first stopping at the chicken-feed jobs.

Before you do one other thing, though, check the fluid level in the power-steering pump. A low level in the pump can cause it to grind and growl as though it were pulverizing itself (which it eventually *will* if you don't raise the fluid level, since the fluid also lubricates the interior parts of the pump).

There is no question about it—it is much easier for those who have a brother-in-law who is service manager of the dealership where they bought their car. But for most of us, learning these 10 sounds and the fixes is next best.

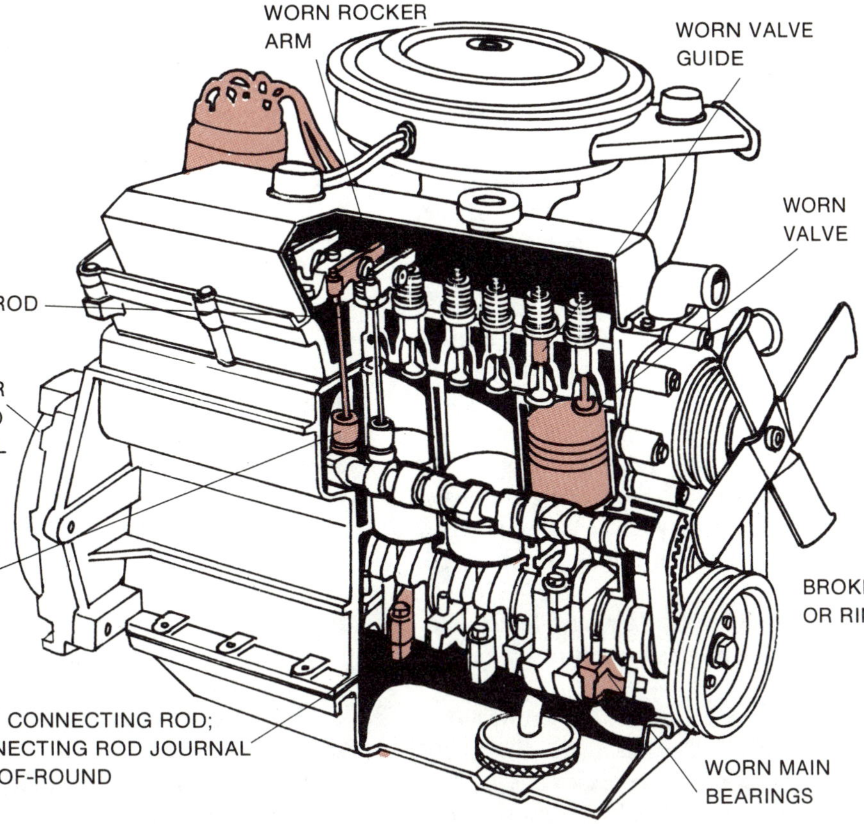

ENGINE NOISES can originate in a number of areas some of which are shown here.

How to diagnose engine noise

■ SOME ENGINE NOISES indicate major problems, while other noises are easily eliminated. The noise must be identified before a diagnosis can be made. There's a big difference between the noise of a piston slap and the noise from a sticking valve. The problem is recognizing the difference, and understanding the noise from hundreds of other parts both inside and attached to the engine.

The illustration on this page shows a cut-away of an engine, pinpointing some of the major problems that produce internal noise. The noises that these malfunctions and others make are described by mechanics as slap, rap, rattle, click, whine, thump and thud.

Keep in mind that we are now discussing sounds symptomatic of major engine problems. We will cover "minor" problem sounds later. The word **minor** is encased in quotes, because one of these noises—ping—may, in fact, be caused by a major problem, but we'll discuss that further on.

In determining which one of the noises applies to your engine, it's also important to ascertain under what conditions the sound occurs and, if possible, at what pitch.

For example, is the noise loud, faint, sharp or dull? Does it occur regularly or intermittently? Does it happen when the engine's hot, cold, or all the time—during acceleration, deceleration, idling or at high speed?

SEE ALSO
**Engines, auto . . . Leaks, auto . . .
Lubrication, auto . . . Motor oil . . . Noises, auto . . .
Power-train noise, auto . . . Tune-up, auto**

sounds defined

Let's run down each of the various noises that are created by major engine problems and define them:

■ **Slap**—This is described as a sound resembling a hammer striking a metal surface, but not sharply. It's a dull noise. The one part inside an engine that's most notorious for slapping is the piston. It happens when a piston loosens up.

■ **Rap**—A rap is similar to a slap—like a hammer hitting a metal surface—but it's much sharper in intensity. A primary cause of engine rap is putting a load on an engine or running it at high speed when it's low on oil. The noise is actually being made by connecting rods.

■ **Rattle**—This term is quite descriptive. It sounds like a baby's rattle that's being furiously shaken. A loose piston may cause a rattle rather than a slap. So can ignition timing which is too advanced.

■ **Click**—Run a stick along a picket fence, and you have some idea of what is meant by engine click.

A clicking sound is frequently caused by a dry hydraulic valve lifter. As soon as the lifter gets pumped up with oil, the noise ceases.

Clicking can also be caused by excessive valve lash (usually in engines with mechanical lifters—a valve adjustment may help); a piston that's lightly touching the head gasket or cylinder ridge; or a nick on a timing gear.

■ **Whine**—This one is in the gray area. It might indicate a major problem, but then again it might not. A whine is described as a high-pitched, continuous sound. It may be more pronounced at some speeds than at others.

The noise may be caused by nothing more serious than a glazed fan belt. It might be the result of a malfunctioning rotor in the alternator, which again is not that serious. However, whine can also be caused by a loose or worn timing gear, and this means a major repair.

■ **Thump**—A thumping sound is a deep-throated noise that you seem to feel as well as hear. It indicates a serious condition, such as loose main bearings. A thump occurs intermittently—not on a regular rotational basis.

■ **Thud**—A thud is similar in pitch to thump, but it occurs regularly—that is, every revolution. Loose flywheel and excessive crankshaft end play are two possible causes.

zeroing in on noise

Trying to analyze the cause of engine noise from sound alone is tough. However, there is an "old-timer's" test that we'll outline.

Internal engine noise usually falls into one of these classifications:

1. Noise that occurs once every revolution.

2. Noise that occurs once every cycle (two revolutions).

3. Noise that occurs intermittently, having no rhyme or reason.

Do the test as follows:

■ Check engine oil; replenish if necessary.

■ Warm up the engine to normal operating temperature.

■ Set the engine to idle at about 600 rpm, and place a neon-type sparkplug tester on one of the sparkplugs (pull the boot off the plug, of course).

■ Note when engine noise occurs in respect to the flashes of light.

If noise occurs twice for each flash (once every revolution), the cause of the sound is a part driven by or driving the crankshaft. Pistons, rings, pins and main journals are in this category.

If the sound occurs once for each flash (once every cycle), anything driven by or with the camshaft could be causing the noise since the camshaft makes a single revolution per cycle. Falling into this area are valves, oil pump, distributor, fuel pump and the camshaft itself.

If the noise occurs intermittently—neither once nor twice for every flash of light—the cause of the problem is some component that isn't tied directly into the camshaft or crankshaft. Consider excessive end play of one of the shafts or noise being made by some engine-driven components, such as the alternator, starter or distributor.

Noise can often be isolated by shorting out the sparkplug of each cylinder in turn. If the noise stops when a cylinder is shorted, you have isolated the noise to that cylinder.

noise indicating "minor" problems

Pinging usually indicates a minor condition, but it may also tell you that your engine is in big trouble. It depends on whether ping is being produced by detonation of a mild sort, detonation of a serious nature or preignition.

Detonation and preignition are very different and should not be confused.

Ping is a rapid, rattling knock coming from an engine. Ping caused by detonation occurs primarily when the engine is placed under load, such as when the car is climbing a hill. It happens when gasoline isn't able to withstand the heat and pressure inside a cylinder.

Instead of burning evenly and smoothly, as gasoline should, the unburned portion of the mixture ignites violently **after the mixture has been ignited by the sparkplug.** This sudden premature bursting into flame of the unburned gasoline causes the engine's cylinder head to rattle. It is this noise that you hear as "ping."

Detonation can usually be eliminated or at least relieved greatly by seeing to it that ignition timing is set to manufacturer's specification, that the engine isn't overheating, and that gasoline of the needed octane rating is being used. In checking timing, you should also check the condition of those parts affecting engine timing—the distributor and spark advance.

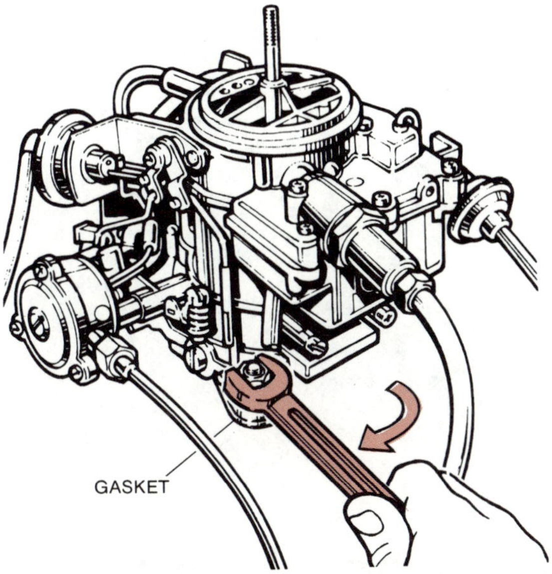

TIGHTEN CARBURETOR mounting bolts to prevent air leaks and loss of power.

Ping caused by preignition occurs when there is combustion of gasoline in a cylinder **before the sparkplug ignites the fuel.** Combustion is caused by a "hot spot" (red-hot carbon usually) in the cylinder.

Preignition places moving parts under extraordinary stress and can cause the most serious damage. There is no such thing as harmless preignition, and at the first sign of the condition the engine should not be operated—but should be disassembled for a carbon cleaning.

But how do you tell the difference between ping caused by detonation and that caused by preignition? It's very difficult to listen to the noise and distinguish between the two.

So, if engine ping doesn't clear up at once by setting timing, assuring proper engine operating temperature and changing to high-octane gasoline, watch out. You have a preignition problem.

If you have a whistling noise coming from the engine compartment, it could be a drive belt that's too tight or glazed. But many times a whistle coming from under the hood is produced by a vacuum leak because of loose intake manifold attaching screws, loose carburetor mounting bolts or a leaking gasket.

To determine if this is causing the noise, spread a mixture of oil and kerosene around the manifold and carburetor with the engine running. If the whistle ceases or changes pitch, you have found the reason.

Tighten up on all bolts. If this doesn't help, the gasket should be replaced.

engines that run on

If your engine continues running after you turn off the ignition, the engine is dieseling. This is ignition in the absence of spark. It occurs when fuel in the combustion chambers is ignited by heat.

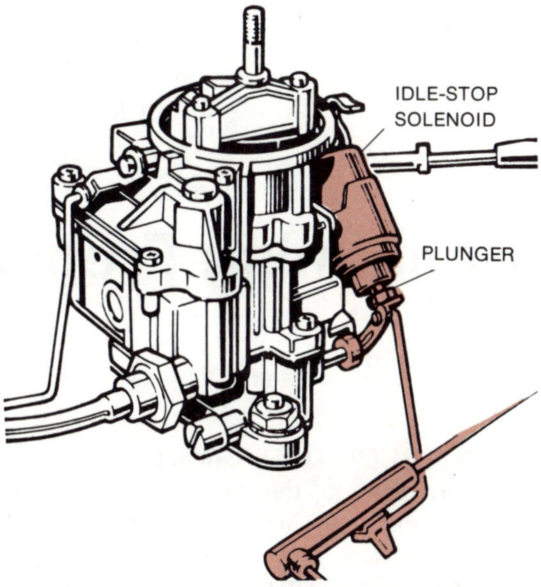

DIESELING can be caused by an idle-stop solenoid that's not working properly.

To help prevent dieseling, manufacturers have added a device called an idlestop solenoid to the carburetors of most engines coupled to automatic transmissions. The solenoid's job is to shut the throttle at once when the ignition is turned off, keeping excess fuel from entering the combustion chambers where it can be ignited by high temperature.

If your car has an idle-stop solenoid, dieseling will occur if the solenoid isn't working.

A special 'touch' in this occasional table is the tambour doors that slide open easily on a curved track

A charming French Provincial table

By C. L. WIDDICOMBE

■ CONSTRUCTED OF cabinet-grade ¾-in. mahogany plywood, this handsome occasional table of French Provincial design can be used singly, or in pairs, in living room or bedroom. Though not a project for a beginning woodworker, it is easier to build than it looks. The design, however, does require the use of some sophisticated shop equipment such as a bandsaw, router and table saw. The original table shown above is one of a pair; if your need is for a couple of end tables, you can save time by doing all the cutting and assembly for both at the same time.

SEE ALSO

Bridge tables . . . Butcher block furniture . . . Butler's tables . . . Coffee tables . . . Dining tables . . . Game tables . . . Hutch tables . . . Party tables

Begin work by cutting the top and bottom pieces 19½ x 21¼ in. and face three edges with ¾ x 1¾-in. strips of solid stock. These are mitered at the front corners and attached with glue and splines. Then shape the three edges with your router. The grooves in which the doors slide are ¼-in. deep by ½-in. wide. These are made using a router, collars and template. The template is simply a piece of ¾-in. plywood cut to a size that will result in a groove cut in the bottom of the top and the top of the bottom when the router collar is guided around the outer edge. Next, run a blind rabbet along the back to accommodate the back panel. Then cut a slot at a 45° angle and tangent to the back circles. This tangent slot permits insertion of the doors from the back after which the slot is filled in with a small piece.

Make up the two corner posts and the front rail from the pattern given and attach the front rail to the corner posts with dowels or mortise-and-tenon joints, and then secure this subassembly to the front of the bottom by driving screws up through the corner of the plywood and into the end of the corner posts. Next, cut the two 11 x 12½-in. plywood sidepieces and cover the exposed front edges with wood tape. Bandsaw the two side rails, dowel them to the posts and side panels, then drive three 2-in. No. 8 fh screws up through the bottom and into the side panels.

The base is composed of four feet and rails. The feet are bandsawed from blanks of 2$^{7}/_{16}$-in.-sq. stock. These can be either laminated or solid blocks. The front and side rails are of stock thick enough to follow the contour of the tops of the legs.

In the original, I used ⅞-in. mahogany backed up by ¾-in. maple as shown in the details. Cut the leg and rail blanks to the correct lengths and mark them for dowels. Notice that the back rail is simply a flat board cut from ¾-in. stock. Take care that the dowel holes are positioned in such a manner that they won't show when the contours of the feet and rails are cut. Bandsaw the four legs and remove excess material from the rails on your table saw. Now assemble the base section. Plane the rails and tops of the feet to match and finish up with a thorough sanding of all members. After attaching the four corner blocks, the completed base should look like that shown on page 1977.

Now you can make the doors—they make the completed table stand out from run-of-the-mill furniture. With a little extra care along the way, you will be assured of a professional-looking piece of furniture. The slats are of $^{7}/_{16}$-in. mate-

CLAMPS ARE used in gluing the side rails to corner posts and side panels after you glue the front rail.

SLAT DOORS are inserted in track from the rear of the cabinet before the ¼-in. plywood back is installed.

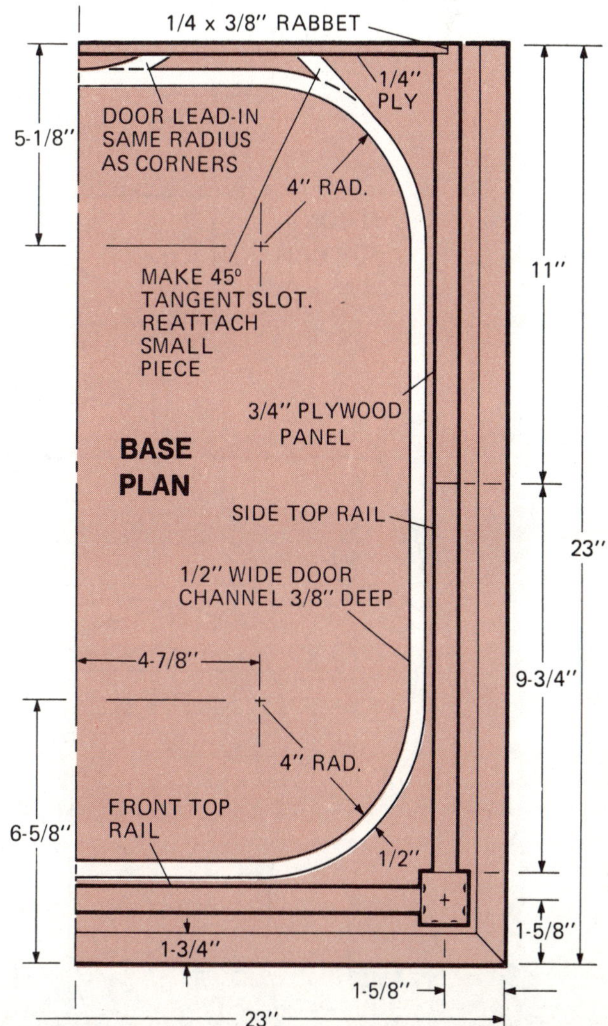

rial; 36 slats are ⅞ in. wide and two—the front ones where the knobs go—are 1¼-in. wide.

Remove the sharp edges from all pieces and sand the front faces only. There's no need to sand the backs of the slats; they're not seen because of the canvas backing. Lay all slats for one door face down on a flat piece of plywood and, using a pipe clamp, clamp them together reasonably tight. Make certain the slats are aligned and square, and clamp the ends down with C-clamps and strips of thick wood.

Cut two 2-in. widths of heavy canvas slightly shorter than the overall length of the clamped-up doors, apply two coats of contact cement to each slat and the canvas strip. When the cement sets, place the canvas strips in contact with the slats and smooth all wrinkles. Keep the assembly in clamps for at least 20 minutes. *Caution:* When you apply the contact cement to the backs of the slats, do not let any glue run onto the exposed sides (the cement will bleed through the lacquer finish).

When the doors are completed, insert each one in the routed groove or track. Apply a coat of paraffin wax to the bottoms of the slats to ensure sliding ease. It's best to make a dry run of the doors with the top temporarily secured. If necessary, sand slat ends for smooth operation.

It is a good idea to stain the parts before assembly. The original tables were given a coat of sealer and three coats of satin lacquer. However, an antique-white finish with the tambour doors in mauve, makes a handsome piece. Either way, it will be one you will treasure for years to come.

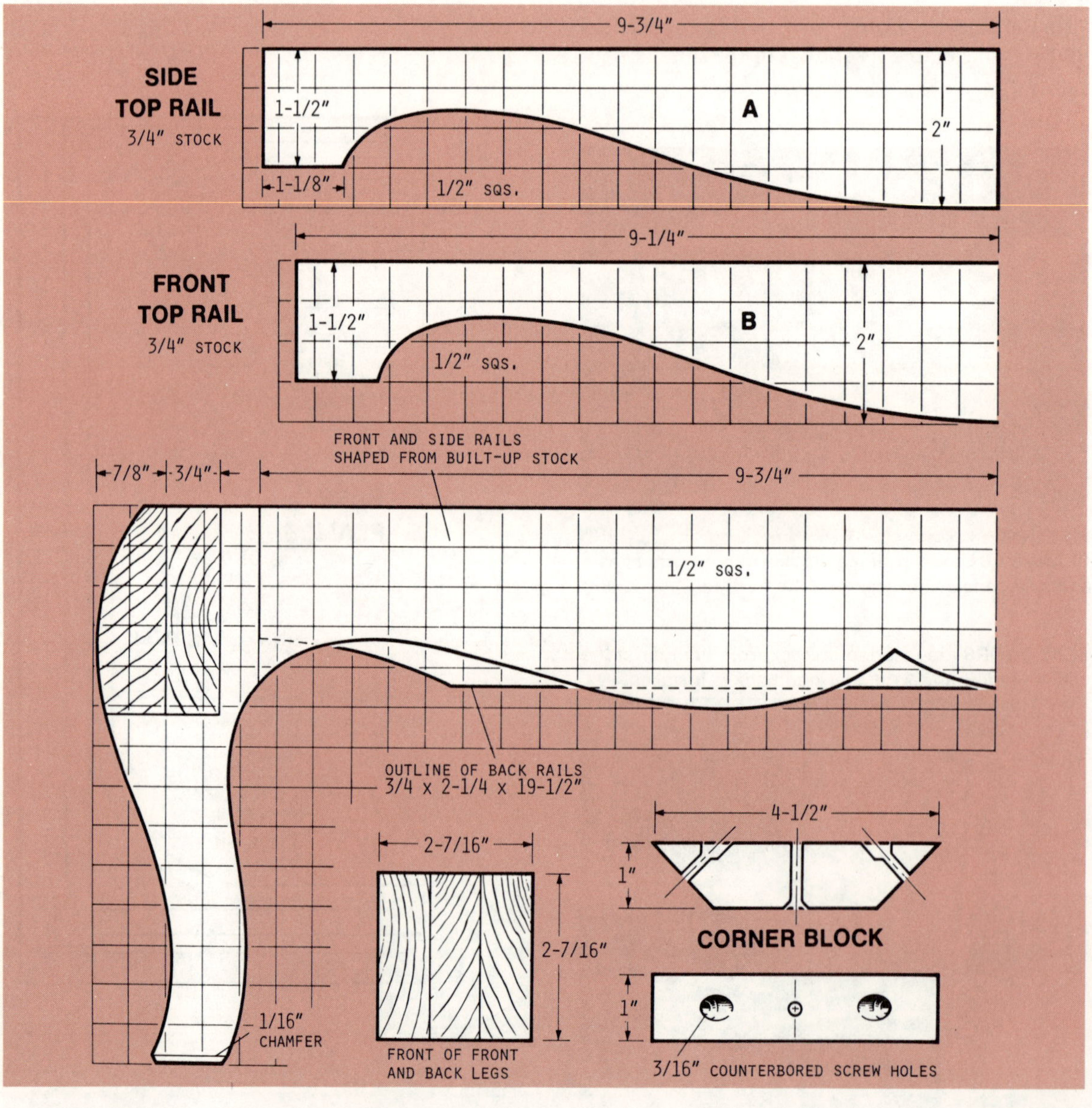

TAMBOUR TABLE

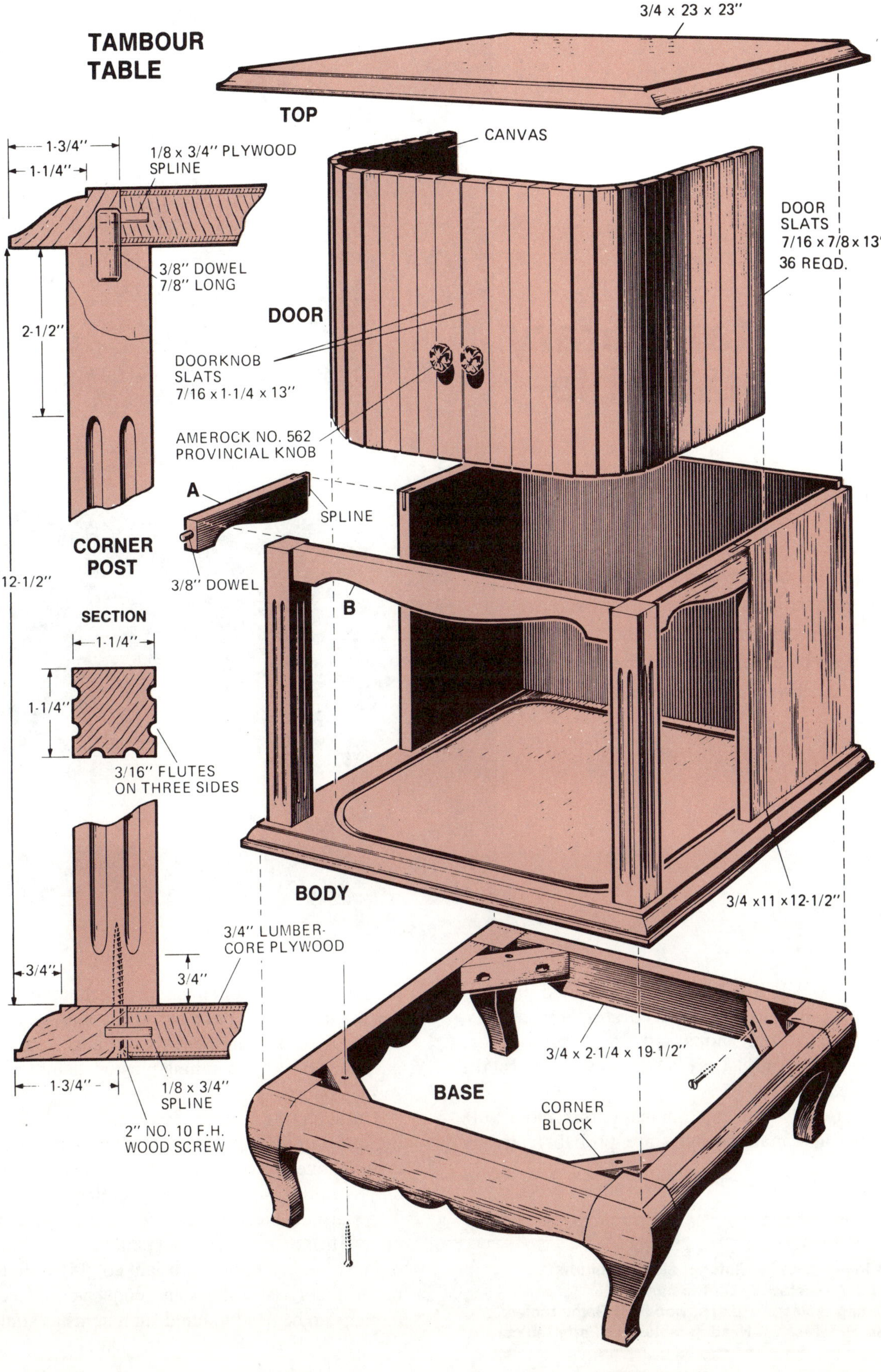

A contemporary pedestal table

By JACKSON HAND

Here's a table you can make with a new and interesting technique. The construction method can be applied to other types of modern furniture for your home

■ YOU'VE SEEN gracefully formed pedestal tables such as this in decorators' magazines, smart boutique shops and fine-furniture store windows. And just as likely, you've gulped at the prices they sell for.

Happily, you can duplicate this table with tools and materials you are probably already familiar with by utilizing a new technique. You can make it for the price of a sheet of plywood, a short piece of pipe and two flanges, a few packages of vinyl patching plaster, paint, some screws and glue.

The sculpting involved is simple, yet challenging and interesting. The technique is a sort of cross between using a potter's wheel and doing clay sculpture—with a little spackling thrown in. The finished piece is graceful, but rugged and heavy. For a finish, you can paint it white, black or one of today's popular bright colors to suit the room decor. And the same construction techniques can be used to build such items as stands for TV, hi-fi speakers and the like.

SEE ALSO
**Bridge tables . . . Butcher block furniture . . .
Butler's tables . . . Coffee tables . . .
Dining tables . . . Discs, wood . . . Game tables . . .
Hutch tables . . . Nesting tables . . . Party tables**

The dimensions for the table shown are entirely arbitrary; the piece was made to be used as a fairly large occasional table. You can make it, of course, any size you wish; in practice, you're limited only by the standard 48-in. width of a plywood sheet.

The basic skeleton of the table is a pair of built-up plywood discs—one for the top, one for the base. The stem is a length of 1½-in. galvanized pipe fastened to the top and the base with pipe flanges and lagscrews. All of the parts are then given shape with a patching plaster such as Savogran Crack Filler or Durham's Rockhard Putty. Drill a small hole through the center of each disc to form the pilot-point for penciling the circle. These holes also let you slip a nail through the plywood discs to insure accurate centering when assembling.

To assemble the discs, spread glue evenly on the first disc, center the next smaller size and put

THE PEDESTAL BASE is formed of glued-together plywood discs. Pipe determines the table height.

THE FINAL HEIGHT of the table on the opposite page (in which a 16-in. pipe was used) is about 24 in. If you decide to increase the table's height, increase pedestal and top circumferences in direct proportion.

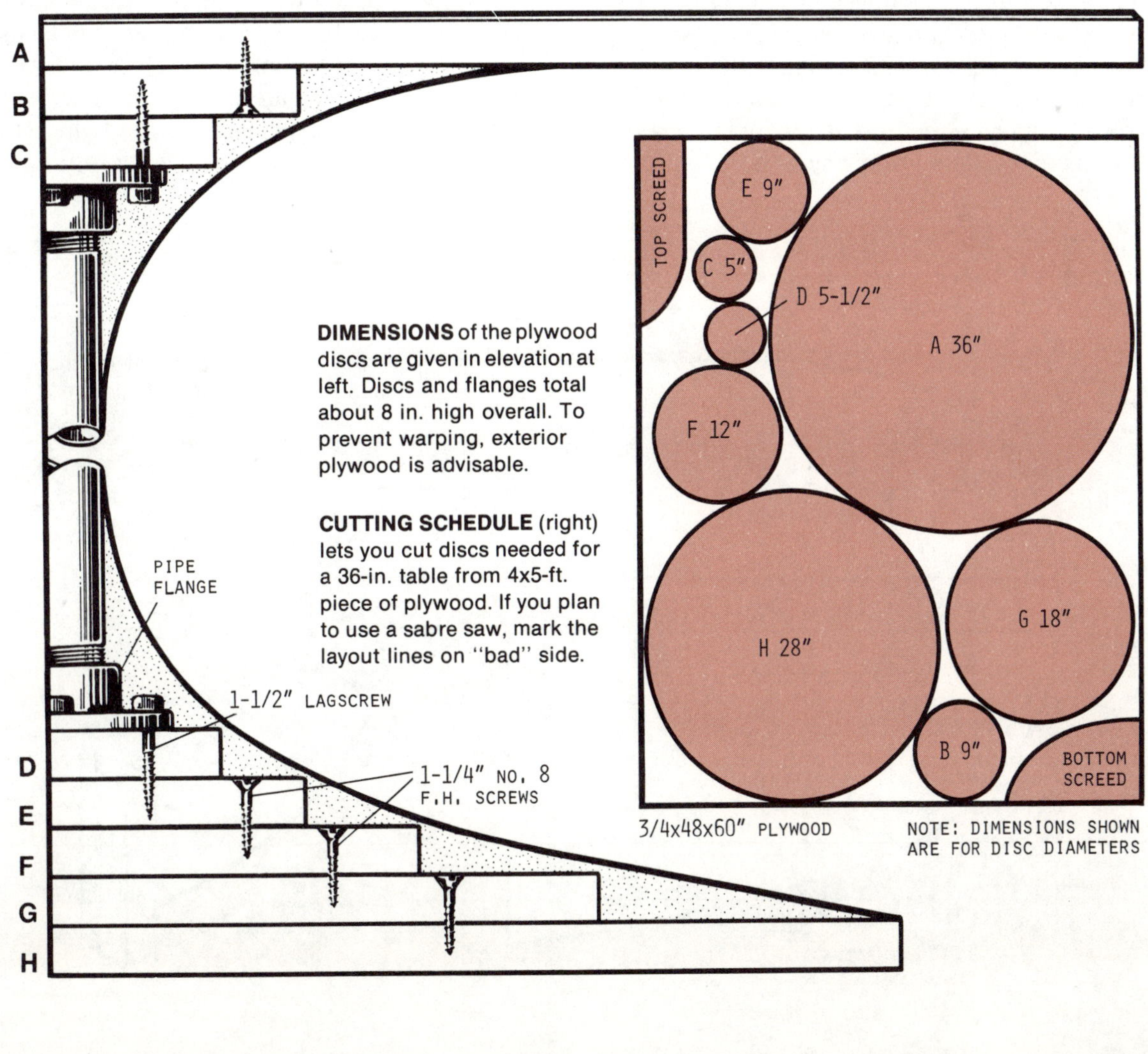

DIMENSIONS of the plywood discs are given in elevation at left. Discs and flanges total about 8 in. high overall. To prevent warping, exterior plywood is advisable.

CUTTING SCHEDULE (right) lets you cut discs needed for a 36-in. table from 4x5-ft. piece of plywood. If you plan to use a sabre saw, mark the layout lines on "bad" side.

THE FIRST STEP in molding the gracefully curved pedestal is to fill in the "steps" using plaster of paris.

THE FINAL SHAPE is made by screeding patching plaster with a special plywood screed built as shown.

a nail in the hole. Drive the 1¼-in. No. 8 screws and move on to the next disc. When all discs assembled, center the two pipe flanges and fasten in place with lagscrews.

You can save time and money by using ordinary plaster of paris for the initial filling. It's best to apply the plaster in two or three coats, starting with a thick mixture and ending with a mixture the consistency of heavy cream. Glob on a trowel-full and screed the shape by holding the tool (notched block) firmly against the pipe and the cleat against the plywood edge. You'll end up with the shapes quite true, but *not* entirely smooth. Do the final smoothing by laying on joint compound the same way you do when finishing a plasterboard wall.

When the plaster is dry, apply several coats of flat enamel, sanding thoroughly between coats.

If you prefer a durable top for use as a work surface, plastic laminate is a practical choice. In this case, apply a laminate self-edge strip to the plywood edge before laminating the top.

THE SCREED can be cut from scrap plywood lying about the shop. The notched block guides it around the pipe.

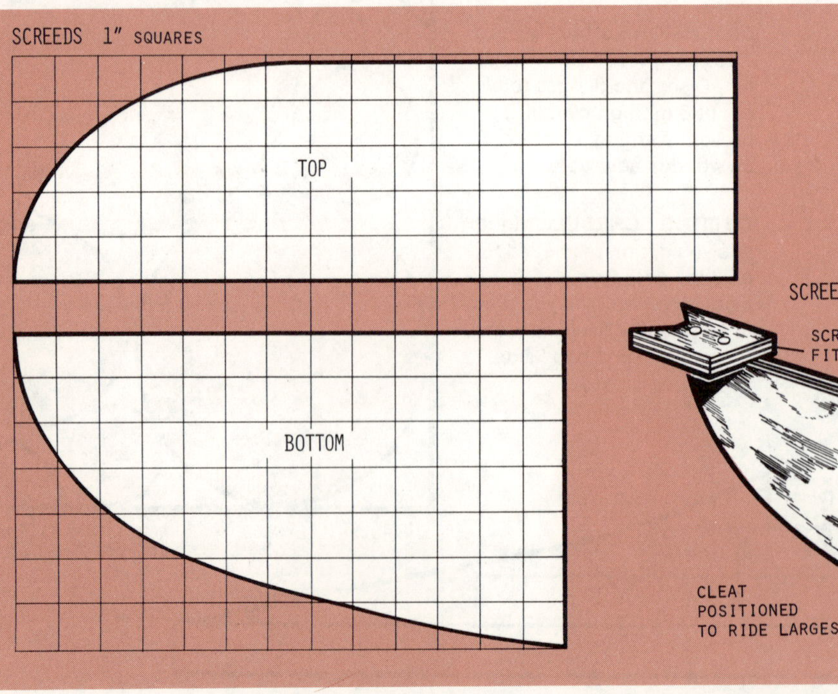

SCREEDS used to shape the contours can be cut from the same plywood panel as the discs. Be sure to cut curves accurately and sand smoothly.

A service manual for your outboard motor

By MORT SCHULTZ

This article is divided into five sections that correspond to the five major systems of your outboard motor: (1) ignition; (2) starting; (3) fuel; (4) powerhead; (5) lower unit. It is a comprehensive discussion, carefully arranged in step-by-step fashion, that will permit you to make both minor and major repairs on your motor

1. The Ignition System

THE CONVENTIONAL, non-electronic ignition system of every one and two-cylinder outboard engine consists of a magneto, sparkplugs and high-tension cables.

The heart of this system is a magneto (Photo 1). They're all pretty much the same—if you can repair one, you can repair all. You'll need two pieces of equipment—a flywheel puller and a magneto analyzer.

You can get both from a dealer of outboard equipment. Be sure the magneto tester is accompanied by an instruction book.

Keep in mind that all components of the ignition system should be tested once you pull the flywheel, even though you may find and replace a bad part at the start of your checks. New breaker points, for instance, may increase the spark. But if a weak condenser (that caused failure of the points in the first place) goes undetected, the trouble will soon reappear.

Ignitions of two-cylinder engines have two of everything: plugs, points condensers, coils. In one-cylinder engines there's one of each.

How do you know when your outboard ignition system is giving trouble? If the engine refuses to start or is hard to start, pull a sparkplug after cranking the engine to see if fuel is getting to the cylinders. If the plug is wet, but the motor isn't starting, the trouble is undoubtedly ignition. Occasionally, an engine that misses at high speed or won't get up to full speed signifies an ignition breakdown.

You can check for ignition trouble another, more positive, way. Remove a sparkplug lead and hold it ¼-½ in. away from a ground on the engine block. Crank the motor. A spark should jump the gap.

Another way to test for spark is to start the engine and pull a lead from a plug. Hold it ¼ to ½ in. away from the plug terminal to see if a spark jumps the gap. Be careful if you do it this way. Make the test for just an instant. It puts a strain on the coils and might cause a good coil to break down.

Caution: To avoid the possibility of a shock when holding a sparkplug lead to ground or a plug terminal, grasp the lead with insulated pliers.

Sparkplugs, loose or shorted wiring, and breaker points account for practically all ignition failure. Occasionally, a condenser or coil will go bad. Rarely, if ever, do the magnets in the flywheel give trouble.

What follows is how to test, replace and adjust each ignition component. Keep in mind that the specifications we give are general; that is, they apply to most model outboards 1965 and later that possess conventional magneto ignition systems. However, it's advisable to get the exact specifications for your engine from a dealer or from the manufacturer.

spark plug testing

Start with sparkplugs. If you find them the reason for your ignition failure, you don't have to go further. Look for dirty plugs, improper electrode gap, worn electrodes, broken or cracked insulator and plugs of the wrong heat range.

SEE ALSO
**Boating, safety . . . Boating, storage . . .
Pontoon boats . . . Propellers, boat . . .
Repairs, boat . . . Sailboats**

IGNITION SYSTEM

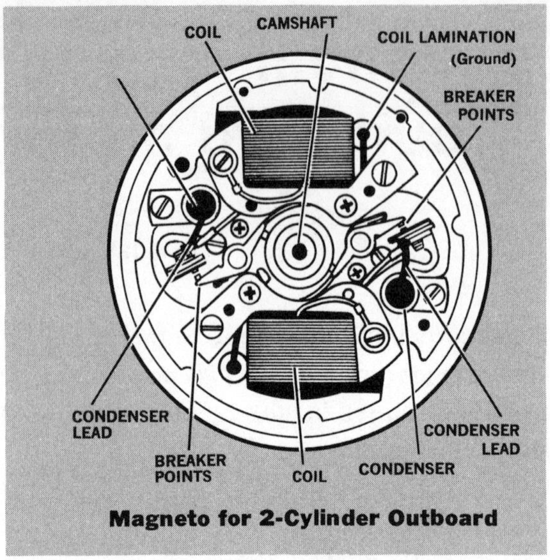

1. MAGNETOS are all about the same, except that one for a 2-cylinder engine has two of everything, one for a 1-cylinder engine just one of each part.

5. BREAKER-POINT spring tension should be 33 to 37 lbs. Replace if point tension is not firm to touch.

Heat range is important. If the plug insulator tips are blistered, indicating that the plugs have been running hot, switch to the next colder plug. If they are fouled, indicating improper combustion, they are running too cold, so switch to the next hotter plug.

Replace damaged plugs, and those that have a ground electrode worn to 1/16-in. below the edge of the shell. Clean dirty electrodes with a strip of emery cloth and check gap. The usual sparkplug gap for OMC and Chrysler engines is 0.030 in. Plugs in most Mercury engines are gapped to

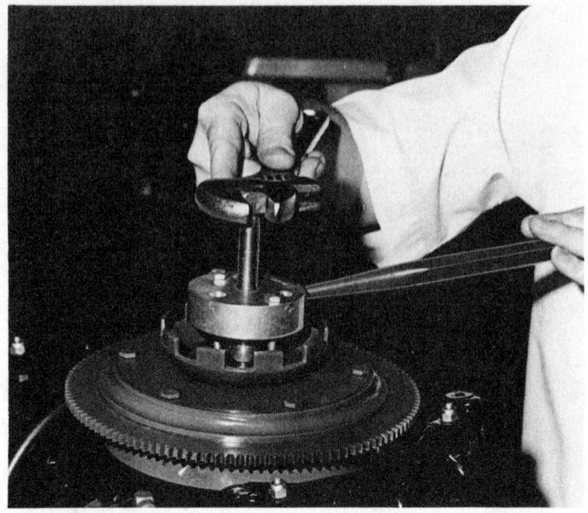

2. WITH FLYWHEEL NUT and attaching screws removed, use puller to remove flywheel. This uncovers magneto.

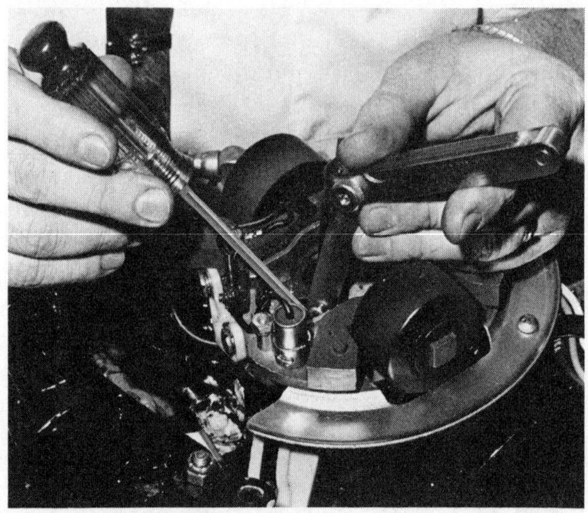

6. WHEN ADJUSTING POINTS, the important thing to remember is that the breaker arm must be on the high lobe of the cam so the points are fully open.

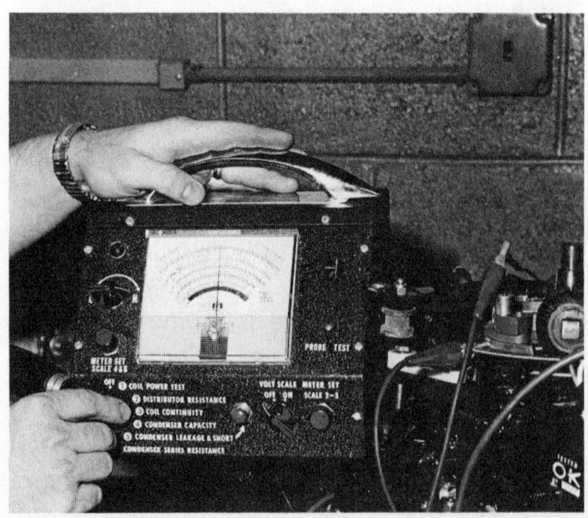

9. TO TEST COIL, use the magneto analyzer book to find the correct way to make the right hookup and to set the meter for a coil check.

3. TIGHT CONNECTIONS are a must. A critical one is where condenser lead joins coil primary leads.

4. REPLACE BREAKER POINTS by disconnecting the condenser lead, unscrewing points. Parts lift out.

7. CAM LUBRICATOR WICK is shown here. It's good for about 100 hours of operation. You should replace the wick when you replace the breaker points.

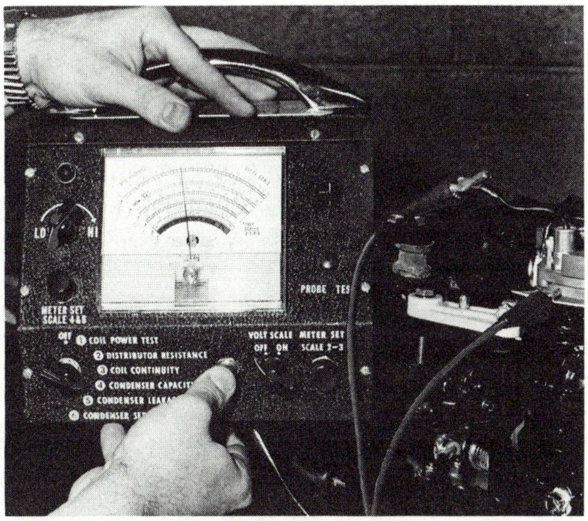

8. WITHOUT A MAGNETO ANALYZER to check motor properly, you can merely replace different parts. Condenser capacity here shows 0.17 mfd.

continued

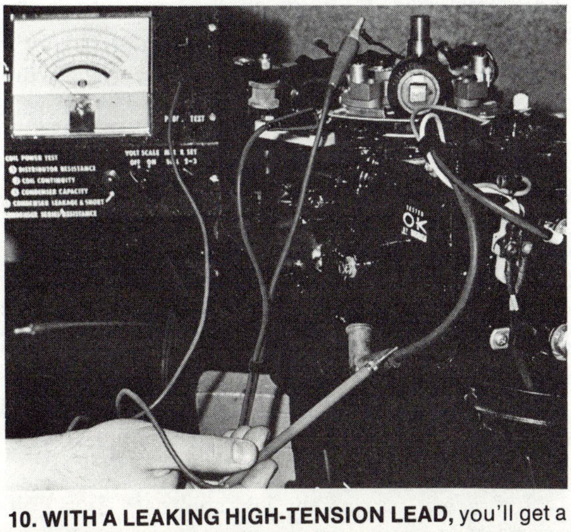

10. WITH A LEAKING HIGH-TENSION LEAD, you'll get a flash between the lead and the meter test probe. If there's a flash, replace the leads.

11. MAGNETS IN THE MAGNETO should hold up for the life of the outboard. But should a sharp blow damage them, you will have to replace the flywheel.

0.025 in. Those in McCulloch outboards are gapped to 0.035 in. *Important:* To adjust gap, bend the side electrode only.

In replacing plugs, torque to 20 ft.-lbs. A loose plug will cause loss of compression; a tight plug will overheat.

Give sparkplug cables a close inspection. Replace if cracked or split, and check boots, too. Discard if damaged. You will give each high-tension lead a closer test for leakage when you test the coils later.

removing the flywheel

If sparkplugs are not the cause of trouble, you must now remove the flywheel to investigate further. All flywheels are removed in much the same way. Unscrew the flywheel nut and screws (usually two or three) holding the flywheel to the magneto armature plate. To remove the flywheel nut, you have to hold the flywheel steady. This can be done with a strap wrench. Using the flywheel puller, remove the flywheel from the crankshaft (Photo 2).

(Remember that when you reinstall the flywheel it is important that the nut be torqued to proper specifications. This spec is normally 40 to 50 ft.-lbs.)

Next, check all electrical wires for tightness at connections and for frayed insulation (Photo 3). If a section of wire is bare or the insulation is worn, shorts will keep the engine from running. If the insulation isn't too badly frayed, repair it with a strip of insulating tape. If shot, replace the part. Notice that each component of the magneto—points, condensers, coils—is held by a screw or screws. Replacement is easy by removing the screw(s) and lifting the components from place (Photo 4).

Breaker points can wear, become dirty and go out of adjustment. To check them, first inspect for corrosion and wear. Test the tension of the breaker arm with your finger or a screwdriver (Photo 5). It should be firm. Replace points that are questionable.

cleaning points

Although dirty and oily points affect good performance, they can usually be salvaged by cleaning. Apply a drop of alcohol or trichlorethylene to the points and pass a strip of bias tape up and down between them. Never file points. You'll ruin a good set and make a bad set worse.

Use the magneto analyzer to test points for good electrical contact. Connect the proper test lead to the breaker-arm lead and the other test lead to ground. Consult the magneto-tester instruction book for exact details on how to use it.

Set the analyzer for the breaker point test. If the meter needle shows that point contact is poor, make sure test-lead connections are tight before rejecting the points. Tight connections are necessary for accurate test results.

The final service done to breaker points, whether new or old, is to adjust them. This is important and must be done exactly to specifications since the breaker-point gap controls the timing of the ignition by the number of degrees the points open before the piston reaches top dead center. Mercury, OMC, Chrysler and McCulloch engines generally have a breaker-point gap adjustment of 0.020 in., but it is advised that you double-check to make sure this specification is correct.

To set gap, make sure the points are *fully* open by having the breaker arm on the high lobe of the cam (Photo 6). Use a feeler gauge and adjust by loosening the breaker-arm screw and moving the points wider or closer together. When one set of points is gapped properly, rotate the crankshaft 180° clockwise to open the other set. Repeat the procedure.

Every magneto has a wick for lubricating the cam. No additional lubricant should ever be added. A new cam wick is usually supplied with new breaker points and should be installed when points are changed (Photo 7).

testing condensers

Condensers may look discolored. Don't worry about that. Discoloration doesn't affect condenser functioning.

Each condenser is tested for leakage, capacity and resistance. Leakage must be more than one megohm, but the capacity depends on the condenser. Most are rated from 0.17 to 0.22 microfarads (mfd.). However, some have different values. For example, some Mercury engines use condensers that have an mfd. capacity of 0.15 to 0.19 and 0.22 to 0.27. Check with a dealer or the manufacturer of your engine.

To test a condenser, disconnect the condenser lead to the breaker point assembly. Connect one test lead of the magneto analyzer to this pigtail and the other test lead to ground. Check the condenser for each of the parameters mentioned above by switching from one to the other on your analyzer (Photo 8).

Be careful during the leakage test. High voltage is being applied to the condenser by the analyzer. Don't handle test leads. Before disconnecting the leads from the condenser, be sure the turn selector switch of the analyzer is off.

handling coils

In newer outboard engines, a coil that's removed from the magneto and then reinstalled can go on in only one way—the right way. This is not true of all magnetos, however. In some, a correct airspace has to be left between a coil and its core.

To be on the safe side, if you have to remove a coil, first measure exactly the distance between the face of the coil and the edge of the coil seat. When putting the coil back in place, set it to this specification. Do not tamper with the core.

When connected to the magneto condenser, the coil is tested under actual operating conditions. The analyzer provides an interrupted primary current and measures the induced secondary voltage. If the coil's okay, the meter will show it.

Test leads from the magneto analyzer are connected to ground, to the coil primary and to the secondary (Photo 9). Adjust the meter as specified in the instruction book. Note the meter reading.

A low reading means that the coil is weak and must be replaced. You can get a higher reading by increasing primary current, but this is false. The coil is shot if it won't come up to spec with the primary current that's specified in the instruction book.

Now, check the coil for leakage by running a test probe over the housing. Replace any coil that's leaking.

checking plug leads

To test a sparkplug high-tension lead with its respective coil, disconnect the meter lead that runs to the secondary. Leave the other leads in place and probe the entire surface of the sparkplug lead (Photo 10). If insulation has broken down, you'll get flashover. Replace the lead.

Magnets are located in the flywheel (Photo 11). They could be damaged by a hammer blow or a dropped flywheel, so be careful. Before replacing the flywheel, use mineral spirits to clean magnets of foreign matter that could hamper their function.

The importance of periodic inspection of sparkplugs, followed by cleaning or replacement, cannot be overemphasized in your preventive maintenance of an outboard ignition system. Dirty or worn plugs are the major cause of ignition failure.

When installing new plugs, be sure gaskets are replaced. Start the plug into the cylinder with your fingers to avoid cross-threading. Run them up finger-tight and torque to 20 ft.-lbs.

If your outboard motor is equipped with an electronic ignition system, you can confine your activities to inspecting and, if necessary, replacing sparkplugs and inspecting sparkplug leads. In the event of a problem that suggests ignition-system failure (see above), the outboard should be referred to a factory-trained service technician. Luckily, electronic ignition system failure is not a common occurrence.

2. The Starting System

■ OUTBOARD MOTORS have manual starters or electric starters, or both. We'll explain how to repair a manual starter first; then we'll talk about electrics.

Most outboard motors employ a manual starter of the type similar to that shown in Photo 12.

Manual starters are extremely reliable. Most will last the life of an outboard motor if treated properly. The commonest problem is a damaged rewind spring. This happens most often when the operator steps back and gives the rope a yank that exceeds its length. It's also possible for the rope to break, but this isn't as common as some people believe. Starter ropes are exceedingly strong.

You'll need a spring rewind tool to repair a manual starter. You'll also need a rope-threading tool to pull the rope through the handle.

You must be very careful in handling manual starter repairs. The rewind spring is under great tension and could cause serious injury if allowed to fly loose. Wear safety glasses. Also make sure you hold the starter housing and pulley parts firmly together once the connecting spindle has been removed. This will prevent the rewind spring from slipping loose.

repair steps

Here is how to repair a manual starter:

1. Remove the attaching screws holding the starter housing to the powerhead and lift the housing from place.

2. Remove the pawl retainers, pawls, spindle, and friction ring (Photos 13 and 14). Examine the pawls. If worn, replace. Note how parts come out of the housing so that replacement will be simplified.

STARTING SYSTEMS

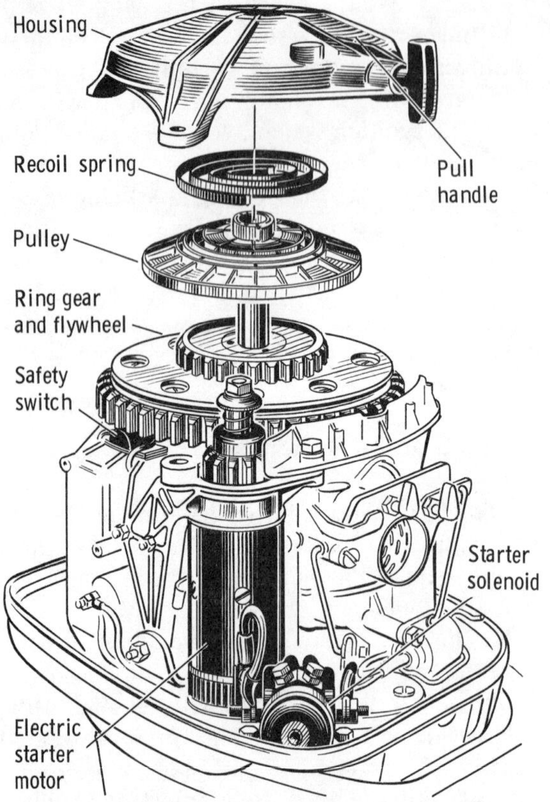

12. UPPER THREE PARTS are used in manual-start systems, the lower parts in electric-start systems.

3. Now, drop the starter, bottom side down, on the floor (Photo 15). This will separate the housing, pulley and spring (Photo 16).

4. If it isn't broken, pull the starter rope out far enough for you to tie a slipknot. Then pry open the rope anchor and remove the rope.

5. Spread some Type A lubricant on the end of the rope to allow easy removal of the handle.

6. Replace a damaged starter rope or rewind spring.

7. To put the starter back together, insert the base plate of the rewind tool into a vise. Place the starter pulley in position on the base plate, making sure that the center pin fits into the center loop of the spring. Insert the tool's bushing and handle into the pulley and base plate, and crank up the rewind spring (Photo 17).

8. When the spring is tight, release it slowly until you're able to slide the dowel pin through the hole in the pulley and into the spring loop. This pin holds the spring in place while you reassemble the starter.

9. Lubricate the spring with some Type A grease and place the pulley and spring into the

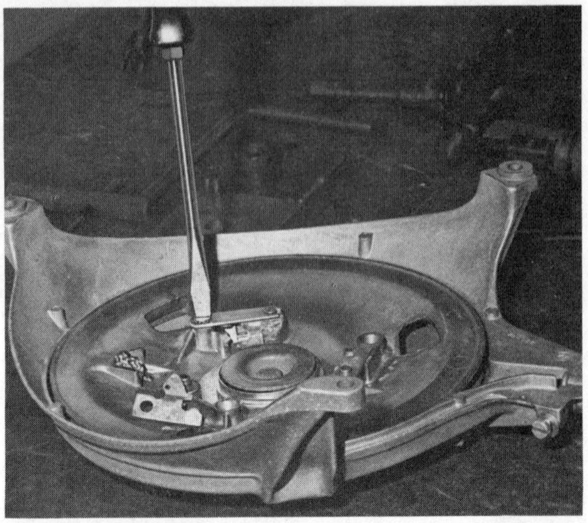

13. REMOVE PAWLS from starter housing (some are shown in lower part of housing). Check them for wear.

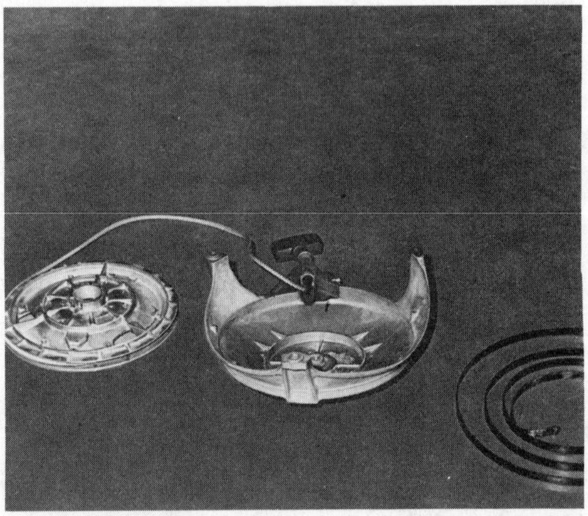

16. THE THREE manual-start parts can be worked on. If there's an "S" in spring, untwist and reuse.

19. GROUNDING safety-switch wire should make motor operate. If not, the switch could be bad.

14. REMOVE SPINDLE from housing. Hold housing and pulley together until ready to separate the two.

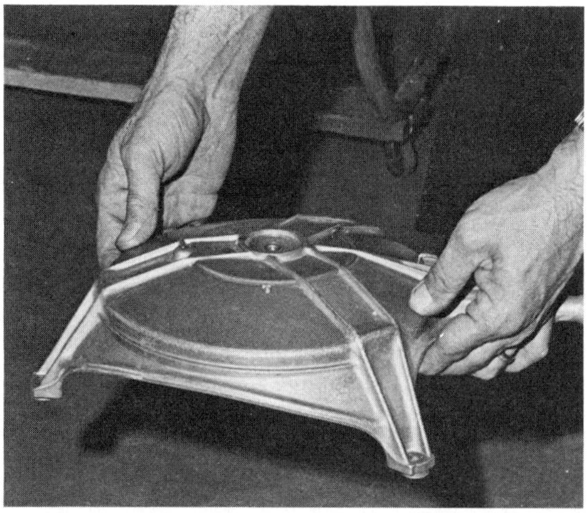

15. DROP ASSEMBLY. Step back quickly to avoid being struck by rewind spring located in assembly.

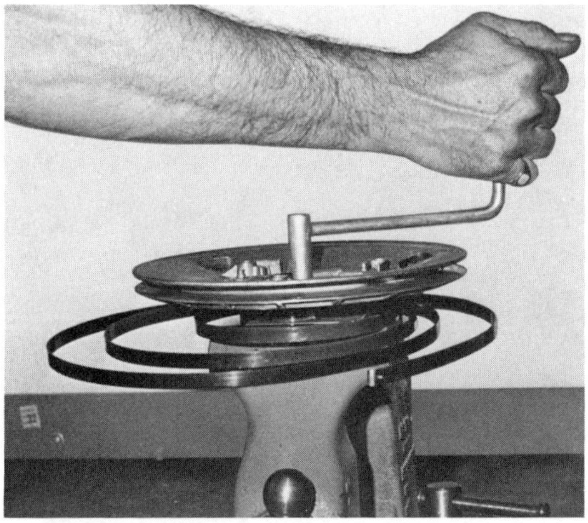

17. REWIND TOOL is needed to reassemble spring into pulley. Crank until spring is tight. Insert dowel.

18. DOWEL PIN, inserted in pulley, holds spring in place until pulley is fitted into starter housing.

20. THE SAFETY SWITCH is usually held in place by one bolt. This is easy to remove and to replace.

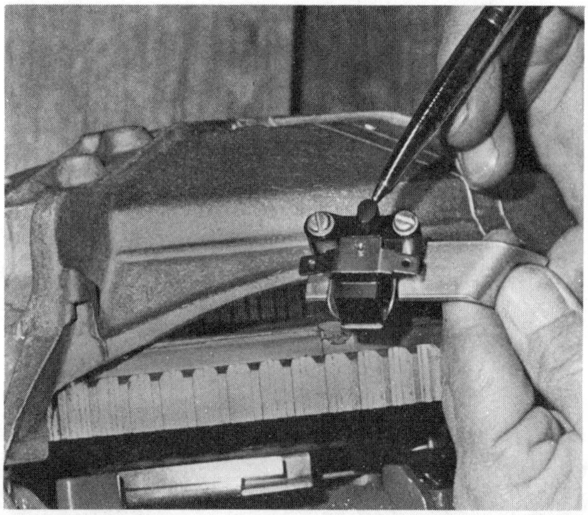

21. THE PLUNGER of the safety switch is so positioned that it actually rides on cam seen at lower left.

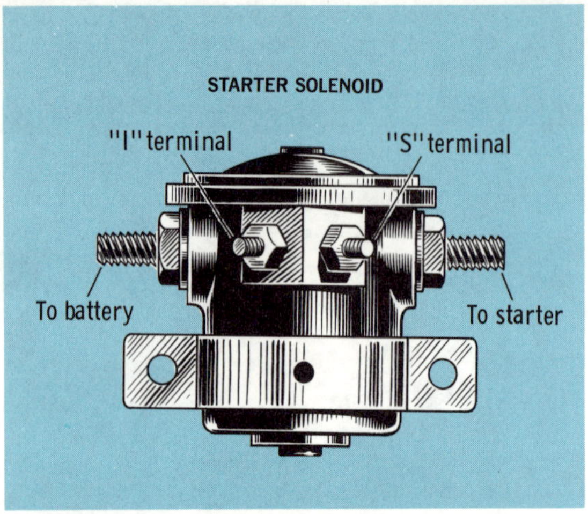

22. STARTER SOLENOID (above) is the key to the electric-start system. Jumper wires (right) connected to the solenoid terminals help you to determine whether or not the solenoid is in good condition.

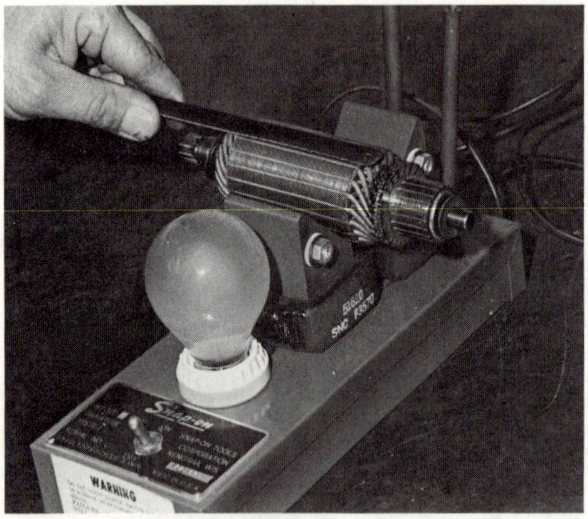

23. TURNING THE ARMATURE of the starter motor in growler is the best way to check for malfunctions.

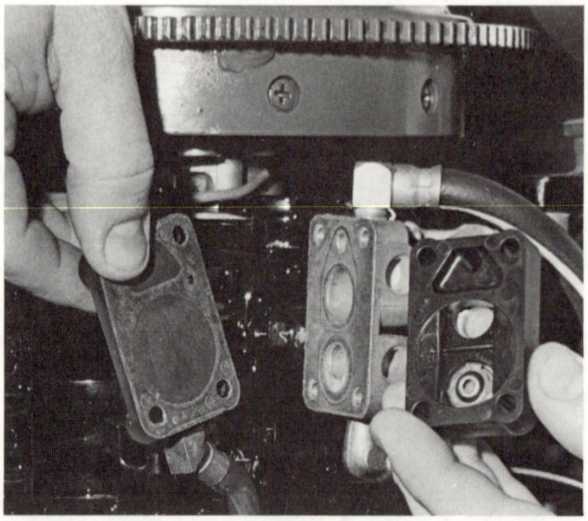

24. FUEL PUMP consists of diaphragm (left) and booster chambers (right). Replace a worn diaphragm.

starter housing, making sure that the outside spring loop is on top of its stud in the housing (Photo 18). Press down so the stud forces the dowel pin out.

10. Tie a slipknot into the rope to keep it from winding up. Now, reassemble the starter.

11. A tough job is usually that of putting the handle back on the rope. If the rope is too stiff, use plenty of lubricant.

electric starter repair

Next is the repair of an electric starting system which consists of a storage battery, starter motor, starter solenoid, safety switch and cables. This is a very easy system to troubleshoot, and it's one of the simplest in your entire outboard engine to repair.

To do the work, you should be equipped with a battery hydrometer to test battery condition and a voltmeter to check the voltage drop of the starter motor. The voltmeter should be graduated in tenths of a volt, but it doesn't have to be an elaborate instrument.

You will need a "growler" for testing starter-motor components if the motor has to be disassembled. However, I wouldn't advise buying this instrument for the rare time you might need it. First, check your local rental center—A to Z, or the like—to see if you can rent one. If not, try to borrow one from the gas station with which you do business. Growler testing takes only two minutes.

If you can't borrow a growler, take the starter motor to a starter repair shop and get it tested.

problems defined

How do you know when you have a problem in the starting system? Either the starter won't function or it will grind away very slowly (r-r-r-r-r) without the engine starting.

Should you experience a malfunction, such as starter grind or no-start, the cause could be loose or dirty electrical connections. The next most likely cause is a weak battery, followed by a defective starter solenoid or a bad safety switch. Seldom will you experience a breakdown within the starter motor itself although it can happen.

At the first sign of a starter-system failure, remove all electrical connections at the battery, starter solenoid and starter motor. Scrape them clean with a wire brush. Then reattach them firmly, making sure that attaching bolts are securely fastened.

Coat connections with liquid neoprene to seal them and prevent further corrosion. Liquid neoprene can be purchased from a dealer of marine supplies.

Next, check the battery by taking a specific gravity reading of the electrolyte with a battery hydrometer. In selecting a hydrometer, buy one that has a built-in thermometer and correction chart.

To take a specific gravity reading, draw electrolyte from each cell in turn. Be sure that the hydrometer float is free, hold the hydrometer at eye level, and note the reading. Be sure to return the electrolyte back to the cell from which it was taken.

The specific gravity of a fully charged battery is 1.260, but a battery with a specific gravity of 1.150 could start your motor. However, if specific gravity is this low, have the battery charged. If charging does not result in an increase in specific gravity in each cell, the battery has just about had it.

testing the safety switch

Now go to the safety switch and starter solenoid. The purpose of the safety switch is to prevent the engine from starting in gear and in neutral at too high an rpm. The switch also completes the ground circuit of the starter solenoid.

The starter solenoid makes and breaks the electrical circuit between the battery and the starter motor. If the safety switch or starter solenoid fails, there will be no starting.

To check the functioning of the safety switch, disconnect the starter terminal wire. There's only one wire. Hold the wire terminal to ground, bypassing the safety switch, and activate the ignition (Photo 19). If you get starter-motor action, it means the safety switch is either out of adjustment or is bad.

To readjust the switch, loosen it and work it back and forth (Photo 20). Place the switch's plunger on the cam of the armature plate (Photo 21). Try starting. If there is still no start, replace the safety switch.

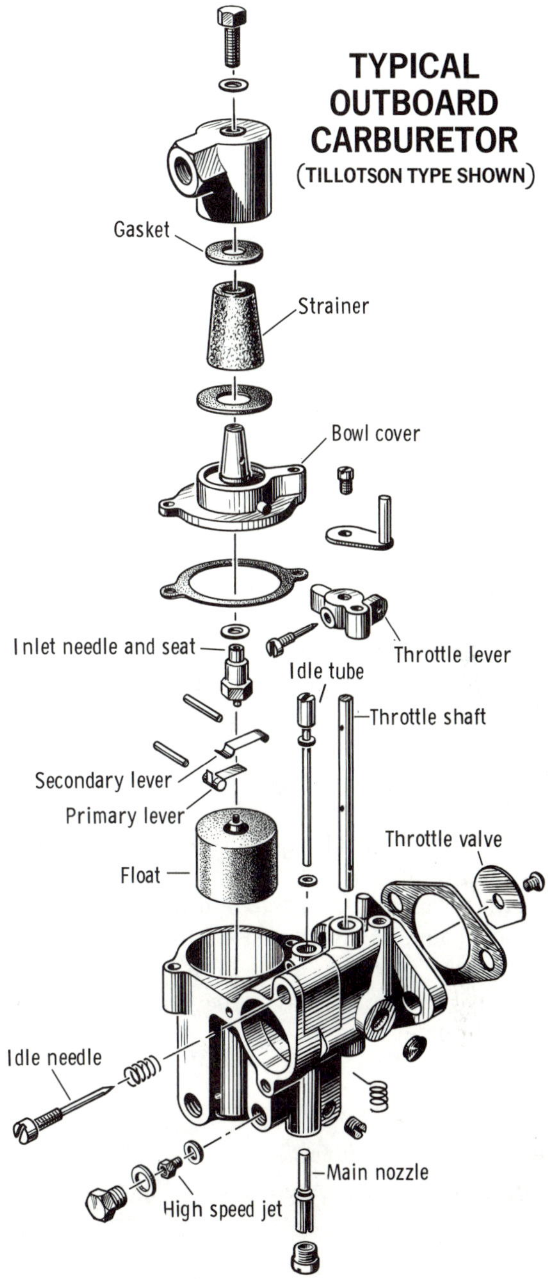

25. THIS EXPLODED VIEW of a typical carburetor will help you work on the one on your outboard.

continued

checking the solenoid

To check the starter solenoid, place a jumper wire from either the "s" or "i" terminal to ground, and connect another jumper from the solenoid's battery terminal to either the "s" or "i" terminal—that is, the terminal not possessing the grounded jumper (Photo 22). Turn on the ignition. If the solenoid switch is in good condition, you'll hear it clicking away and the starter motor will crank as you activate ignition. If not, replace the starter solenoid.

Before replacing the safety switch or starter solenoid, there is one test you'd better make. There's always the possibility that the ignition switch and its wiring, which technically aren't part of the starter system, could be bad and thus make starting impossible.

To test the ignition switch circuit, probe the "i" ignition terminal of the starter solenoid to ground with a 12-v. test light or voltmeter. If the light doesn't glow, it means that juice is not getting to the starter solenoid and, consequently, not to the safety switch either. There's a failure either with the ignition switch or with the wiring that extends from the switch to the starter solenoid.

If switch and solenoid check out, go to the starter motor. Connect a voltmeter to the starter motor terminal. Be sure to determine the polarity of your electrical system first. Generally, Mercury, Chrysler and OMC engines are negative-grounded. Thus, the positive lead of the voltmeter is connected to the starter motor terminal, and the negative lead of the meter is grounded.

meter reveals trouble

Crank the engine and observe the meter. A reading of about 9.2 volts is normal. If the drop is excessive—let's say 7 volts or less—there's a problem inside the starter. It will have to be disassembled and checked for a dirty or worn commutator, shorted turns in the armature, damaged armature windings and condition of the brushes. Here's where you need the growler (Photo 23).

Before doing this, however, see if the starter drive is worn by checking it for side-to-side play. Play should be just about perceptible. Excessive movement indicates a worn starter drive.

Whether you want to have a bad starter motor repaired or buy another is something you'll have to decide for yourself, but sometimes it costs just as much to turn a worn and pitted commutator on a lathe, for example, as it does to buy a rebuilt starter motor. It's advisable to check prices. Naturally, only a single part, such as brushes or an armature, may be needed. Replacement parts for starters can be purchased.

Both electric and manual starters are practically maintenance-free. The only part that actually requires periodic servicing is the battery of an electric starting system.

Keep the top surface clean by flushing it with water every so often. Make sure posts and terminals are free of corrosion. And be sure the electrolyte is up to level at all times.

26. STRAINER COVER comes off top of carburetor to reveal the filter, which should be cleaned.

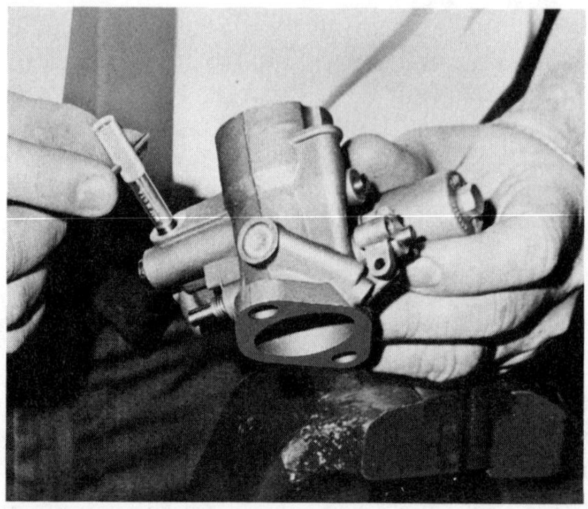

29. REMOVE fixed-jet by uncovering and unscrewing with a fixed-jet tool or an exact-size screwdriver.

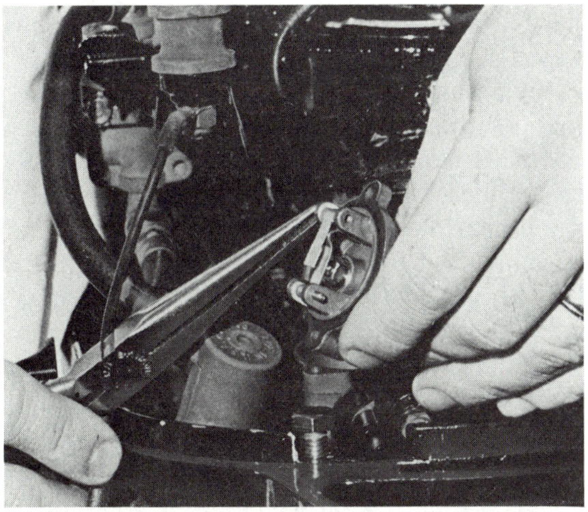

27. REMOVAL of upper float-level pin and the lever permits removal of the needle valve for inspection.

28. FLOAT is removed from bowl. Check condition. If damaged, replace. If hard rubber, clean in solvent.

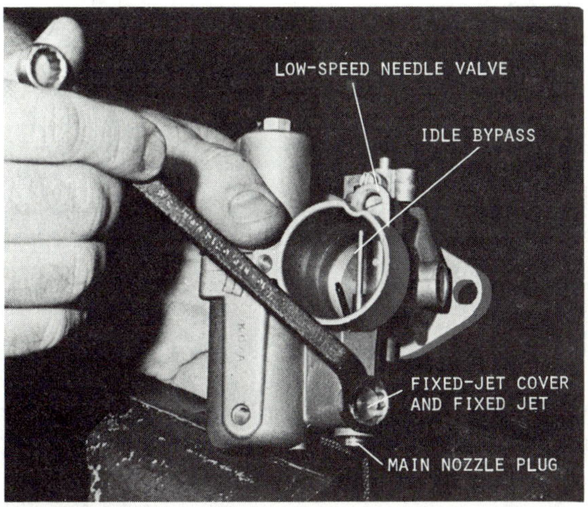

30. UNSCREW the idle bypass, low-speed needle valve and main nozzle plug. Check the parts for damage.

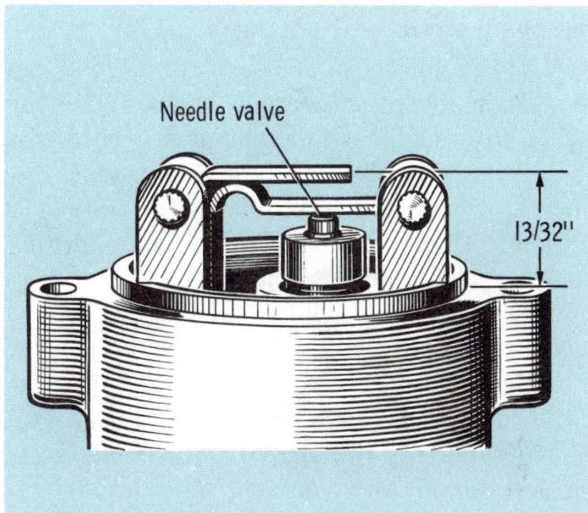

31. ADJUSTMENT of most fixed-jet carburetors is done with the carb upside down, as shown here.

continued

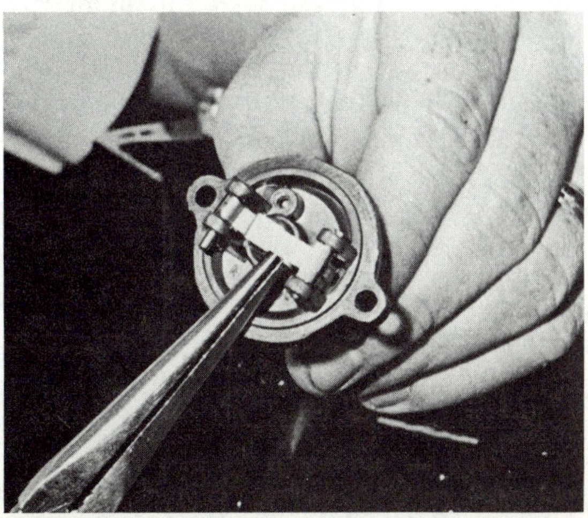

32. BEND the lower float-arm lever to adjust the float level on fixed-jet carburetors.

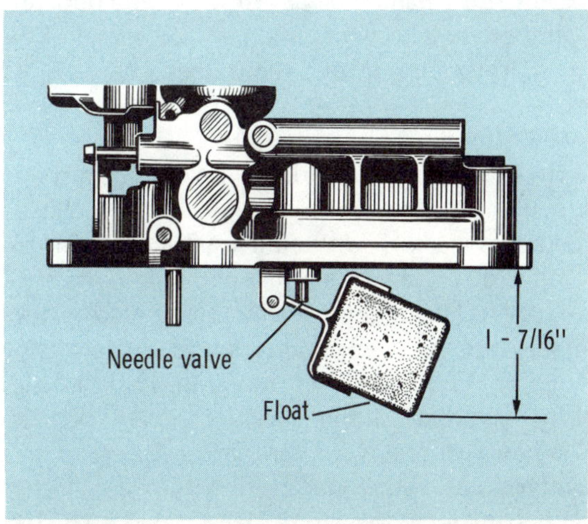

33. FLOAT of most OMC fixed-jet carbs is adjusted by bending cork-float arm to these measurements.

3. The Fuel System

■ FUEL-SYSTEM ASSEMBLIES on outboard motors are simple in make-up and easy to repair. There are two types: gravity-feed (least common) and pressure-feed.

You can recognize a gravity-feed system by the fuel tank mounted on the powerhead above the carburetor. Fuel flows downward without pressure and enters the fuel bowl. Generally, gravity-feed is used on one-cylinder models.

In the more common pressure-feed system, fuel is contained in a tank that's remote from the carburetor and is forced into the bowl by a pump. Most two-cylinder outboards use this system. This article will concentrate on maintenance of a pressure-feed system; if you can repair it, you should have no trouble with gravity-feed.

fuel pump service

A fuel pump consists of a diaphragm and a booster chamber that contains check valves for fuel to enter and leave the chamber (Photo 24). Some pumps, such as those used in OMC engines (Johnson and Evinrude), also contain a fine-mesh filter screen that removes impurities from fuel as it enters the pump.

Fuel-pump parts, including the filter, seldom need to be replaced. The only exception is the diaphragm which can become cracked and pitted. It should be replaced every year. Also check the condition of the diaphragm should your motor suddenly develop fuel-starvation problems.

To keep a fuel pump in good shape, unscrew the pump body, remove the filter if one's used, remove and replace the diaphragm, and remove the booster chamber. Wash the filter and booster chamber in a solvent, such as kerosene. Let parts dry before putting them back.

carburetor service

How far you go in working on your carburetor depends on what's wrong. Usually, all that's needed is a takedown and a wash in solvent to remove dirt and varnish that can clog parts and passages. These impurities can come from the oil-gas mixture if allowed to settle inside a carburetor. You shouldn't have to replace the parts—just clean them.

When you remove a carburetor for cleaning, arm yourself with a gasket kit that you can buy from your local marine dealer. Make sure you get the right kit for your carburetor. Replace all gaskets with the new ones. These include the flange, bowl, fixed-jet, strainer cover and low-speed needle gaskets.

If parts of the carburetor show wear, replace them. If things are very bad, you may decide a complete overhaul is necessary. You'll need a rebuilding kit that contains, among other parts, a needle and seat, a filter screen for those carburetors with filter at the carburetor inlet, idle bypass, gaskets and jets.

If you're working with a fixed-jet carburetor, you'll need a fixed-jet tool or an exact-size screwdriver to remove and reinstall the jet.

Most outboards in the 5 to 20-hp class built since 1959 use the fixed-jet concept. The high-speed control is set at the factory. Generally, it doesn't have to be adjusted. But for operation above 4000-foot elevations a smaller orifice jet is needed. Outboards in the 20-hp and larger class require a high-speed adjustment (except Mercury—all of whose models use fixed-jet carburetion).

Here's how to disassemble a carburetor (Photo 25):

1. Remove the strainer cover and strainer (filter), provided the filter is at the carburetor inlet instead of in the fuel pump (Photo 26).

If the motor is having fuel-starvation problems, remove this filter and hold it to the light. If you can't see through it, it's clogged.

2. Detach the float-bowl cover and discard the gasket. Remove the pin that holds the upper float lever and remove the lever (Photo 27).

3. Invert the float-bowl cover. The needle valve will drop into your hand. Inspect the tapered end of the valve for grooves, nicks and scratches. If the valve is damaged, replace it and its seat. Another indication of a worn needle valve or needle-valve seat is a carburetor that floods constantly. The seat is removed by loosening it from the float bowl cover.

4. Remove the float from the bowl (Photo 28). If the float is made of cork and has become oil-soaked, replace it. Do not wash a cork float in solvent. OMC engines in general use cork floats.

If the float is made of the hard-rubber compound used generally in Mercury and Chrysler outboard motors, it can be cleaned in solvent. If the float is damaged, replace it.

5. Unbolt the carburetor body from the engine.

6. If the carburetor is of the fixed-jet type, remove the fixed-jet cover and, with the right tool, remove the jet (Photo 29).

7. Unscrew the idle bypass, low-speed needle valve and main nozzle plug (Photo 30). If the

carburetor isn't fixed-jet, remove the high-speed needle valve. Check each part. If damaged, replace it.

Wash all parts in solvent and let them dry. Then, in reverse order, put them back into the carburetor body. Use the fixed-jet tool to run the jet up tight.

making adjustments

With the carburetor reassembled, and before putting the float bowl cover back, you have to adjust the float setting. Then, with the carburetor all in one piece, you have to adjust the low-speed needle valve according to the owner's manual. If the carburetor isn't a fixed-jet type, you also have to adjust the high-speed valve.

There is no single adjustment measurement for the float setting. It varies.

Mercury fixed-jet carburetors of the type seen in this article call for a setting of 13/32 inch. The measurement is made as seen in Photo 31. To adjust, bend the lower float arm lever (Photo 32).

With most OMC fixed-jet carburetors of modern vintage, the measurement is 1 7/16 inches. Invert the float body so the float drops and measure from the bottom of the float to the bowl cover body (Photo 33). Adjust by bending the float arm.

To make the low-speed needle adjustment, warm the engine and idle it in forward gear. Open the needle until the engine starts to load up and fire unevenly. It's running rich.

Now, close the needle slowly until the motor slows down and starts to misfire. It's running lean. The best adjustment for the low-speed needle valve is halfway between these rich and lean settings.

By the way, if you can't make the adjustment, check the needle. It's probably damaged and has to be replaced.

high-speed adjustment

In an engine without a fixed-jet, you have to adjust the high-speed needle. Warm up the engine and operate it at full throttle. Run the needle up slowly until it is firm. Do not force it. Now, back it off from a half to three-quarters of a turn.

Now that the carburetor is adjusted, let's check the last part of the fuel system—the fuel tank. Remove the filter and clean it. A clogged filter cuts off fuel.

The only regular maintenance needed on the fuel system of your motor is a periodic cleaning of filters. Also, run the carburetor dry before stowing your motor for the day. This cuts the possibility of varnish and residue accumulating.

The following troubleshooting chart will allow you to pinpoint the fuel system component that is causing a headache:

FUEL-SYSTEM TROUBLESHOOTING CHART

PROBLEM	POSSIBLE SOLUTION
Engine hard to start or won't start	•Make sure you have fuel •Check gas-tank vent to make sure it's open •Check fuel line for kinks •Check fuel for water. Let some fuel evaporate in your hand. Water, if any, will remain •Check fuel filter for clogging dirt •Check carburetor adjustments. The mixture could be on the lean side
Motor misses at low speed, or motor doesn't idle smoothly	•Low-speed needle may be out of adjustment •Check fuel mixture
High-speed motor miss	•Check for water in fuel •Make sure fuel-pump cover is not leaking air •Check fuel-pump diaphragm
Engine coughs, spits, slows down	•Check high-speed adjustment. It might make the mixture too lean. •Check float level. It might be too low •Check fuel-pump diaphragm for dirty check valves and loose cover •Check to see that fuel-tank filter is not clogged •Fuel passages in carburetor may need cleaning

4. The Powerhead

THERE ARE TWO WAYS to tear down a powerhead: minor and major. A minor disassembly allows you to repair such damage as a blown head gasket, a reed-valve failure and carbon buildup in exhaust ports and around cylinder heads. It also lets you look inside the motor to see if a major tear-down is necessary.

If there's an indication of damage that you can't observe directly—such as worn main bearings or a bent connecting rod—you'll have to commit yourself to a major disassembly.

A list of powerhead troubles and how they usually make themselves known is provided at the end of this section. However, a word of caution: Be sure that all other causes of a problem are investigated before you tear into the powerhead. Wouldn't you be red in the face to find out that the cause of an engine knock was advanced ignition timing and not the pistons you're holding in your hand?

THE POWERHEAD

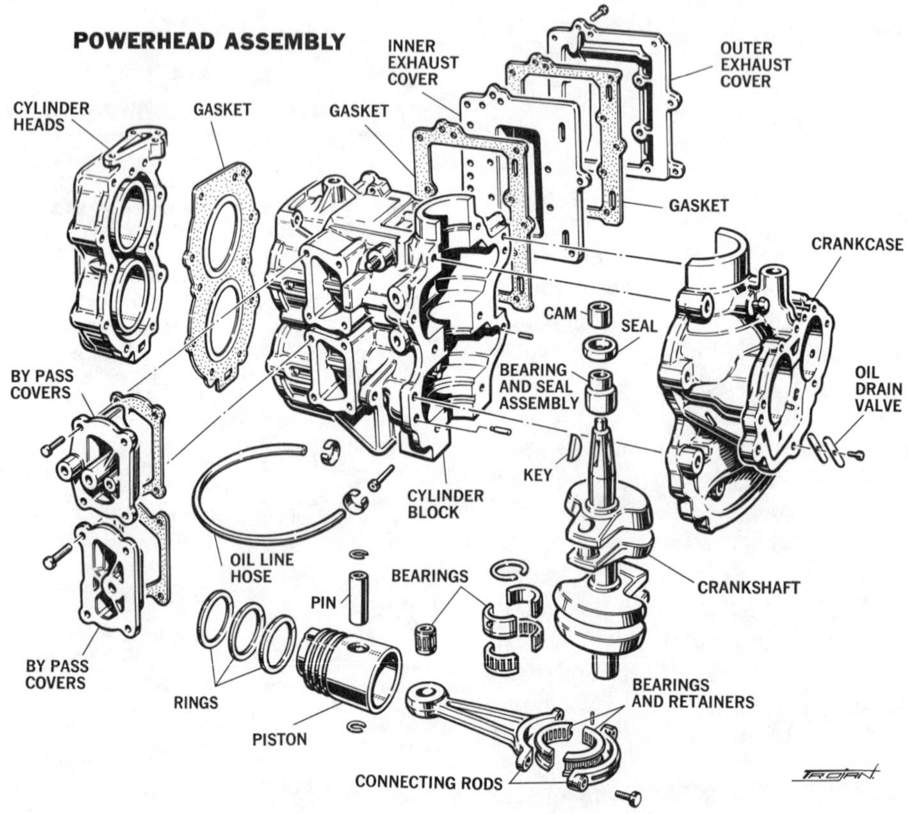

34. THIS DRAWING of a typical powerhead assembly will help you in a minor or major assembly.

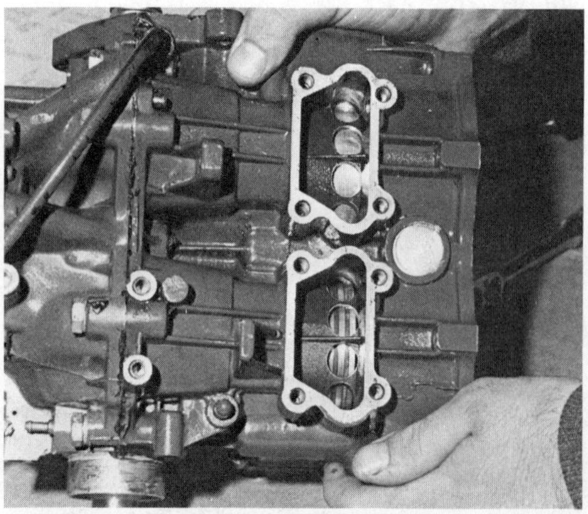

39. PART OF THE PISTON RINGS and some of piston surface are exposed when bypass cover is removed.

40. WITH CYLINDER HEAD removed, examine tops of pistons, part of cylinder wall, all of cylinder head.

35. LIFT POWERHEAD from exhaust housing after all external engine parts and screws have been removed.

36. IF YOU DECIDE to rip the powerhead down completely, you must remove carbon seal. Pull retainer.

37. CYLINDER HEAD often has carbon build-up. Remove it and clean it thoroughly in a solvent.

38. TAKE OFF the bypass covers. Once they are removed, you can get an idea of block's condition.

continued

41. WITH EXHAUST COVERS removed, you'll see side pistons opposite from view through bypass cover area.

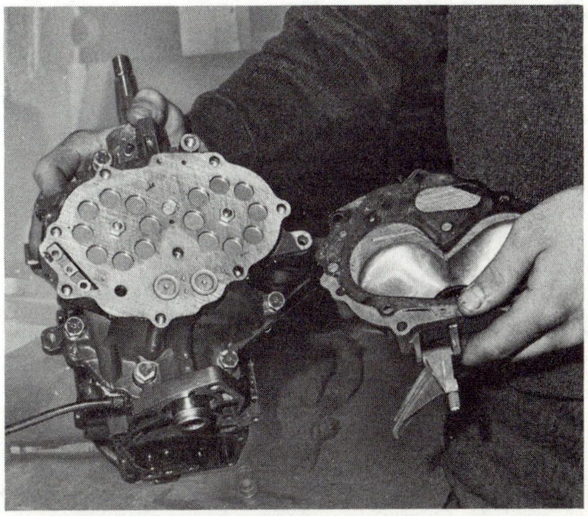

42. REMOVE INTAKE MANIFOLD COVER to reach reed valves. Reed valve plate is held by single screw.

43. BE SURE TO EXAMINE reeds carefully for gum deposits, varnish, distortion, any broken pieces.

44. REMOVE CRANKSHAFT after connecting rod retainer and bearings are disconnected and removed.

important question

An important question you will have to answer is whether to do a major disassembly yourself or to let a professional shop do it for you. There's no doubt that any competent reader can tear the engine apart. But then what are you going to do afterwards?

Suppose, for example, that the cylinder walls show wear, requiring reboring to accommodate oversize pistons. Do you have the reboring tools necessary for this job? If not, would it be less expensive for you to let an outboard repair shop do the whole disassembly and repair job?

Even if reboring isn't necessary, the cylinder walls should be honed and new rings installed while the engine is stripped down. Do you have a cylinder wall honing tool? Do you have a ring expander? Would it be worthwhile to buy them?

All two-cylinder outboard motors are disassembled in pretty much the same way. As you work, be sure to follow these basic guidelines:

• Place parts with their respective fasteners in order of disassembly. This will facilitate reassembly.

• As you perform disassembly, make notes and diagrams of the procedure so that reassembly will be simplified.

• Be observant. Examine everything before you take it off so you'll know how it goes back on. For example, a piston has to be put back into the cylinder with the concave (intake) side of the deflector toward the intake port.

• Keep things clean. Replace worn parts, also all old gaskets and seals.

starting disassembly

To disassemble the powerhead (Photo 34) you have to start by removing the powerhead from the rest of the outboard. Remove all external engine parts: carburetor, flywheel, fuel pump, starter, magneto and so on.

Now, remove the screws that attach the powerhead to the exhaust housing, and lift the powerhead carefully to disengage the crankshaft from the driveshaft (Photo 35). Place the powerhead on the bench.

Remove the carbon seal from the lower end of the crankshaft (Photo 36). This seal sits atop the crankshaft lower main bearing. (However, you need not remove it if you are not doing a major disassembly.)

Remove the cylinder head, bypass (cylinder block) covers and the exhaust covers (Photos 37 and 38). You can now peer inside the block and partially check for cylinder wall damage, carbon accumulation, piston wear and scoring, and piston ring wear (Photos 39, 40 and 41)

The final task in performing a minor disassembly is to remove the intake-manifold cover, which reveals the reed valves (Photo 39). These components do the same job as intake valves on a car—they allow fuel to enter the combustion chambers in measured amounts.

reed valve inspection

Remove the reed valve assembly and inspect the leaves to be sure that they're free of varnish and gum, that they lie flat and aren't distorted, and that none are broken (Photos 42 and 43). If one is damaged, replace all the leaves by simply unscrewing the leaf assembly from the leaf plate.

If this is as far as you're going, carefully clean all parts and castings, especially the cylinder head. Replace all gaskets.

Now, if you determine that the rest of the engine has to come apart, detach the crankcase

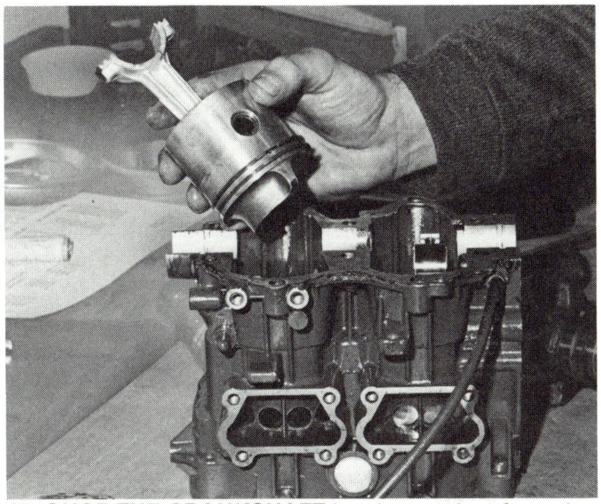

45. ONCE THE CRANKSHAFT has been taken from the engine, you can lift pistons out for inspection.

from the cylinder block to uncover the crankshaft. Disconnect the connecting rod retainers from around the crankshaft and carefully remove the connecting rod bearings.

Next lift the crankshaft from the cylinder block (Photo 44). Remove the crankshaft main bearings for cleaning and inspection. Lift the pistons and connecting rods from the cylinders (Photo 45). You are now ready for overall inspection.

Start with the crankshaft. Check all bearing surfaces for any rust and pit marks. Clean rust off with a very fine emery cloth. If the shaft is pitted badly enough so that your fingernail catches as it scrapes over the surface, replace the shaft.

checking alignment

Each journal and each throw of the crankshaft should be checked for alignment with a dial indicator.

Check connecting rods for rust and alignment. If a rod shows the least sign of being bent, discard it.

Before you check the connecting rods, disconnect them from the piston. Make sure the piston pin that holds the rod to the piston provides a sound fit when you reassemble them. The piston should not feel loose.

Replace needle bearings. Ball bearings, if undamaged, can be cleaned and reused.

Check pistons for scoring and cracks. If a piston has been scored or the metal is damaged, replace it. Clean off all carbon. Replace piston rings.

Check cylinders for wear and accuracy with an inside telescopic gauge and micrometer. If the cylinder is out of round, you can either rebore it so that it will accept oversize pistons, or replace the block.

Inspect the block thoroughly for cracks. Hone the cylinders to remove glaze and to provide a slightly roughened surface for seating the new rings properly.

POWERHEAD TROUBLESHOOTING CHART

PROBLEM	POSSIBLE TROUBLE
Hard to start or won't start	Reed valve failure
Low-speed miss (rough idle)	Leaky or blown head gasket Leaky or blown reed plate gasket Leaky crankcase seal Bad carbon seal
High-speed miss	Leaky head gasket Leaky exhaust case gasket Carbon in combustion chambers
Coughs and spits	Reed valve failure
Runs, then slows and stops	Fouled combustion chambers
Won't start, backfires	Reed valve failure
No acceleration, low top rpm	Reed valve failure Blown head gasket Blown exhaust cover gasket Scored cylinders or stuck rings Carbon buildup on piston head
No power under heavy load	Scored cylinders or stuck rings Carbon buildup on piston head
Engine won't crank over	Broken connecting rod
Motor overheats	Obstructed water passages Bad seals and gaskets Cracked cylinder housing
Motor knocks	Worn or loose bearings, pistons, rods or wrist pins Carbon in combustion chambers and exhaust ports
Motor stops suddenly (freezes up)	Rusted cylinder or crankshaft Bent or broken connecting rod, crankshaft Stuck piston

5. The Lower Unit

ENEMY NUMBER ONE of a lower unit is lack of proper maintenance. Failure to use the correct lubricant as recommended by the manufacturer is a greater cause of damage to your lower unit than those occasional underwater obstructions you may bump over.

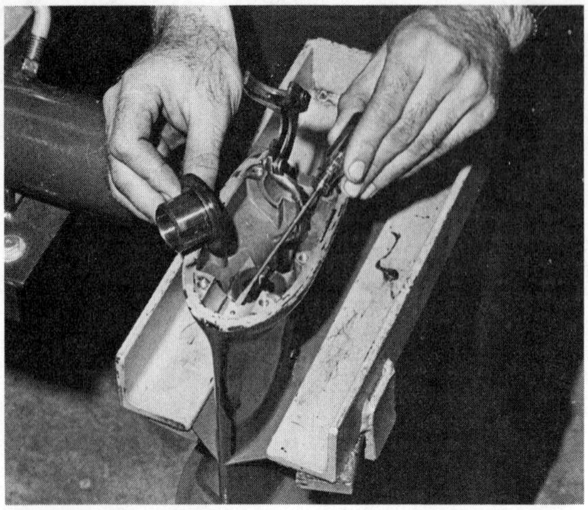

46. EXAMINE EACH PART carefully on disassembly so you'll be prepared to reassemble correctly.

47. THIS INSPECTION PLATE is found primarily on Chrysler, Johnson and Evinrude outboard motors.

THE LOWER UNIT

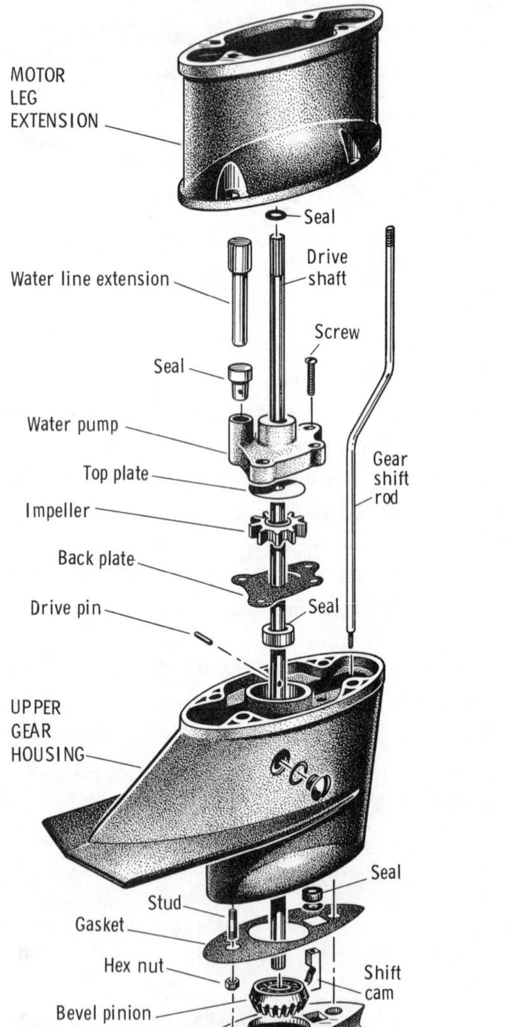
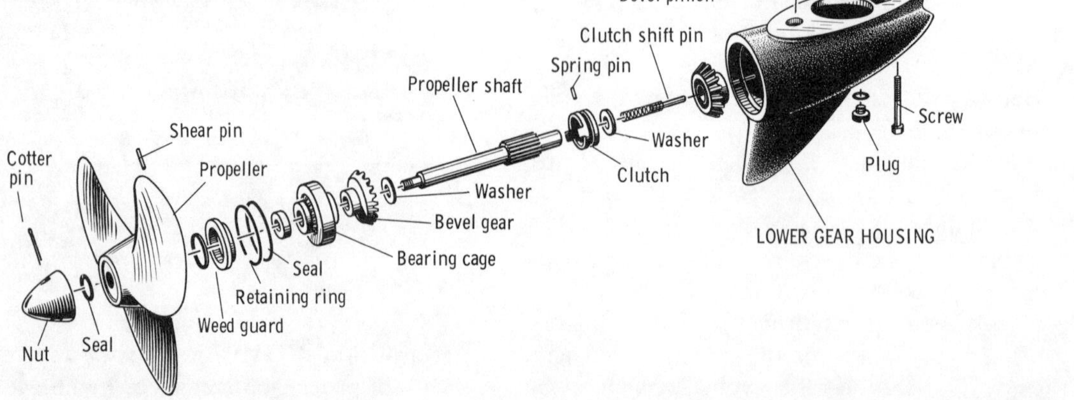

48. EXPLODED VIEW of a typical lower unit will assist you in disassembly of your outboard's unit.

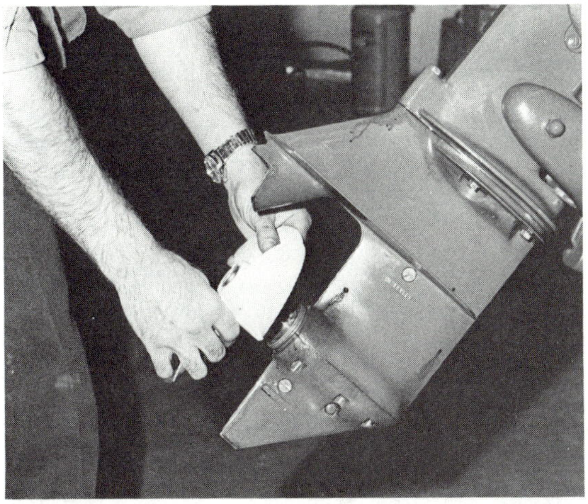

49. BEGIN LOWER-UNIT REPAIR WORK by removing the propeller and draining the gearcase of lubricant.

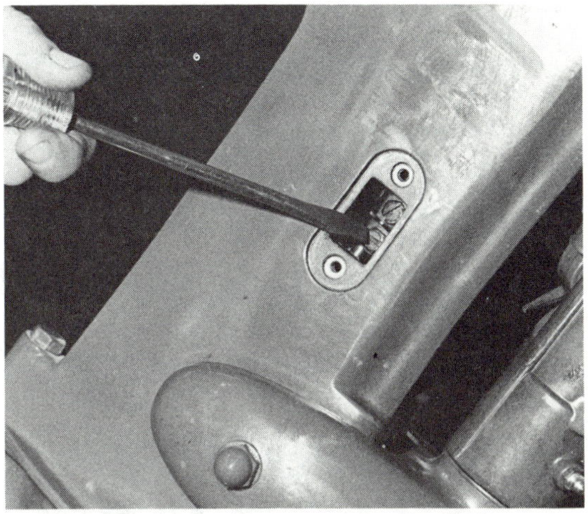

50. IF YOUR UNIT is this type, remove inspection cover and unscrew lower pin to disengage shift rod.

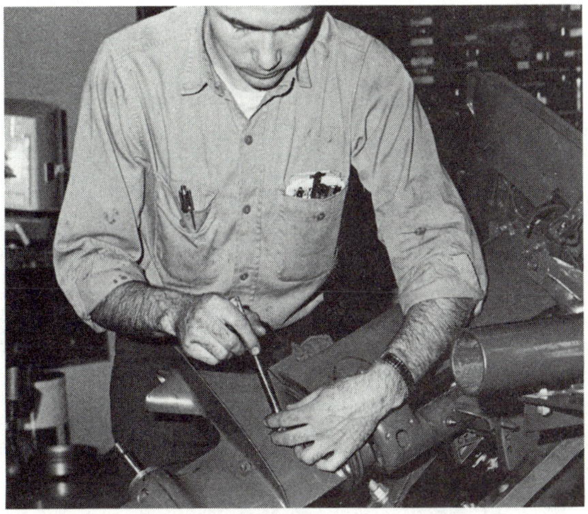

51. REMOVE FASTENERS that hold gearcase to the exhaust housing; store in handy place for reassembly.

52. PULL GEARCASE FREE of exhaust housing. Inspect the machined surfaces for nicks.

continued

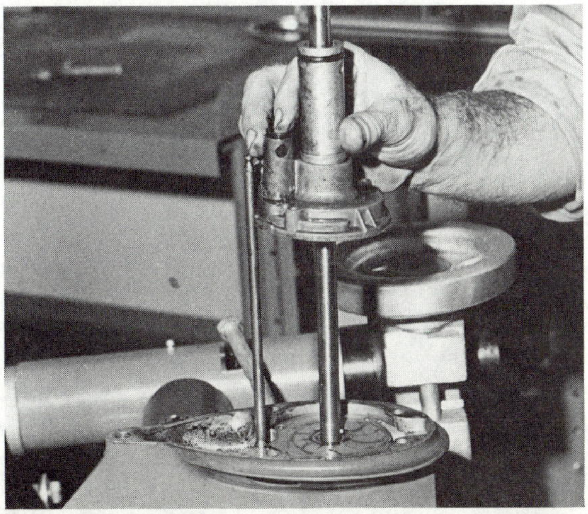

53. DETACH WATER-PUMP HOUSING, slide off shaft.

54. REMOVE IMPELLER from the water-pump housing.

55. REMOVE PIVOT PIN and screws to free the skeg.

56. EXPOSED GEAR TRAIN, after removal of skeg.

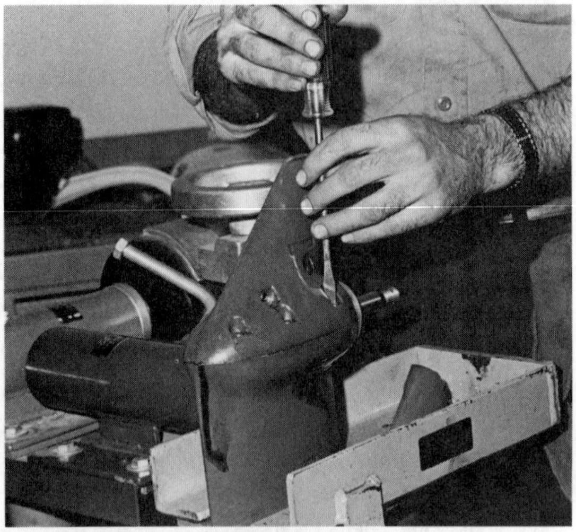

57. LIFT GEAR TRAIN carefully from the gearcase.

58. REMOVE PINION GEAR, then the thrust washer.

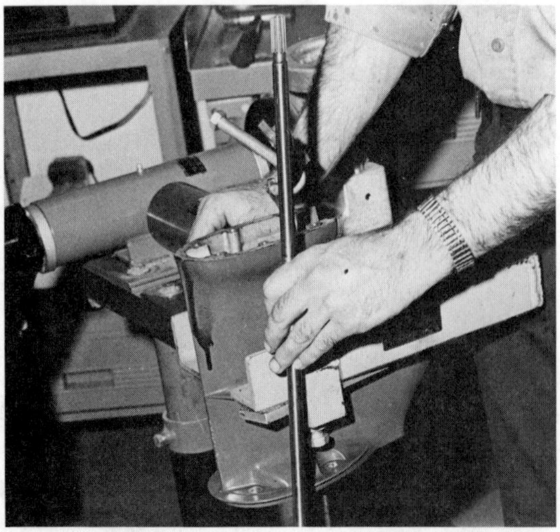

59. REMOVE DRIVESHAFT and, if bent, replace it.

60. CHECK WATER TUBE fit in water-pump housing.

Lower-unit trouble can be detected in one of three ways:

1. The engine won't shift into foward and/or reverse.
2. It can be shifted into forward, but not back into neutral.
3. It jumps continually in and out of gear.

Do you have a remote-control shifting arrangement? Before tearing into that gearcase, better make certain the remote control mechanism isn't the cause of your problem. To test it, disconnect the remote-control unit cable at the motor and shift the motor by hand. If the engine now shifts properly, the problem is the remote control unit. If not, the trouble is in the gearcase.

guidelines for repair

You need no special tools to disassemble a mechanically operated lower unit. But you do need patience, a go-slow approach and a keen eye, especially in your first attempt at lower unit work. If you observe the following guidelines, you should have little trouble:

- As you disassemble, make notes and diagrams of what you've done so that reassembly will be easier.
- As you take down each part, examine it carefully to determine if there's anything special about the way it goes together (Photo 46). For example, in the 18-hp Evinrude used in the illustrations, there's a slot in the front roller bearing that has to fit into a small dowel pin in the gearcase. Otherwise the entire gear train is thrown out of line!
- Keep everything clean, especially when reassembling. If dirt gets on the gears, they will grind themselves to pieces.
- Discard all old seals, O-rings and gaskets for new ones. Most manufacturers issue these in kit form, and you can get them from a dealer of marine supplies.
- If any component, such as a water-pump impeller, is bad, buy it separately.

Basically, there are two types of lower units. One employs a spring-loaded ratchet-type shift dog in forward gear. Mercury makes wide use of it. The other type has a nonspring-loaded, ratchet-type shift dog in forward gear. You'll find it primarily on OMC and Chrysler motors. Its shift rod has to be disconnected before you can drop the lower unit.

To tell which setup you have, examine the lower-unit case. If you find a little inspection cover, your unit is a nonspring-loaded type (Photo 47).

Follow the step-by-step plan of photos 48-60 to take your lower unit apart. Clean all parts in a solvent—kerosene is okay—and let dry. Compressed-air drying is best, but normal air will do. Inspect all parts carefully. If you're not sure whether a part is damaged, don't take a chance. Get rid of it.

Here are a few tips for inspecting lower-unit parts:

- Inspect the driveshaft splines for wear and replace the shaft if it's bent.
- Inspect the gearcase. If it's nicked on any machined surface, the damage must be repaired and the case face resurfaced. The same applies to the surface of the exhaust housing. Let a professional do this. He has the surface plate, surface gauge and scriber needed for such work. If the gearcase is bent, replace it.
- Inspect water tube for obstructions.
- Inspect the water-pump impeller and replace it if vanes are damaged or worn.
- Inspect water-pump housing, drive gears, clutch dog, pinion gear, bearings, and thrust washers for wear. Replace all damaged parts.
- Don't forget the propeller. Minor nicks can be removed with a file. But a broken or cracked blade means that the propeller should be replaced. It's also a good idea to check the prop pitch on a pitch block.

reassembling advice

When reassembling remember that machined surfaces between two parts, primarily between skeg and gearcase, and gearcase and exhaust housing, must be sealed with a marine sealer. Also be sure that screws holding these components are sealed. Dip them in a sealer, such as Perfect Seal No. 4, before they're run up tight.

When the lower unit is reassembled, refill it with gearcase lubricant. It's wise to lubricate all other parts relating to the unit, such as clamp screws, swivel-bracket fittings, throttle-shaft bushings and gears.

Finally, outboard-engine manufacturers stress two basic rules for proper handling of the gearshift.

1. Shift at recommended idle speed only. (Consult your owner's manual—it's usually 600 rpm, plus or minus 100.)
2. Shift smartly with a quick motion of the gearshift lever. Don't ease into gear, and don't wrench your control over.

If you follow these guidelines and the manufacturer's suggestions, your takedown of an outboard motor's lower unit should be limited to a once-in-a-lifetime experience.

NUMBERS LOCATE the parts of this electric-start outboard motor referred to in the text.

Troubleshooting an outboard that won't start

By HENRY B. NOTROM

■ NOTHING DEFEATS a boatman quicker than an outboard that refuses to start. Before you yank your arm off pulling the starter cord, or kill the battery on an electric start, take a few minutes to troubleshoot the problem.

First, make sure you've got fuel in the tank.

Second, make sure the fuel line is pushed *all the way* into the fuel tank at one end and to the fuel pump line connection at the other (1). (See the photographs on these two pages.

Third, squeeze the fuel-line pressure bulb. It should be hard.

Fourth, determine whether fuel is contaminated. Let some drip into the palm of your hand then blow on it. If fuel is loaded with water or dirt, you'll see it as the gas evaporates. Dump that bad fuel.

If this doesn't get you started, find out whether the problem is a clogged fuel system forward of the carburetor. Unscrew the high-speed needle or drain plug at the head of the carburetor (2). If fuel doesn't pour from the hole, you know immediately that a stoppage exists somewhere between the gas tank and the carburetor inlet. Here's how to track it down.

Look for a kinked or ruptured fuel line, and make sure the fuel tank isn't lying on top of the fuel line (3). Check for chipped O-rings inside the fuel-line connectors at both ends of the line (4). These are used to seal the line. If one's bugged, air can be diluting fuel, preventing easy starts. Replace it.

Check for a clogged fuel tank vent. Remove the gas cap. If air rushes in, put the cap back on and try to start the engine. If it starts, you can figure the vent's clogged.

Some tanks have the vent in the upper housing

SEE ALSO

Accident prevention, water . . . Boating, safety . . . Planing speed, boats . . . Pontoon boats . . . Propellers, boat

and fuel line assembly (5). Replace the entire assembly. Other tanks are vented by means of a vent hole in the gas cap. Replace the cap.

filter screens can clog

A clogged filter screen inside the gas tank can keep fuel from getting to the fuel pump. Unscrew the upper housing and fuel line assembly. Pull it out. Clean off the filter screen at the base of the long pipe.

Check the fuel pump (6). You could have a clogged fuel filter inside the fuel pump housing (7). Some model outboards, like the one shown here, have the filter in a housing over the pump. Other models have this filter cut into the fuel pump-to-carburetor inlet. In any event, when a fuel stoppage shows up, always remove and clean the in-line fuel filter.

Tighten fuel-pump housing bolts. If this doesn't get the engine started, remove the fuel-pump cover and replace the pump diaphragm.

Okay, suppose when you removed the high-speed needle or drain plug, gas did pour forth. You have to see whether fuel is getting from the carburetor to the combustion chamber, so prime the engine and remove a sparkplug (8).

A wet plug means the engine's getting gas, but maybe it's getting too much or not enough. Check the choke plate to make sure it's not stuck in either the closed or open position. (9). Follow with a check of the low-speed idle adjustment (10). Turn the adjustment screw a little at a time

ANOTHER VIEW of the same motor shows other parts you should be familiar with as you troubleshoot.

to one side, and then the other. Try to start the engine at each setting.

If fuel is not getting to the combustion chamber but is getting to the carburetor, the trouble lies inside the carburetor or with a reed valve that isn't working right. To fix it, you'll have to remove the carburetor (11). Take it down; clean it; and install any new parts if needed.

You remove the reed valve assembly by taking off the manifold (12). If you're faced with this project, you can forget about fishing for the day. Reed valves that are gummed up—a rare problem—can be cleaned with gasoline. If it is damaged, replace it.

ignition system checks

The cause of your engine problem could lie within the ignition system. So, while you have the sparkplug out checking for fuel in the combustion chamber, hold the plug one-half inch from a clean ground on the powerhead and crank the engine. Absence of a strong blue spark signifies ignition troubles. But where?

Probably with the sparkplug itself, since 90 percent of ignition problems involve this part. Replace a cracked or damaged plug. Make sure the electrode gap is set to specifications.

Check lead wires for breaks in insulation (13). Replace any defective wires.

check magneto or distributor

If nothing to this point helps, the flywheel has to come off for a check of magneto components (14) or, if your engine is so equipped, you'll have to remove the cap for a check inside the distributor.

Inspect ignition points first for proper gap and a burned or dirty condition. If the points seem okay, the cause of your ignition failure is probably a weak coil or condenser.

With an engine that has a distributor, check the distributor cap for cracks and burned contacts, and check the condition of the rotor before replacing the coil.

There's one other major cause of an outboard's refusal to start—a ruptured cylinder head gasket (15). If everything else so far has failed to help, that's a good place to turn.

Simple troubleshooting of today's larger and more complex motors can often reveal a minor problem that you can quickly put right. But when it comes to digging deep into a large sophisticated motor—75 hp and up—take it to trained personnel unless you're a mechanic.

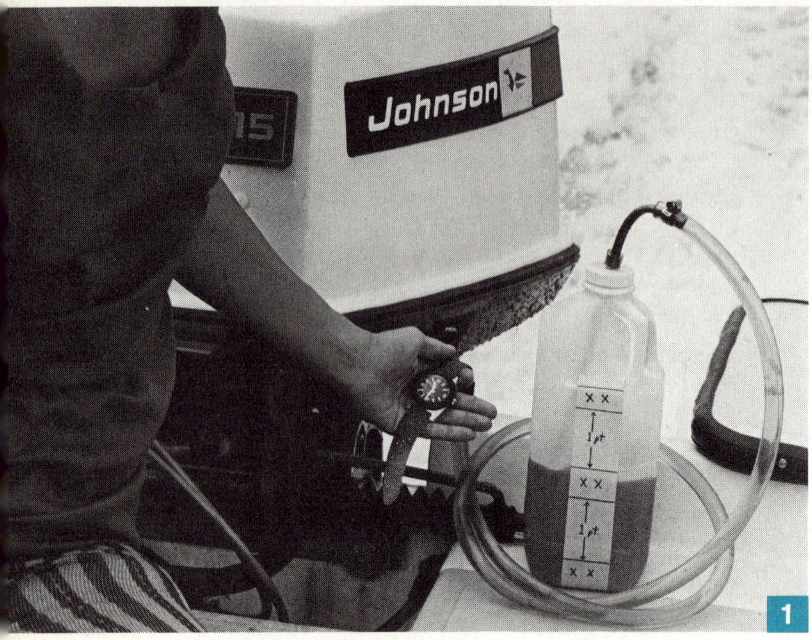

1

2

Determine your outboard gas consumption

By ROBERT D. STEARNS

How far will your boat go on a tank of gas? Are you sure? This simple test will help you determine the proper figure for your boat and tank

SEE ALSO
Boating, white-water . . . Planing speed, boats . . . Propellers, boat . . . Repairs, boat

FUEL SHORTAGES make knowing the gasoline consumption of your outboard more important than ever. If you can figure out in advance your most efficient cruising speed, miles per gallon and range of action on a tank of gas, you're sure to increase your boating safety and enjoyment.

Most large outboards burn about one gallon per 10 hp per hour at full throttle. A 100-hp mill uses up approximately 10 gph wide open, but a 10 percent reduction in rpm can cut gas consumption by 20 percent, while an 80 percent drop in rpm may mean a 35 percent gas saving. These averages apply generally to planing hulls riding over, rather than through, the water, but they can vary greatly from boat to boat with different-size motors and loads. It's certainly worth the small amount of time and expense, using the method shown here, to determine what your fuel requirements really are. Almost any outboard with separate fuel tank can be tested; with adaptations the system should also work for inboards.

Total cost is only about $4 in parts. Assemble a fuel-line connector for your make of engine, a small stainless-steel hose clamp, three feet of 5/16-inch i.d. clear vinyl tubing and enough 5/16 o.d. copper tubing to reach the bottom of your measuring container with a couple inches to spare. For our use, vinyl tubing is better than

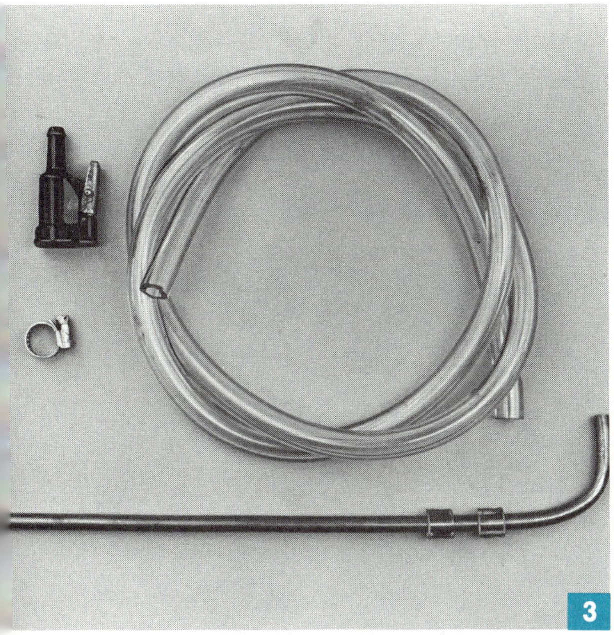

3

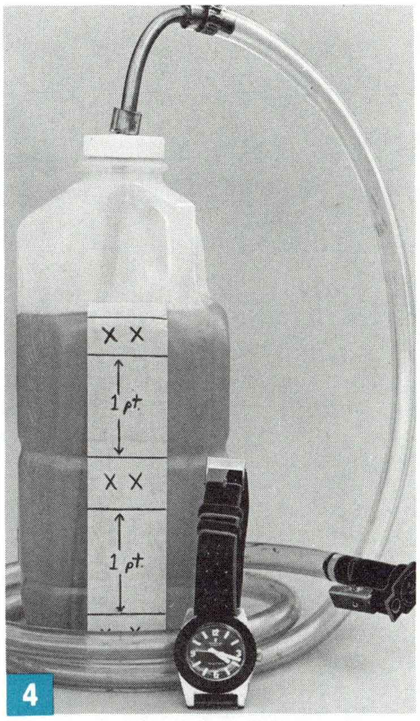

4

5

1. THIS INEXPENSIVE JUG and tubing rig, plus a wristwatch are the only requirements for this simple fuel-consumption test for outboards.
2. A PLASTIC QUART or half-gallon milk bottle, top and kitchen measuring cup are often already available. A strip of tape makes marking easier.
3. BUY A LENGTH of $^5/_{16}$-inch outside diameter (o.d.) copper tube, three feet of $^5/_{16}$-inch i.d. vinyl tube, stainless-steel hose clamp and fuel line connector.
4. A COPPER TUBE to the bottom of the jug fits through a large hole in the top. Add a small hole to serve as an air vent to let the tank "breathe."
5. BURN GAS from the one-inch separation marks between the pints to get the boat on plane and running smoothly before starting to take the time.

rubber (other than neoprene) since gasoline will not cause vinyl to deteriorate, and its transparency allows monitoring a bubble-free flow of gas. An ideal fuel container is a discarded semi-transparent plastic or half-gallon milk jug. Glass would work, but there is the hazard of breakage in a bouncing boat.

First, apply a strip of masking tape vertically on your jug. You will make your calibration marks on it. Marking directly on the jug with a felt-tip pen didn't work well when I tried it; gasoline made the markings run. To calibrate the jug, first pour in an inch of water and draw a line on the tape at that level. Next add one pint of water using a kitchen measuring cup (two eight-ounce cups equal one pint), and draw another line. With a half-gallon jug you can add and mark another inch of water, measure in another pint, and top it off with one more one-inch marking.

The inch separations between pints are important since they allow getting the boat up on plane and running steadily before timing starts. The bottom inch makes it unnecessary to run the engine dry, and avoids the chance of getting extra miles from fuel in your lines and carburetor. Once your jug is calibrated, dump your measuring water, rinse with gas and then fill with your fuel mix on the dock to avoid the chance of spilled gas and vapor aboard.

Test runs are easy. Find a calm water area for easier reading of your jug markings and, preferably, with buoys or markers spaced a known distance apart, if you don't have a boat speedometer. Use up your extra inch of gas, once you're plugged into your engine, to get settled on a smooth run and then time your run while burning one pint.

The arithmetic is simple. A pint is ⅛th of a gallon so by multiplying your pint time by eight you have your time for burning one gallon. Divide that figure into 60 for gallons per hour. Let's say you use one pint in two minutes. Two times eight is 16, and 60 divided by 16 is 3.75. Your engine is burning 3.75 gallons per hour at that throttle setting. For an even easier way, divide your time for one pint into 7.5 (which is 60 divided by eight) and you get the results in one step.

THE LONG shadows of sunrise and sunset bring out details that likely would fall flat if photographed in the light of mid-day as in these desert badlands.

How to get great outdoor pictures

By E. P. HADDON

A professional wildlife photographer tells his secrets. It takes the right equipment, but even more important are the correct exposure, framing, composition and patience to get the perfect shot

SEE ALSO
Bird photography . . . Boat photography . . . Camera gunstocks . . . Close-up photos . . . Hunting . . . Map reading . . . Night photography . . . Panorama photos . . . Photography . . . Underwater photography

FOR THE SPORTSMAN, outdoor photography is a hobby within a hobby. And it's a hobby you can master with nothing more than a small camera that fits in your shirt pocket, plus some knowledge of and attention to simple techniques.

The basic requirement is a good camera that's easy to tote—but even the least expensive Instamatic can give good results if it's used properly. And even heavy telephoto outfits are totable on long hikes: Just transfer the camera's weight to your pack frame with two belt hooks and some nylon tape.

Good pictures start with good framing and composition. An effective picture has good balance, it is pleasing to the eye and it contains no unnecessary distractions.

Low camera positions are a helpful compositional trick many photographers ignore. Shoot-

BACKLIGHTING IS most effective in an open meadow, snow-covered landscape, or on the beach. This proves to be especially true when there is some wildlife around to cast extra shadows for added effect.

ing upward from a low angle, you can dramatize subjects by making them look taller and by emphasizing the texture of the foreground. And aiming upward to shoot your subject against the sky eliminates much background clutter.

To make the sky more interesting, clouds can be emphasized with filters: For black and white, you can use yellow, orange or red filters for increasingly dramatic (and decreasingly natural) effects; with color, you can use only a polarizing filter, which darkens that portion of the sky at a right angle to the sun, and which also can be used with black and white film. When shooting distant scenics, or whenever shooting color at altitudes above 5000 feet, you should use skylight or haze filters to eliminate excess blue. Shooting bighorn in the Sangre de Cristo mountains, two miles above sea level, I find my shots look sick without such filters.

A SPOTLIGHT held this frog fascinated while we shot from 3 feet away with a 90-mm tele. Flash on camera was augmented by slave flash held by a friend.

TRANSFER YOUR camera's weight from your neck to your packframe when backpacking, to make it easier to hike for days. The author uses nylon tape and a couple of hooks for support (circle).

Focusing also affects your background. If it's cluttered and unattractive, use a wide-open lens to throw it out of focus. But for general scenics or action whose exact distance you can't foresee, use the smallest lens opening that permits an adequate shutter speed, to keep the greatest possible range of distances in focus; and use your lens' depth-of-field scale (most nonautomatic cameras have one) to place that depth where it will be most useful.

The subject's angle to the camera is also important. Animals and people are best shot facing the camera, and action is best shot moving into or across the picture, not out of it—basically a matter of aiming the camera a bit ahead of the action.

Action that's moving toward the camera is also easier to stop than action moving across the camera's field of view. A deer coming head-on at full-speed might be stopped with a shutter setting of 1/500 second; but running broadside across the camera's field close by, he might need 1/1000.

Where you expect to be shooting action in subdued light (or where you'll need fast shutter speeds to reduce the effects of tele lens shake)

AUTHOR HID, flash at the ready, by a log where a crocodile was likely to climb. Author's patience really paid off with this shot. He used a flash off the camera on a 5-foot cord to catch the drama of the eye and teeth. This was the correct sidelighting.

DEADLY COTTONMOUTH moccasin was shot from 20 inches with a 90-mm lens and close-up attachment. Fortunately, he couldn't strike as he was not coiled. Notice the way the tongue is stopped with electronic flash.

BIRD PHOTOGRAPHY takes patience. It is best to hide where birds nest, feed or gather. Blinds are necessary for close-ups of waterfowl and other nervous birds. This prairie falcon was snapped from hiding, with a 180-mm telephoto lens held ready for the right moment.

use a fast film such as High Speed Ektachrome for slides, or Tri-X for black-and-white prints. But slower films, such as Plus-X black and white, Ektachrome and Kodachrome for color slides, and Kodacolor for color prints will give you finer detail.

A faster film also helps you shoot on overcast or rainy days, when colors are soft and greens especially vivid. When the sun is out, try to shoot in the early morning and afternoon when the light is most dramatic and long shadows accentuate landscapes and the animals that move across them. Early light is especially good for features of distant mountains that fall flat at high noon. If you find sunset or sunrise light too red, you can cool it down a bit with an 92A filter; if you want to accentuate the redness, try a Sky 1A or Haze.

Noon, oddly enough, is a good time for flash. Use it to fill in the shadows under noses and hat brims. When the sun is lower, flash fill-in lets you face subjects away from the sun, for more relaxed, squint-free expressions; properly done, such backlighting is more dramatic, too. Fill-in is also good with sidelighting. The technique of fill-in flash is basically a matter of juggling flash and sunlight exposure so the subject gets its main exposure from the sun and a bit less exposure from the flash.

Flash is about your only choice when shooting game at night. The flash is too quick to scare the game, and it stops action beautifully. Nighttime flash shots do have an artificial look, with dark backgrounds, washed-out foregrounds and red eyes. But you can eliminate the red eyes and get more natural lighting by using a long flashcord and holding your flash off the camera. You can attach the flash to an overhanging tree limb with a camera clamp.

Electronic flash beats bulb flash on the trail. A pocket-sized flash can give you as many as 150 shots or more on two sets of alkaline AA batteries (more batteries are easy to bring along), and there are no used bulbs to be carted back or

BARBARY SHEEP, among the wariest of big game, are hard to stalk. These were shot from a hiding place across the canyon, with a 500-mm telephoto lens on a 2¼ x 2¼ single-lens reflex camera. Telephotos are among the most useful lenses for wildlife.

to litter up the trail.

Both electronic flash and cameras can be damaged by moisture. So take plenty of plastic bags to protect them from rain. You can even shoot single-lens reflex cameras while they're in a bag: Just cut holes for the lens and eyepiece, and clamp the edge of the bag to the lens with a lens hood.

If you're going to expose your camera regularly to heavy rains, snow, salt spray or canoe upsets, the Nikonos is tops. Sealed for underwater use, it also makes a great all-weather camera.

Whatever game you're stalking with a camera, you need the same tricks hunters use. Cling to the shadows, keep upwind from easily spooked game, walk slowly with a light tread, and anticipate what lies ahead. Preset your shutter speed and lens opening for existing conditions (automatic, electric-eye cameras do this for you) so you'll have nothing to do when an animal appears but aim, focus and shoot. If you're lying in wait at a water hole, salt lick or wherever the animal's location is predictable, you can save even more time by prefocusing where you expect to see him.

The right equipment does make a difference in wildlife photography. A camera clamp is among the most useful pieces of gear, holding the camera so you can set a self-timer and get in the picture yourself, steadying it for time exposures, or holding a flashgun away from the camera. Add a long rubber-bulb or cable release and a camouflage poncho, and you're equipped to shoot birds in their nests. For close-ups of plants, insects and trout flies, use a single-lens reflex camera with auxiliary close-up lenses or extension tubes. With a polarizing filter, to cut through water-top reflections, you can even shoot a

USING TREES for concealment, the author shot this elk herd storming past. For such head-on action, 1/500 second is fast-enough. But broadside close-ups taken just as the elk moved past the camera required a faster shutter speed, 1/1000 second.

SNOW AND BEACHES can fool exposure meters. To solve this problem try taking a reading from your gloved hand. Another solution is to carefully follow the recommendations on your film's instruction sheet.

90-MM MEDIUM tele knit together this carefully planned shot of a falconer and his dog bringing the distant peaks into greater prominence.

CAMP SCENES are a must for good thorough coverage of your pack trip. Here, the low morning light is used to bring out considerable detail in the light-colored sand, tent, and the inflatable kayak.

close-up portrait of a feeding fish. And reflex cameras are great with long telephoto lenses, so you can photograph wary wildlife.

Since telephotos magnify camera shake, it pays to learn some rifleman's tricks, too: Squeeze off your shots as slowly with a camera as you would with a rifle. Steady your camera by bracing your arms against trees, rocks or fences, or drop into a rifleman's crouch. "Gunstock" mounts, many of which can be folded up compactly, also help.

On the other hand, you can travel light and still get good pictures. I often take along the 15-ounce Rollei 35, a full-frame 35-mm camera that features a brilliant viewfinder, a built-in exposure meter, shutter speeds from ½ to 1/500 second, and a 40-mm Tessar f/3.5 lens that folds in for compact carrying. My whole Rollei outfit, complete with lens hood, filters, Rollei electronic flash and film, can be carried in a jacket pocket or a small Camp Trails belt pouch. Similar, but less expensive (and a bit less compact), cameras are available from Fujica, Konica, Minolta,

WITH SELF-TIMER and pocket-sized camera clamp, you can become a part of your own picture. For this shot, a wide-angle lens caught the depth of field.

Olympus, Petri and Yashica, many with coupled rangefinders and most with automatic exposure control. Many outdoor photographers swear by the rugged, compact old Leicas which, unlike other compacts, take interchangeable telephoto and wide-angle lenses.

Simple cameras, which are usually even lighter and easier to carry, can also yield good shots, of course (I've seen some nice results from Pocket Instamatics).

At the other extreme, 2¼ x 2¼ cameras, such as the Hasselblad single-lens reflex, the Mamiya interchangeable-lens twin-lens reflex (especially the current models, which are lighter than the old ones) and the light, rugged Rolleiflex, are also used on the trail for the greater detail and tonal range their larger negatives provide. Some really dedicated nature photographers even pack 4x5 view cameras!

But whatever your camera, it's not the equipment but the thought and care you put into your shooting that make your picture trophies true records of the drama and beauty of your trips.

TRIPOD STRAPS easily to the "Expedition" pack. When an ice ax is carried, the tripod can be strapped to the top of the pack frame. This Vivitar tripod will add less than five pounds to your load.

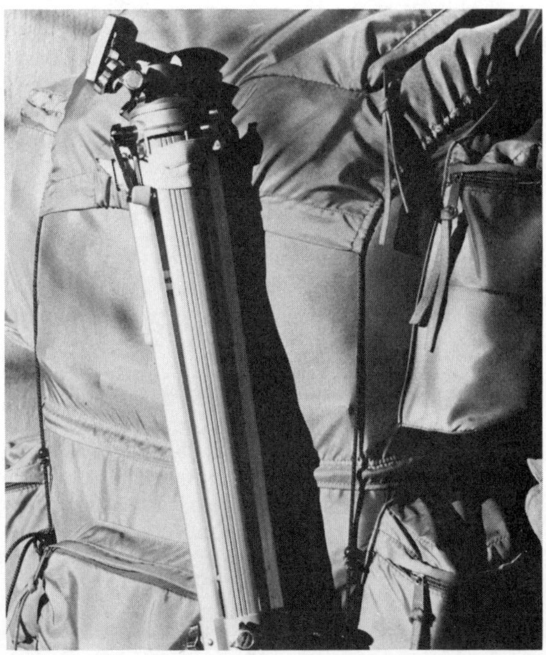

IF YOU FIND yourself in need of spade lugs during a late-night or Sunday work session when stores are closed, make your own from a piece of brass chain as shown: A, remove link; B, cut off the ends; C, cut the link in half. You'll end up with D, a neat lug that can be soldered to the end of the conductor.—*Hugh M. Gordon, Burlington, Ont.*

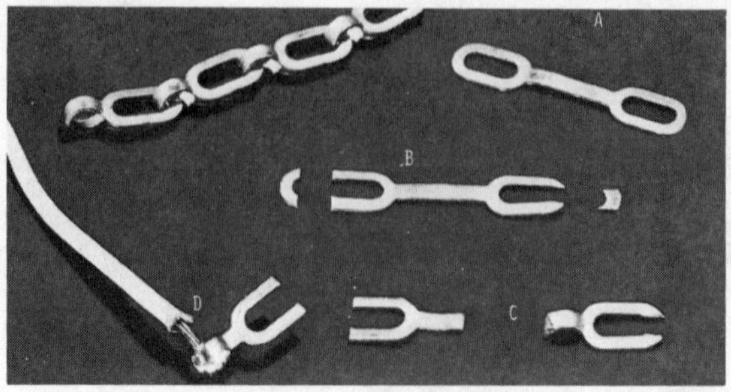

WHEN USING a cutter on highly finished metal tubing you can minimize surface scratches by first wrapping the tubing with two thicknesses of sheet plastic (such as the type used for bread wrappers, vegetable bags and the like). Hold plastic on tubing with clear tape, use low or moderate feed-pressure on the cutting wheel.—*Burt Web, Skokie, IL.*

SMALL AND FINE NEEDLES are frequently lost or tend to rust if not protected. A good holder can be readily made from the cap of a ballpoint pen and a small cork. Trim cork to fit cap opening tightly and stick needles into the cork so that when it is pulled, the needles will come out along with it.—*Harry Radzinsky, Charlotte, NC.*

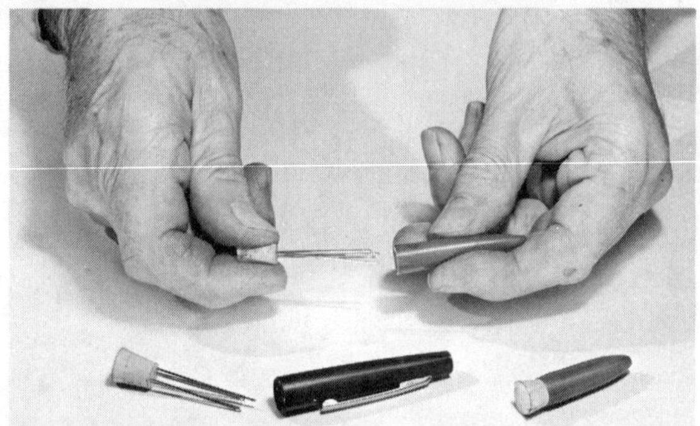

ORDINARILY, small, standard wood moldings are difficult to hold absolutely motionless in a miterbox because of their size. I've discovered that a pair of spring-type photolamp clamps will hold such pieces firmly while the molding is being cut. To do this effectively, fasten one clamp per side as shown in the photo.—*Ken Patterson, Regina, Sask.*

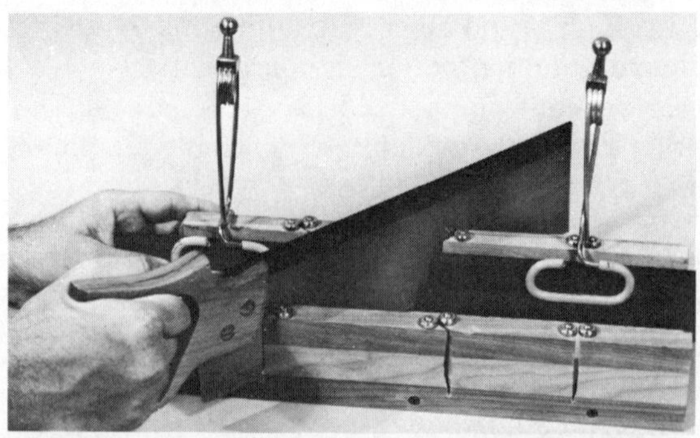

AN EASY WAY to make stencils for use with airbrushes, spatter-brushes, or similar applicators is to block squares selectively in a piece of wire screen. The stencil shown was made using household cement to block double rows of squares outlining figure, then painting over with lacquer. A toothbrush was used to spatter paint through.—*Walter E. Burton, Akron, OH.*

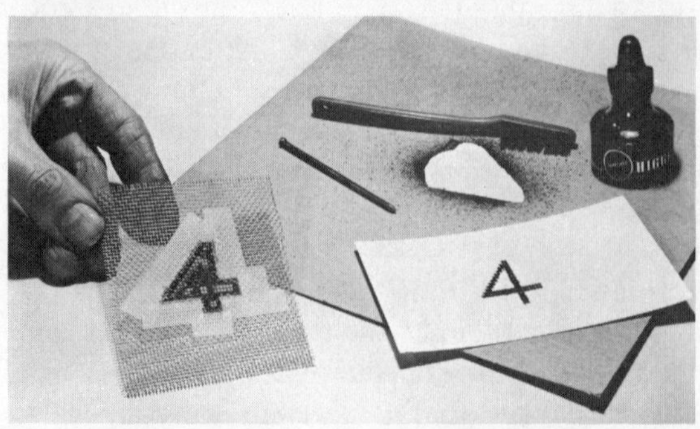

THE TABLE ABOVE can be opened on one or both sides for serving and closes to only 7 inches wide. Table below breaks down into four separate parts for easy storage

Two stowaway tables for the outdoors

IMAGINE HAVING a Christmas display on your lawn 12 months of the year simply because it is too big and bulky to put away! You can liken this to a bulky picnic table that sits around from one summer to the next, too large to stow away come winter, a headache to move each time you must mow around it. And before long, its ap-

pearance starts disintegrating from constant exposure to the elements.

Not so with the two unique tables shown on these pages. You can take them apart, close them up, move them indoors if you wish, or park them in the garage in a minimum space.

The 3x6-ft. table in the large photograph on page 137 breaks down into four parts—two benchtops, stretcher and a table that folds flat. To set it up, you place the table face down and open the wood turn-buttons which hold the legs in tow and the metal ones which anchor the leg braces. Lift one leg, back off the wingnuts, swing open the twin bench legs and insert the stretcher part way in its slot. Then lift the opposite leg, swing out the bench legs, raise both side braces, shove the notched stretcher in place and pull up on it to lock it. Turn the table right side up, open the notched rails on the underside of the benchtops and fit them into the notches in the legs. This procedure may sound complicated but once your family gets used to it you will be surprised how quickly the table will be ready for your picnic.

two sheets of plywood

It takes two 4x8-ft. sheets of plywood (with some waste) for the legs, table and benchtops, and 1x2, 1x3, 1x4 and 2x4 lumber for the rest. You'll need 20 3-in. plain butt hinges, four wingnuts and bolts, six metal turnbuttons and about six dozen 1¼-in. No. 8 flathead screws, along with some water-resistant glue. A couple coats of a marine-type spar varnish inside and out give good protection for the plywood table and benchtops. We used Zip-Guard by Star Bronze Co., Box 568, Alliance, OH 44601. Two coats of acrylic latex house paint will keep the legs in good condition and will add some color to the table.

You'll need a saber saw to cut the legs, but it's worth the small extra charge to have the lumberyard saw your plywood into the nine individual pieces required. This way, there won't be much cutting to be done and a handsaw will handle what's left. Kerfing of the table and benchtops adds to the looks, but is optional. The kerfs are easy to cut if you have a router or portable circular saw.

It's important that the leg hinges at the top fit flush in their rabbets so the side braces will pass over the barrels when moved up or down. Note too that the end-view drawing shows a ¾-in.-sq. block added to the tops of the bench legs to bear against the underside of the benchtops for added support.

the second table

The fold-down table is light enough to carry to a deck or yard and elegant enough to use inside, too. It doesn't look like a plywood table (even though the panels are) because the edges are banded with ¾-in. solid stock. You can use any hardwood from mahogany (which we used to get

THE FOUR PARTS of this collapsible table are the stretcher (A), benchtops (B), and table (C). The bench and the table legs hinge to the tabletop. Use the cutting diagrams (right) to minimize waste

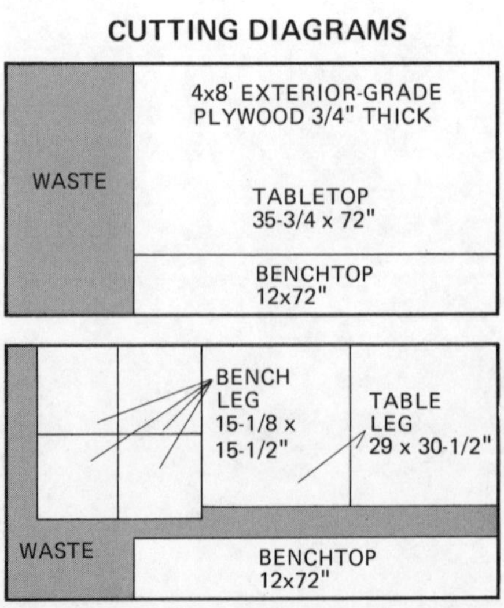

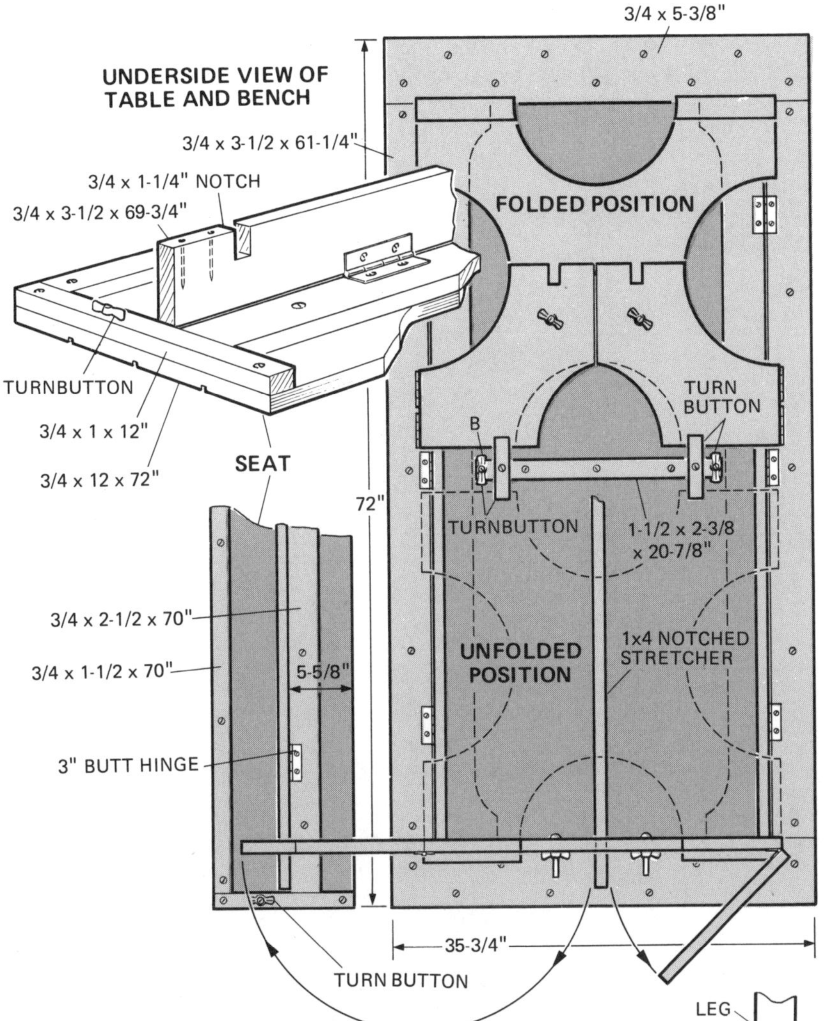

UNDERSIDE VIEW OF TABLE AND BENCH
3/4 x 5-3/8"
3/4 x 3-1/2 x 61-1/4"
3/4 x 1-1/4" NOTCH
3/4 x 3-1/2 x 69-3/4"
FOLDED POSITION
TURNBUTTON
3/4 x 1 x 12"
3/4 x 12 x 72"
SEAT
TURN BUTTON
B
TURNBUTTON
1-1/2 x 2-3/8 x 20-7/8"
72"
3/4 x 2-1/2 x 70"
3/4 x 1-1/2 x 70"
5-5/8"
UNFOLDED POSITION
1x4 NOTCHED STRETCHER
3" BUTT HINGE
35-3/4"
TURN BUTTON

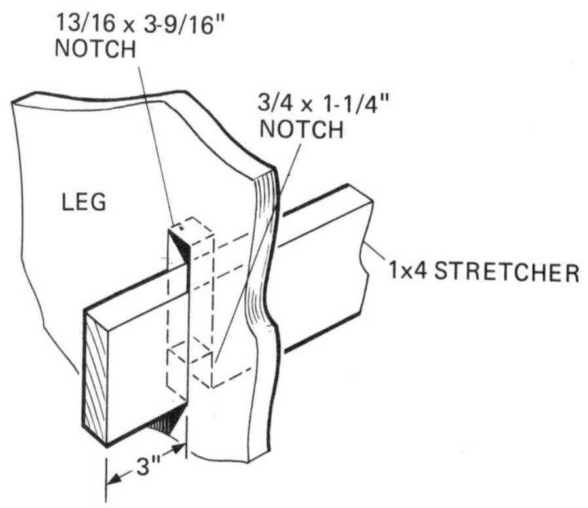

13/16 x 3-9/16" NOTCH
3/4 x 1-1/4" NOTCH
LEG
1x4 STRETCHER
3"

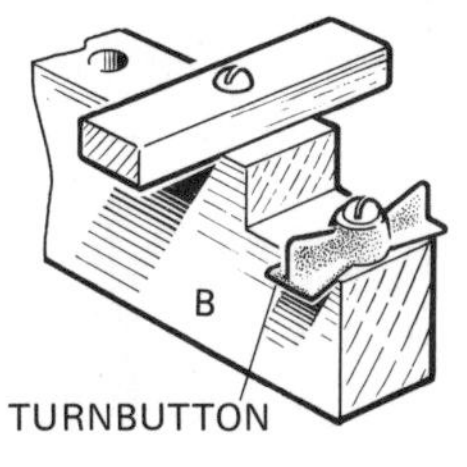

B
TURNBUTTON

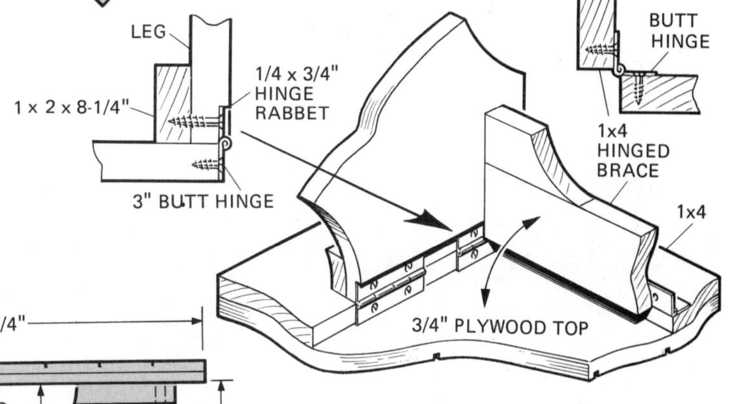

LEG
1 x 2 x 8-1/4"
1/4 x 3/4" HINGE RABBET
3" BUTT HINGE
BUTT HINGE
1x4 HINGED BRACE
1x4
3/4" PLYWOOD TOP

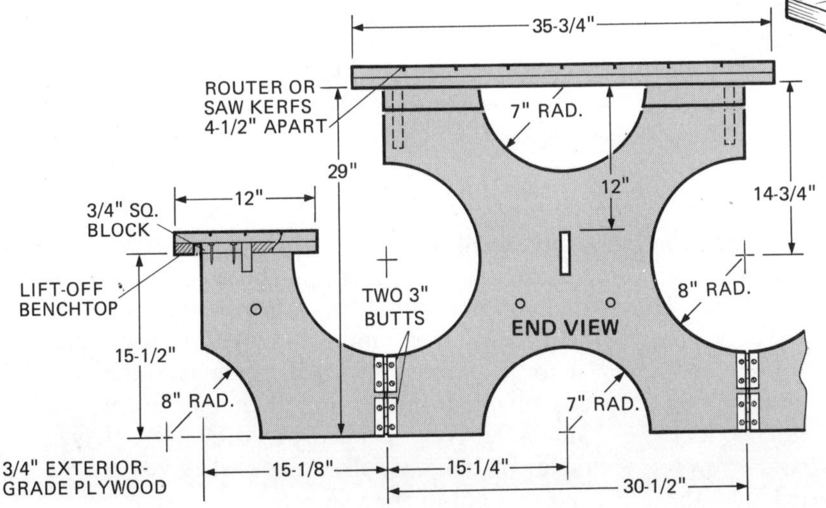

35-3/4"
ROUTER OR SAW KERFS 4-1/2" APART
7" RAD.
29"
12"
14-3/4"
12"
3/4" SQ. BLOCK
LIFT-OFF BENCHTOP
TWO 3" BUTTS
8" RAD.
END VIEW
15-1/2"
8" RAD.
7" RAD.
3/4" EXTERIOR-GRADE PLYWOOD
15-1/8"
15-1/4"
30-1/2"

Clean lines and efficient construction make this table both practical and versatile for outside or in. Its spacious 5½-ft.-long top folds down to 7-in. width for storage

ELEGANT FOLD-UP TABLE

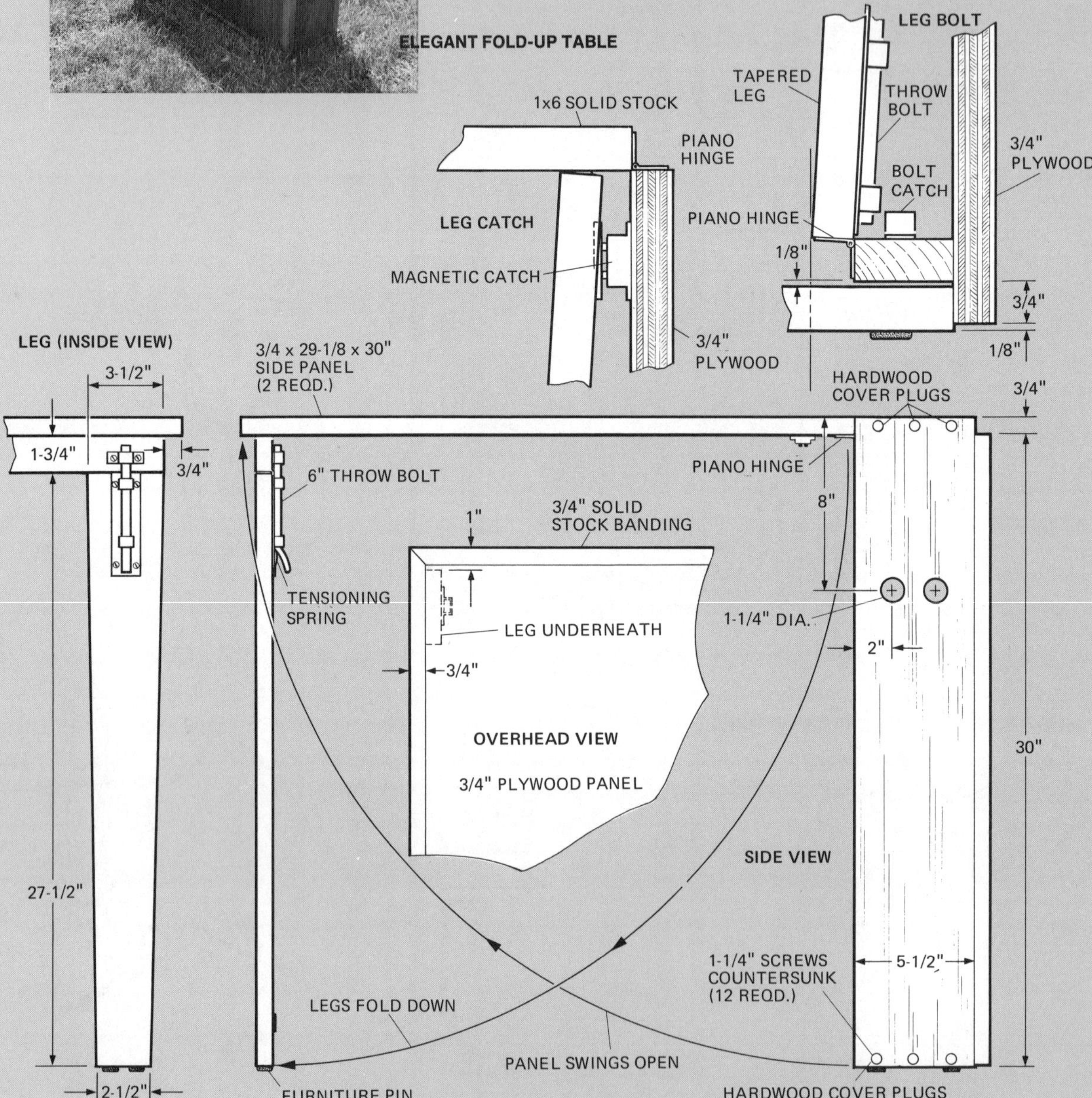

a rich, dark tone) to a light birch. You'll need a sharp blade (carbide tipped is ideal) to cut the panels without damaging the edges. A plywood blade also will do the job nicely.

Assemble the center frame first. For good, tight construction, cut a ¼ x ¾-in. rabbet along the edges of the vertical center boards and lock in the horizontal members with glue and screws. Contrasting wood plugs are inserted into the countersunk holes. Let them extend 1/16 in. to assure a smooth, flush finish when you do the sanding. Furniture pins in the bottom of the legs help steady the completed table. We used teak oil for a lustrous finish. It's made by Watco and is available from Woodcraft Supply Corp., 313 Montvale Ave., Woburn, MA 01801. Whichever table you build, it will be there when you need it and fold out of the way when you don't.

Insulation between furring
I want to panel two outside walls of a room in wood over furring strips. What insulation should I use?—John Agias, Toronto, Ont.

Use a blanket type of insulating material placed so that the foil facing (vapor barrier) is on the room side. Be sure that you space the furring strips so the insulating "blanket" will fit snugly between them, tacking the lip of the facing over the wooden strips to form an effective moisture barrier.

Brass won't polish
My home has brass switch and outlet plates. I don't know how old these are, but they won't polish bright even though I've tried several brass polishes. All have darkened in color, appear dingy. Is there some way of brightening them?—E. Rollins, Pontiac, Mich.

Originally, the plates were coated with a metal lacquer which defies removal by most common metal polishes. This finish tends to darken, accounting for the dingy look. Remove the coating with a lacquer thinner. (Since the solvent is highly volatile and flammable, clean plates outdoors.) Then use your brass polish as directed.

'Drumming' heating unit
Last winter my warm-air heater developed a pecular "drumming" sound when the blower is running. Occasionally there's a sharp, rapid "ticking" noise that sounds like metal hitting metal, especially when the blower comes on. I've examined the blower and nothing seems wrong; the fan spins free at the touch. What's wrong?—Earl Trapp, Moline, Ill.

From your description, it sounds as if the motor mounting is slightly loose. Thus, the running fan wobbles enough for the fan blades to contact the housing due to the torque developed when the motor starts. Tightening the mount and checking the duct system for loose supports should correct the defect.

Uncupping thin boards
I have two boards about ⅜ in. thick, 10 in. wide and 36 in. long which are old door panels. How can I remove the cup and flatten them?—Milton Conners, Perry, Iowa.

I assume the panels are of solid stock, not plywood. Taking the cup out of thin stock is uncertain business at best, but I've had fair success with this method: Dampen the wood on the concave side, lay a damp cloth over the surface and go over the cloth with a hot steam iron. Then place the board on a flat surface and weight it with a heavy object until thoroughly dry.

If this doesn't solve your problem you may have to sacrifice some thickness and have the boards run through a thickness planer to "flatten" them.

Unsticking a stopper
I have an old glass cruet in which the stopper is stuck fast. I've tried heating it in soapy water and also applying penetrating oil, but haven't had any luck. Can you offer a solution for unsticking a stopper?—Alice Holmes, Macon, Ga.

I've used lighter fluid with reasonable success. Squirt a few drops of fluid around the stopper, then apply a light, twisting pressure until it can be removed. You may have to repeat the process several times.

Replacing kitchen countertop
My kitchen countertop is covered with linoleum and I'd like to replace it with Formica. Can you advise how to proceed, how to prepare the top, which adhesive to use and how to apply the new Formica?—A.F. Miller, Dauphin Island, Ala.

You can do this by removing the old linoleum and replacing it with Formica on the existing plywood top. This involves time and considerable labor as *all* of the old residue must be removed down to the plywood surface. It's better to replace the old plywood top with a fully preformed counter, coved backsplash and no-drip front edge topped with Formica. Such do-it-yourself tops are available.

To remove the old countertop, first shut off the water at the meter, then disconnect the sink from the faucets and water lines. Retain the top or all parts of it for use when fitting the replacement. Your local hardware dealer can help with tools and materials.

Gurgling plumbing
Our plumbing is all copper tubing (piping). When either the bathtub or lavatory is drained, there's an increasingly loud gurgling sound. Is a pipe or vent running up through the roof the solution? There's no such vent in the system at this time.—Mrs. J.B. Schian, Saginaw, Mich.

If the system is not vented, as you say, it should be. In fact, the building code requires that all plumbing fixtures be vented. Otherwise, water draining from the tub or lavatory can create, in effect, a vacuum which would cause the "gurgling" noise you describe. Even if there were proper venting, whole or partial vent clogging by leaves or other debris would create the same effect. In this case, you should have your local plumber check the system.

How to build a hood for an oven-over range

By ALFRED OSBORNE

Covering an exhaust fan in the wall, this hood will direct the heat, cooking odors and vapors out of your kitchen. It is made from sheet metal and wood trim

■ WHEN WE INSTALLED a wall oven over our kitchen range and hung it between two hanging cabinets, we couldn't find a hood with an exhaust fan that would fit between the cabinets. They were either too wide or too narrow. That's when I decided to make this attractive colonial hood which fits the space between the soffit and the top of the oven and the two flanking cabinets.

I bought and installed an exhaust fan in the wall over the oven, venting it to the outside and wiring it to a switch conveniently located under the cabinets. The fan not only exhausted the heat from the oven but also the cooking odors and grease-laden vapors from the range as well. Removable filters were used to trap the grease.

I formed the hood from a 36x94-in. sheet of 30-ga. sheet metal, cutting it according to the pattern. Most of the bends are made 90° to form flanges. The exceptions are those along the bottom edges which are bent 180° and hammered flat to stiffen the metal. I used Pop rivets to join the sides to the top. A neat job of bending results from using two straight pieces of wood and clamping them to each side of the metal along the line of bend.

The built-up, 3-in.-wide wood trim along the sides and front of the hood is made in one piece as shown in detail A, then mitered at the corners to fit. The corner trim pieces are preassembled similarly, then cut to fit and attached to the hood with sheet-metal screws. Finally, I Pop-riveted 1x1-in. metal angles to the bottom hood flanges to hold removable grease filters. The corner strips, as well as the strips applied to the face of the hood, not only add decoration, but they actually serve to stiffen the hood.

The finished hood can be spray-painted a complementary color, or covered with the same wallpaper pattern as may be used in the kitchen. In the latter case, it would be best to apply the paper before adding the decorative wood strips. For a bit of Early American decor, I added a brass eagle as a final touch.

SEE ALSO
Appliance repair . . . Kitchen accessories . . . Kitchens . . . Ranges

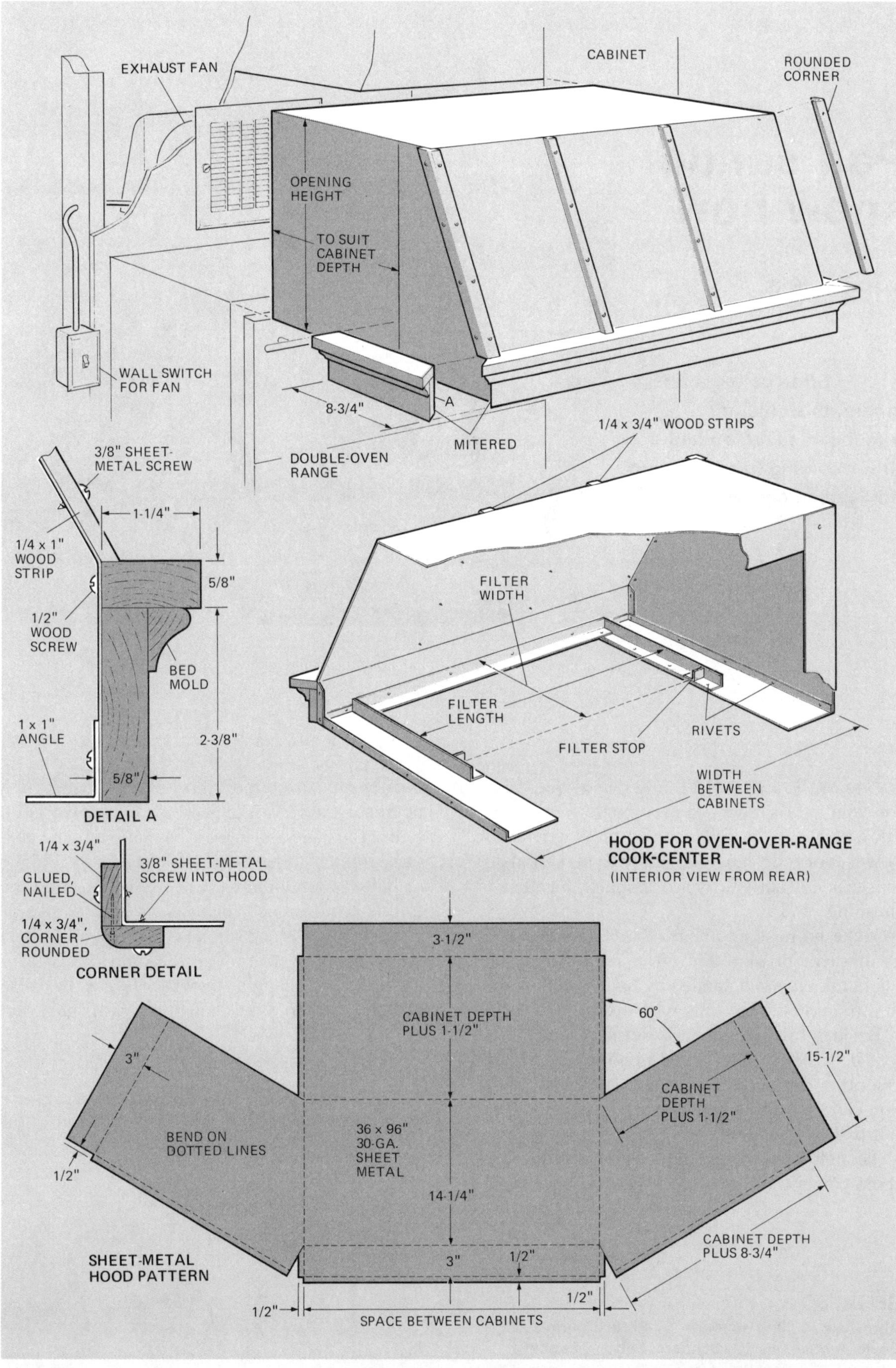

HOOD FOR OVEN-OVER-RANGE COOK-CENTER
(INTERIOR VIEW FROM REAR)

Pad sander know-how

By HARRY WICKS

Often called a finishing sander, this efficient power tool can save you hours of arm-wearying hand sanding if it is used correctly

■ NO MATTER WHAT other uses you have for your pad sander—some people have been known to use the felt pad for massages—this power tool is designed basically to make finishing easier. That's why it's popularly called a finishing sander.

Make no mistake about it, a pad sander is a great saver of time and effort. A project that might take hours if sanded by hand can be done in a fraction of that time with power.

Besides saving time, a power pad sander lets you do a better job. There is no way you can smooth a flat surface by hand as efficiently as you can with abrasive paper clamped about the felt pad of a sander.

Though a finishing sander is one of the first three power tools most do-it-yourselfers buy, it is often a misused tool. It is not uncommon for a beginner (and even experienced woodworkers) to use the pad sander for jobs that would be best performed by other tools such as the block plane or belt sander. In any event, remember that the tool is not designed for heavy stock removal.

Basically, the pad sander is used to finish-sand wood just prior to applying the stain and finish to a project. By changing paper (grits), the tool also can be used to smooth paints, varnishes, lac-

SEE ALSO

Abrasives . . . Belt sanders . . . Motors, shop . . . Power-tool stands . . . Sanders, belt . . . Sanding

PAPERS SIZED to suit various makers' sander shoes come packaged in all-one-grit or with mixed grits.

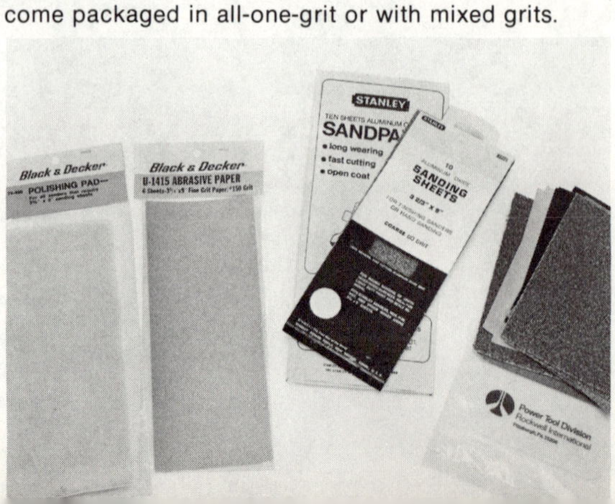

Dual-action sanders

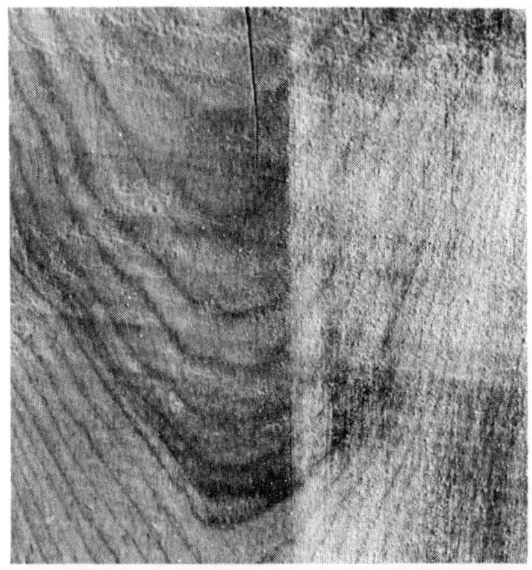

DIFFERENT MANUFACTURERS use various kinds of on-off switches. Sears model shown above has a thumb-operated slide type (inset) instead of toggle switch. A two-way sander (top right) gives you a choice between straight-line (center photo) and orbital sanding (bottom photo).

quers and the like between coats. Finally, when fitted with a lamb's-wool pad, a pad sander can be used with polishes and paste waxes to bring furniture to a high luster.

types of pad sanders

There are two types, straight-line and orbital. The former has a back-and-forth motion which makes it ideal for with-the-grain sanding as you get close to the final stages of the sanding opera-

SANDPAPER COMES in a wide variety of grits, from left—wet or dry fine, 280, 120, 100, 80 and 60.

METHOD OF HOLDING sandpaper varies with makers. The author liked this version from Stanley.

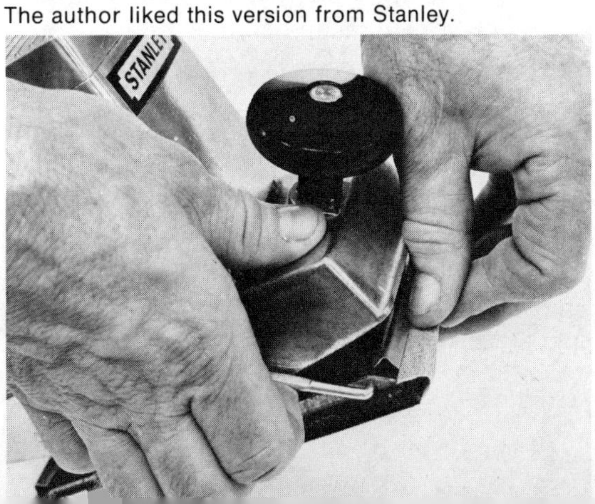

Typical pad-sander chores

TO SAND corner with minimum chatter, let side of shoe (not end) contact vertical.

NARROW SURFACE can be accurately sanded if you work carefully.

PAD SANDER gets into tight corners; the orbital type usually leaves marks here.

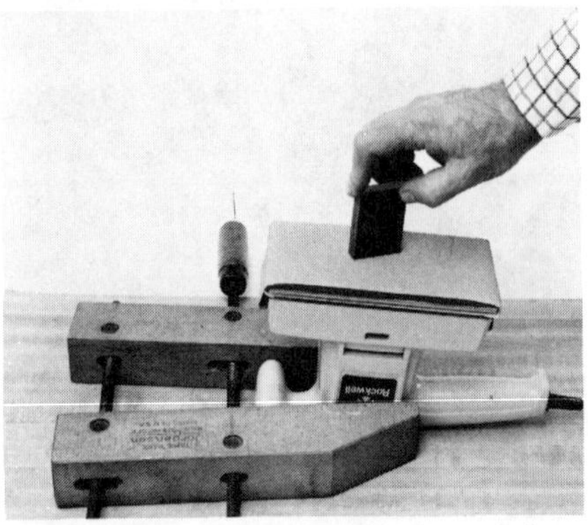

SAND SMALL objects by clamping sander upside down. Don't overtighten the clamp.

FITTED WITH a polishing pad, sander brings paste wax to a smooth, high luster.

WITH CARE and fine emery paper, in a pinch, sander can hone a chisel.

tion. The straight-line action removes stock more slowly than the orbital type, but does a smoother job. On some soft woods, stock removal can be speeded up by sanding across the grain in the early coarse-grit stages.

Orbital sanders, on the other hand, combine a slight side-to-side motion with a back-and-forth motion to form small orbits. If speed is slow, swirls will be obvious on the finished product and mar its beauty.

Both types are readily available, and now most manufacturers offer sander models which combine both actions in one tool.

choosing a pad sander

The pad sander is a simple tool—one which you can learn to use correctly in a short time. Before buying one, the smartest thing you can do is to pick up and heft the various models you are considering. The better hardware and building supply outlets usually have sample boards available for customer tool tests.

By using this service, you will quickly find out that some tools feel extra comfortable in your hand, while others will be just plain cumbersome. Now is the time—before spending—to find out whether or not a tool gives you satisfactory working comfort.

You will also have to decide whether you want straight-line or orbital action or both. Many craftsmen are content with an orbital sander with a high speed and very small orbits. With one of these, it is just about impossible to see any swirl marks in the finished project unless you have super vision (or use a magnifying glass). These models also cost more than their slower, larger-orbiting cousins.

Of course, with coarse-grit paper, almost any orbital sander is certain to produce some swirl marks as shown in the photo on page 2021. Here, a 40-grit paper was used on a piece of birch to demonstrate the look of sander swirls.

If you opt for a dual-action model, make certain that the switch controlling the sander action is easy to use, yet located and operated in such a way as to avoid accidental changing of sanding strokes.

As with all power tools, you get what you pay for in pad sanders. In general, it's safe to say that the higher the price, the better the quality will be: The construction of the tool plus the number and type of bearings definitely affect the sander's price tag.

As a rule of thumb, you can figure that the most inexpensive sanders will serve just fine for the once-in-a-while user. Those equipping a woodworking shop, with the idea of doing most home handyman chores themselves and taking on occasional furniture projects, will usually be content with a tool in the middle price range.

In general, the highest priced pad sanders are geared for the professional market. However, many serious do-it-yourselfers want the best tools; for these, sanders rated commercial or industrial are the only choices.

New on the power-tool scene and something you should think about seriously before buying, as far as I'm concerned, are the short, pigtail-like line cords which now come on many new tools—including sanders.

On these, the line cord measures a mere foot or so instead of the traditional 6 to 8 ft. The reason for shorter cords is both obvious and understandable. The cords are made of copper. When less of it is used, retail prices can be kept down. For my money however, I find the resulting inconvenience an expensive price to pay.

mounting paper

There are as many different ways of putting sandpaper in a pad sander as there are pad sanders. Some tools are easy to load and some are not. Check this feature before buying and pick a sander that makes it easy to mount and remove papers.

No matter how paper is mounted and held, it must remain flat as well as secure. The action of the sander itself is a pulling one, and if the paper is loose and flaps about, it will soon tear and become useless.

Check the maker's instructions for mounting papers and make certain that all papers you mount are stretched tightly across the pad.

The shoe (or pad) on most sanders is sized so you will be able to get three strips of paper from a standard-size sheet of abrasive paper. Some of the commercial-duty sanders have larger shoes; with these you get two sander-size pieces from each sheet. Sized sandpapers are also available as accessories: These are packaged both in assorted grits and in all-one-type papers, as shown on page 2020.

maintaining the sander

No matter what price tool you buy, it will last longer if you use and maintain it properly. Pad sander maintenance, for the most part, consists of little more than keeping the air ports free of dust accumulation (so the tool won't overheat) and periodic lubrication. The best way to do the former is by blowing out the tool with compressed air. If you lack a compressor, periodically take your sander to the local gas station to blow out all dust. If you do own a compressor, use it on the sander after every work session. Lubricate the tool following the manufacturer's instructions with regard to points, frequency and type of lubricant to use. Today, many sanders are sealed and require no further lubrication by the owner. But since that's not the case for all sanders, carefully read that section of the manual covering lubrication.

using the tool

No matter which type of pad sander you buy, it will come equipped with a felt pad on its shoe. The rigidity—or degree of softness—of this pad is intended to suit most of the average jobs a do-it-yourselfer encounters. However, on occasion a softer or harder pad is required.

For example, on some plastics, woods with hard-and-soft grains and for honing of chisels, a more-rigid pad is desirable. In this event, you simply place a piece of ⅛-in. hardboard between the paper and felt pad. To hold it in place, drive three or four brads through the hardboard and into the felt.

If the occasion demands a softer pad, try substituting foam rubber for the felt pad.

Some sanders come equipped with an auxiliary handle. On certain jobs, such as for vertical sanding, this can be very handy. A spare handle is often useful on the bench, too, because two-hand operation will assist you in keeping the shoe flat on the workpiece.

No matter which action your sander has—orbital or straight-line—it is usually best to work the tool back and forth parallel with the grain of the wood.

When edge sanding a narrow surface, use both hands to maintain maximum control. If the job is a critical one, clamp boards on both sides of the surface being sanded to prevent any chance of rounding over corners.

Mount your sander in a stand

By WALTER E. BURTON

This easy-to-make stand will anchor your sander firmly to let you sand small pieces at whatever angle you find most convenient. You can design it to fit any model sander

SEE ALSO

Abrasives . . . Belt sanders . . . Motors, shop . . . Power-tool stands . . . Sanders, belt . . . Sanding . . . Workbenches

■ EVER TRY TO SAND a 1-in. wood cube with a portable finishing sander? If you have, you probably wished you had the sander firmly anchored so you could manipulate the cube instead of the machine.

The wood stand shown here provides a firm mounting for a finishing sander and a convenient means of guiding small pieces, such as model parts, against its vibrating abrasive surface. The stand was designed to fit a Rockwell sander; other makes of machines can be used, of course, although the arrangement of the mounting blocks and other elements might require some altering.

The work-supporting table is of ½-in. plywood; almost all other parts are from ¾-in. plywood. I used ordinary ¾-in. pine lumber for the table column.

The sander platform was constructed first and mounted on the base with its outer longitudinal margin 1 in. from the base edge. The two vertical pieces were attached to the horizontal panel with glue and nails.

It is important that air circulate freely through the sander motor to prevent overheating. To

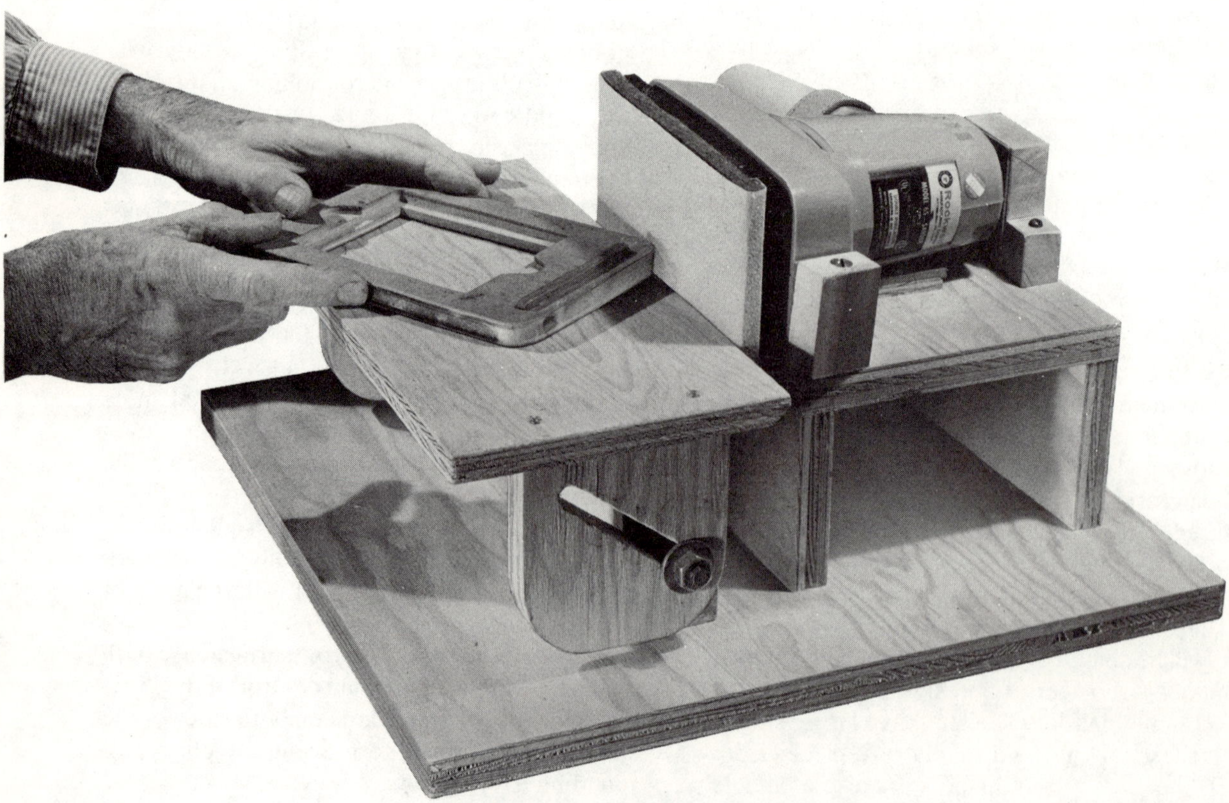

avoid any interference with air discharge from the vent openings nearer the platform when the sander is resting on its side, an opening was cut in the platform opposite these vents.

Three devices hold the sander firmly in position on its platform:

- A 1¼ x 8-in. strip of aluminum-siding sheet that projects ¼ in. above the platform surface, along the edge next to the work-supporting table. A leather strip, ¹⁄₁₆-in. thick, was glued to the side of this strip toward the platform. This acts as a cushion to prevent marring the sander housing. This padded strip projects into the space between the sander-housing edge and the sander pad, and prevents the sander from moving toward the work table.
- Leather-faced wooden blocks installed to hold the sander against the leather-padded aluminum strip. Two of these blocks flank the housing near the sanding pad, the third presses against the outer tip of the motor portion. Two more blocks are under the sander. One supports the motor housing, the other supports the handle.
- A leather strap, attached to the platform with

HOLD-DOWNS go on sander platform (top). At the right, the platform's blocks and strap are in place. Note the opening for air flow from the motor.

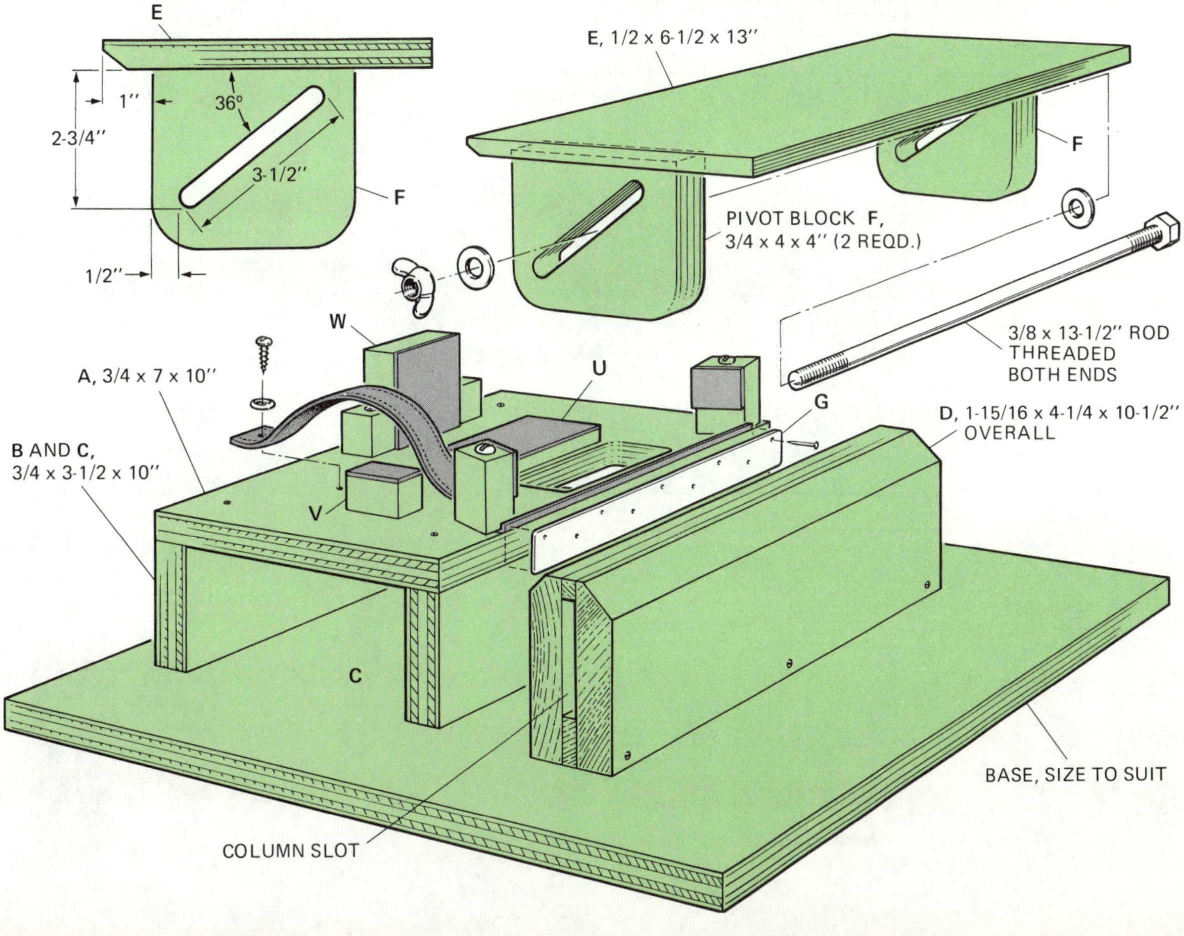

wood screws, and encircling the handle near the motor. Its purpose is to hold the sander in close contact with the two leather-faced blocks underneath. This strap should not be drawn too tight—just enough to keep the sander from moving upward. (For some sanders, it might be preferable to install the strap around the motor portion.) One end of the strap is anchored with two wood screws and washers, the other end by a single No. 8 wood screw installed after the sander is in position.

When a sander has to be removed and replaced frequently, a bolt-and-nut arrangement might be preferable.

The two blocks flanking the housing near the sander pad are secured with single, No. 12 flathead screws 3 in. long, permitting the blocks to adjust to the angle of the housing surface. The block supporting the motor housing was nailed to the platform before leather was applied, and the handle block was similarly fastened with a flathead wood screw. Two No. 8 screws hold the third block.

When the sander is running, there is some vibration transmitted to the platform. No tests were made to determine the long-range durability of the anchoring system, but no tendencies for the blocks to loosen, or other restraints to lessen, were noted.

The workpiece is normally rested on an adjustable table made from ½-in. plywood. Projecting downward from the table are two "pivot blocks," each having a diagonal slot. These blocks straddle the ends of a table column in which there is a vertical slot that measures about 7⁄16 in. wide and 2¾ in. high. This slot was created by assembling the column from two ¾-in. pieces separated by a 7⁄16-in.-sq. and a 7⁄16 x 1-in. spacing strip. The column was mounted with the vertical centerline of its slot about 1¾ in. from the abrasive surface.

Length of the table-supporting column is ½ in. greater than the length of the sander platform. This provides clearance for the slotted pivot blocks to overlap the platform when the table is adjusted to a steep angle. Pivot blocks are positioned on the table so the distance between them matches the column length.

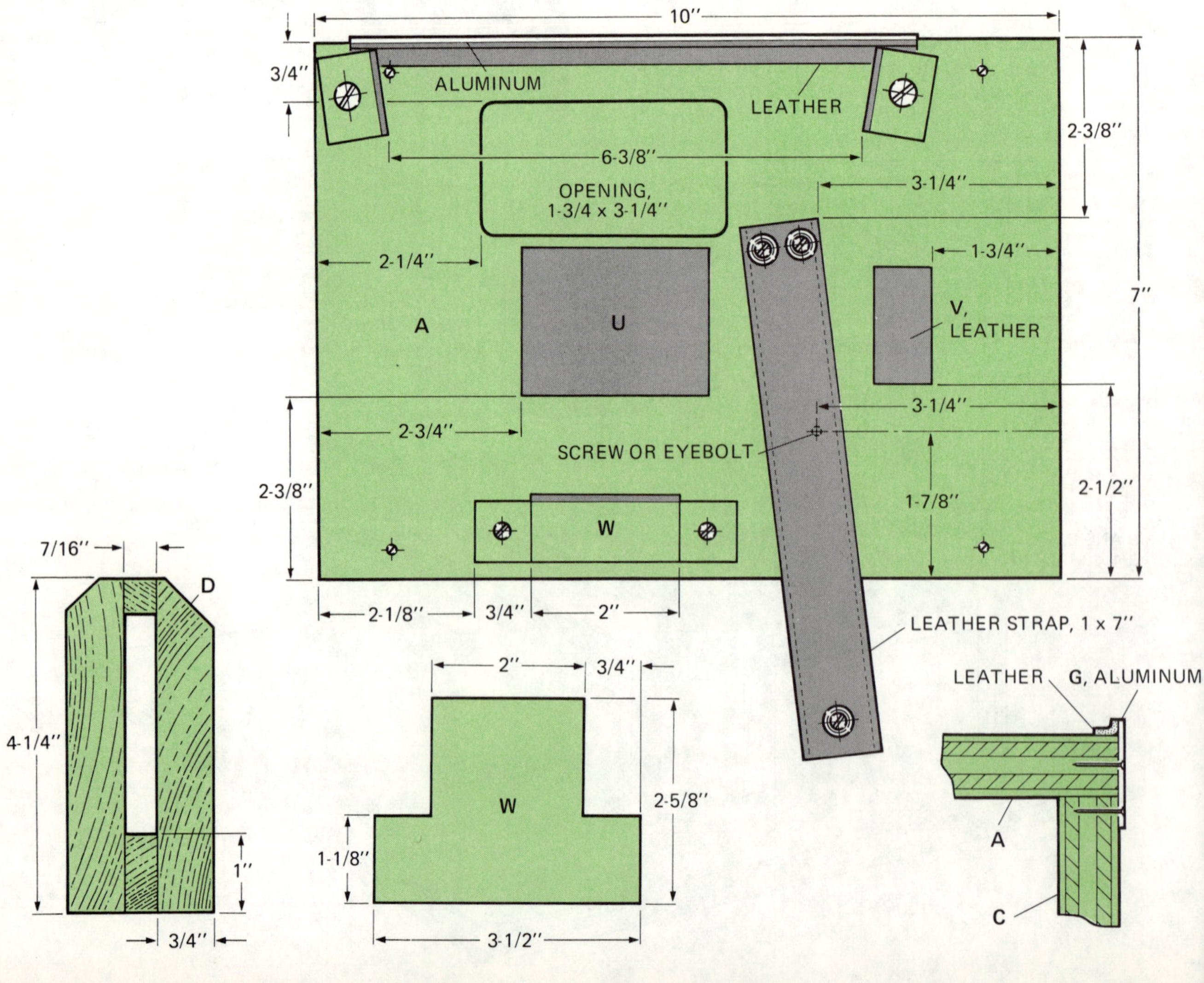

The combination of diagonal slots in the pivot blocks and vertical slot in the column provides for an infinite number of settings for the table with respect to angle and vertical adjustment, and total vertical movement is nearly 2 in.

A 3/8-in. rod, 13½ in. long, threaded at both ends, runs through pivot-block and column slots. It has a wingnut on one end and an ordinary nut on the other plus two washers. Tightening the wingnut compresses the pivot blocks against the column ends, securely anchoring the table.

You may have to trim the column top by trial and error so the table can be tilted up to 45° without moving the table edge too far from the abrasive edge.

Although the sanding stand could be used without anchoring it to the bench, it does have some tendency to "walk." Use either a ¾-in. sponge rubber pad between base and bench or C-clamps to eliminate "walking."

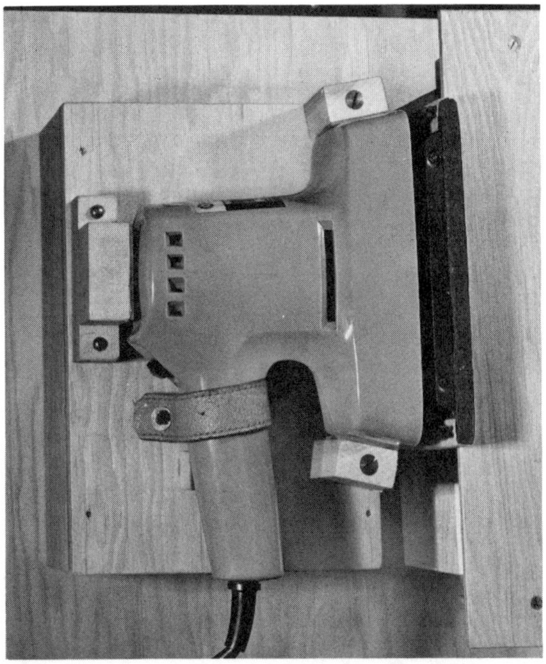

PROTOTYPE stand was tailored to Rockwell's Model 65 sander. Alter dimensions as needed for others.

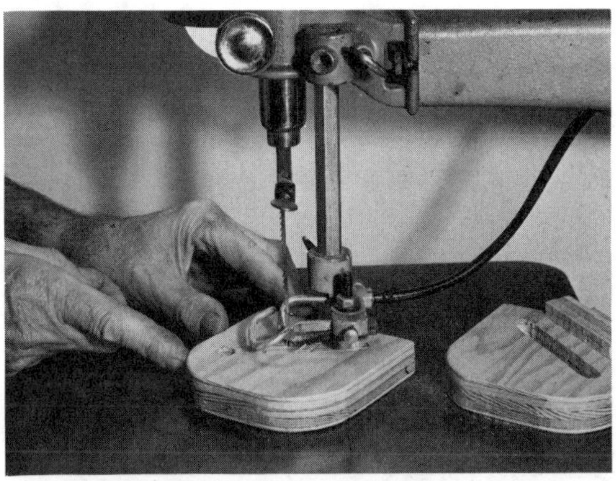

CUT PIVOT block slot by drilling holes at the ends, connecting them with jig or coping saw.

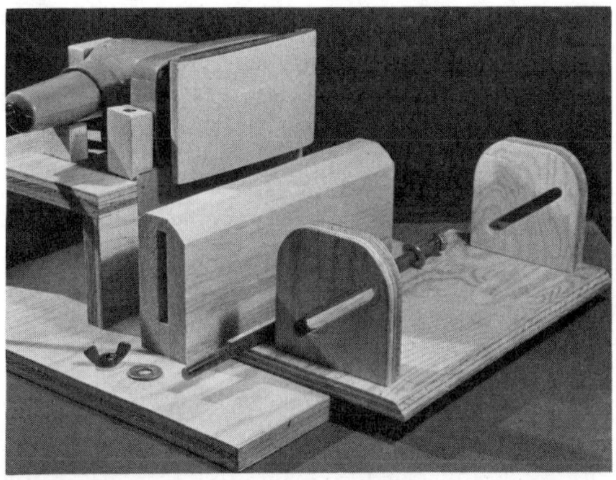

SUPPORT COLUMN is ready to receive pivot blocks for the work-support table at the right.

READY TO GO, the sanding assembly has its table in the upper position for usual right-angle sanding.

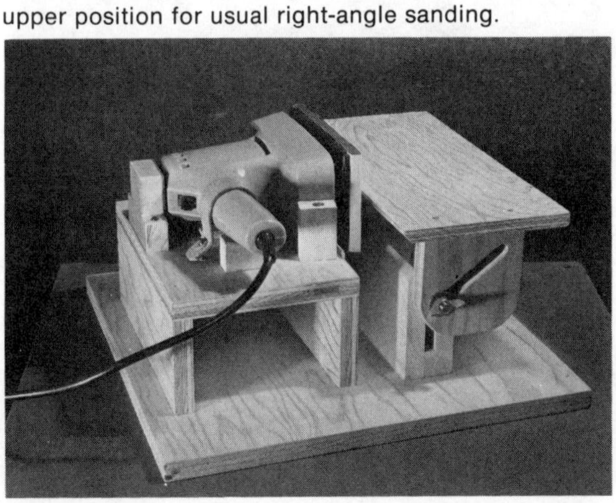

PIVOT-BLOCK and support-column slots combine to let the work table take virtually any angle.

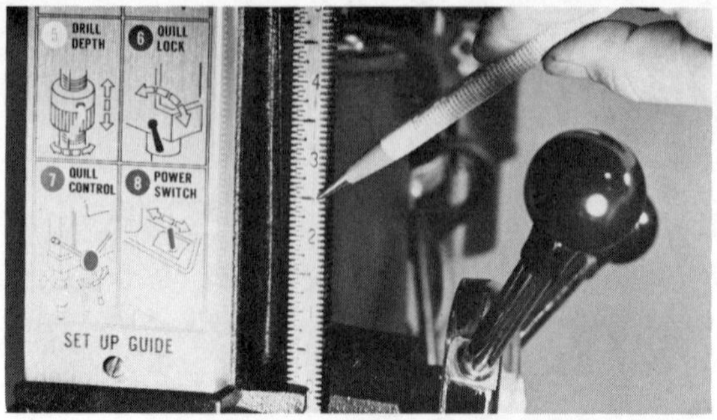

THE DEPTH GAUGE on my drill press had graduation lines of equal length except at the 1-in. markings, which made it hard to read intermediate depths quickly. Using a fine-tipped permanent felt marker, I extended the ¼ and ½-in. marks as well. The trick worked and makes quick readings easy and accurate.—*John F. Pilznienski, Dearborn Heights, MI.*

THE METAL PORTION of a discarded three-ring notebook binder can serve as a good paintbrush holder. Fasten the three-ring device to the top of your stepladder. Tools with holes drilled in their handles can be removed and replaced while you work. When the ladder is to be moved, snap the rings shut and tools will be held securely.—*Ken Patterson, Regina, Sask.*

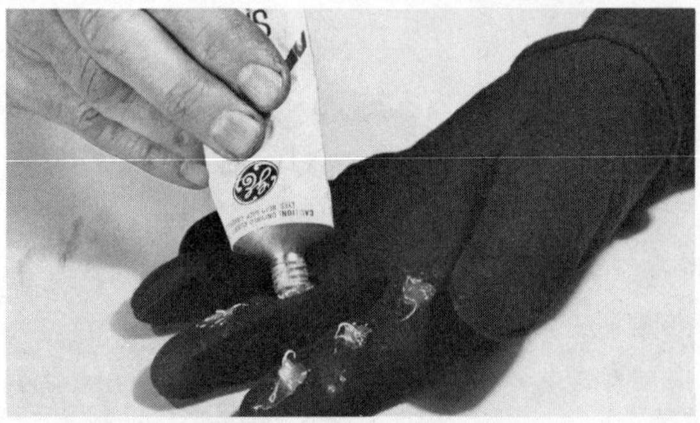

SILICONE COMPOUND spread on the palms of cloth workgloves in a series of dots or beads, lessens the tendency of the gloves to slip when the wearer grasps tool handles and similar objects. The rubber-like coating need not be thick enough to cause appreciable increase in glove stiffness. Let the silicone dry before you use the gloves.—*B.W. Ervin, Kent, OH.*

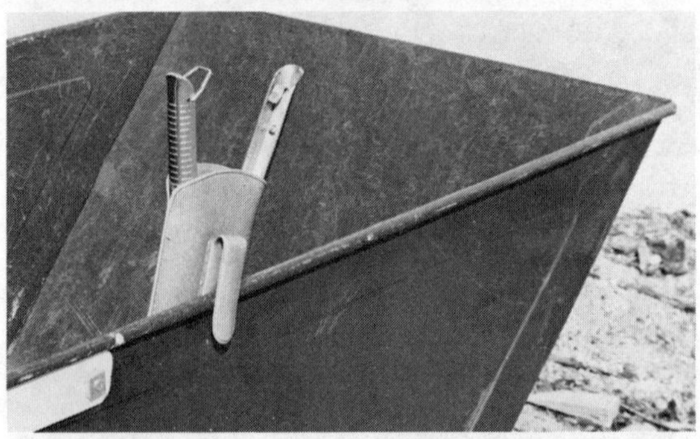

AN EYEGLASS CASE with an attached pocket spring-clip makes a handy carrying case for pruning clippers or other small gardening tools. Attached to your garden cart as shown, clippers are always at the job location. Cutting edges are protected when the tool is not in use, and tools are not apt to be left outside.—*Marshall Lincoln, Wickenburg, AZ.*

A PAGE OR COVER from a spiral-bound booklet can be used for drawing neat dotted (or dashed) lines. Place a straightedge to guide a ball-point pen or pencil across centers of the holes through which the wire spiral had been inserted. To remove a spiral, clip one end and simply "unscrew" the coil.—*Walter E. Burton, Akron, OH.*

Paint your house with a roller

Outdoor painting is much faster and easier if you use a roller instead of a brush. Preparation methods are about the same, but the job goes more smoothly if you are equipped with the right selection of rollers.

MANY PEOPLE seem to prefer indoor painting to outdoor. One reason is the fact that you don't have to fight the elements when working indoors. But the main reason is that painting always seems to go faster indoors because a roller is easier to use than a brush.

However, with a good water-base paint and a few special purpose rollers, there's no reason why you can't tackle the job of painting your house with the same confidence you have when painting a bedroom. The only real difference is in the size of the job.

Preparation is the same as for painting your house with a brush, which in turn is basically the same as preparing to paint with a roller indoors. Surfaces should be reasonably clean—wash any particularly dirty spots—and free of loose paint. Check for areas which may have to be scraped,

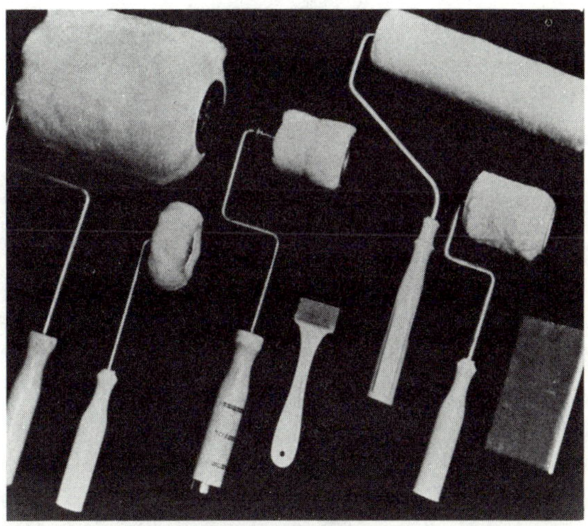

ROLLERS AND PAINTING PADS are special-purpose tools. For best results, don't skimp on your equipment.

SEE ALSO
House painting . . . Ladders . . .
Masonry, painting . . . Painting tools . . .
Painting, exterior . . . Scaffolding

PLANTINGS should be tied back, if necessary, and covered with a dropcloth or plastic sheet.

USE SASH FLATS for window mullions and trim. Other special-purpose pads and daubers will speed the job.

house painting with a roller, continued

and do this a couple of days before you plan to paint.

Putty nail holes and cracks. Reset any nails that have worked out. Renail clapboards or shingles that have pulled away from the surface, using extra nails if necessary.

The day before you paint, stake back foundation plantings. Just drive a couple of stakes in the outer edge of the bed for each bush and tie one end of a line to one stake, then pass the line around the bush so you can pull it away from the wall and tie it to the other stake. When painting, cover the bushes with a dropcloth or old newspapers for additional protection.

Buying the paint should present no special problems. Since you'll be using a roller, you'll have to stick with some brand of water-base paint, and here, as with many other home-improvement materials, it generally boils down to a matter of getting what you pay for. Special sales may offer a chance to save a little on the total cost, but real bargains in paint are rare.

Before you head for the paint store, take a few measurements to get a rough idea of the area to be covered so you'll know how much paint to buy. Make a mental note of the different surfaces

A NONSKID GRID helps you to load rollers. Hardware cloth is shown, but you can buy a commercial unit.

MATCH THE ROLLER to the area to be covered. A small one coats a railing much faster than the standard size.

A SEGMENTED ROLLER on a flexible core wraps around down-spouts so you can paint them in one easy pass.

you'll be working on; this will determine the kinds of rollers you'll need and how many.

Nap length is one important consideration when selecting rollers. It may vary from ¼ in. (most common, and still best for most work) up to 1¼ in. (special-purpose length for extra-rough masonry, chain-link fences and other unusual jobs).

A short-nap roller will lay on the smoothest coat and is best for smooth surfaces. A long-nap roller is better for rough surfaces, because it can reach the bottoms of minor irregularities. For the best compromise between smoothness and coverage capability, always pick the shortest

TO STORE A ROLLER overnight, just wrap it in foil or a polyethylene bag and put it in the refrigerator.

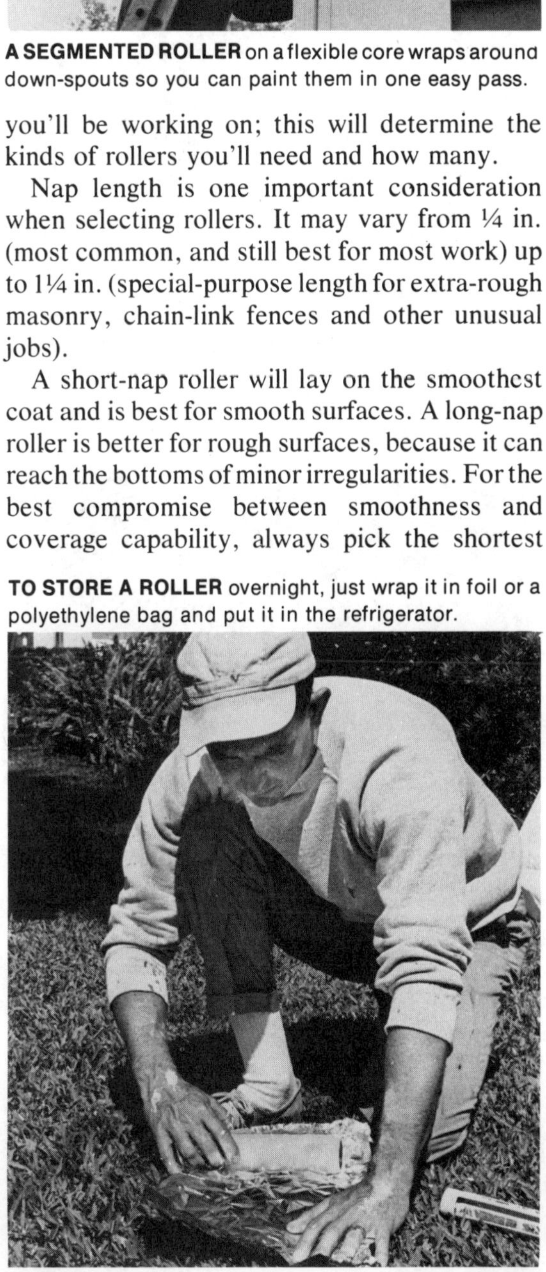

TO CLEAN A ROLLER, hold it by the handle and spin it in a strong blast of water from a garden hose.

nap that will handle the job efficiently.

The type of fiber is also important. *Always* choose a synthetic. Natural fibers such as lamb's wool and mohair will soften and lose body in water-base paint. Stick with Dynel, Dacron, Pronel, Bak-O-Nel or one of the other man-made fibers. These not only stand up to water, but are tailored to suit the job (for instance, fibers for use in long-nap rollers are given more body than those commonly used in short-nap rollers).

Quality of construction is relatively easy to judge. The roller core should be plastic, or at least plastic-impregnated, in order to stand up under heavy use. The ends should be beveled slightly so they won't spread beyond the edge of the core and become overloaded with paint.

Be sure to get a roller frame with a threaded handle, so you can use it with extension poles. Sectionalized poles are best since they can easily be tailored to the desired "reach."

Start painting in the morning, as soon as the dew has evaporated. Begin on the north or west side and work around to the south or east side. Always start at the top and paint down, so you can cover drips and spatters.

When you take a break, saturate the roller with paint to offset drying until you return to the job. Also, watch for paint setting up in the roller while you're using it. This sometimes happens in hot dry weather, and many painters alternate two rollers to avoid it. The one not in use is dunked in a pail of water.

For overnight storage, just wrap the rollers in foil and put them in the refrigerator. At the end of the job, though, give them a thorough cleaning. A good roller is no throwaway tool.

QUALITY PAINTS deserve quality rollers. The typical paint applicators shown above make painting today easier than ever. Care should be taken to select roller covers that best suit the type of paint to be used. Basically, covers to be used for latex paints should not be made of rayon or lamb's wool (water causes softening and matting of the fibers). Oil and alkyd paints (thinned with mineral spirits or turpentine) will not affect most rollers. You can use the chart on the opposite page to help you choose the correct roller cover for most home paint jobs. Just locate the paint and surface for your job.

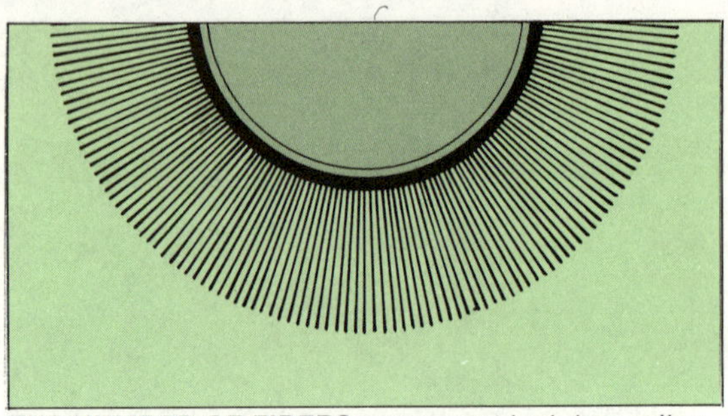

THE NUMBER OF FIBERS per square inch in a roller cover is a critical factor. If they are too dense, they will cut down the paint-holding capacity of the roller. They will also interfere with the roller's ability to meter out paint evenly on the surface.

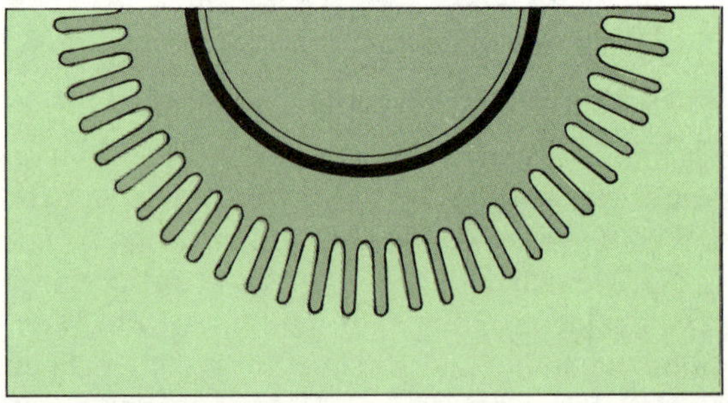

WHEN TOO FEW FIBERS are distributed over a roller surface the result is just as bad as if the roller had too many fibers. Having an insufficient number of fibers, a roller lacks the capacity fo flow paint on the surface evenly. The result: a spotty paint job.

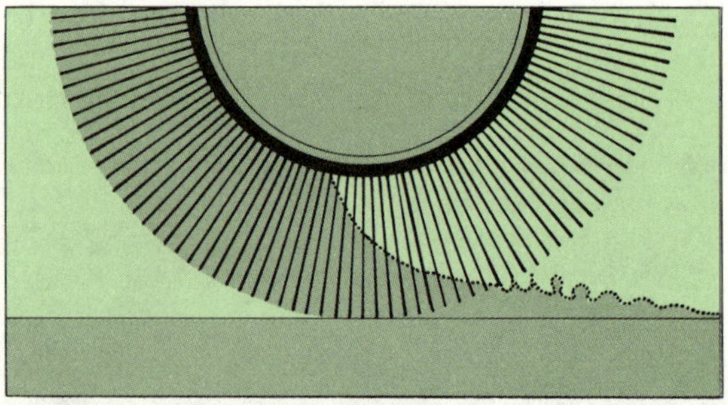

THE PROPER NUMBER of fibers on a roller will distribute a uniform coat of paint that is relatively smooth as it goes on. Such a roller also carries a good paint load and cuts down on the number of passes between the surface and the paint tray.

How to pick the right paint roller

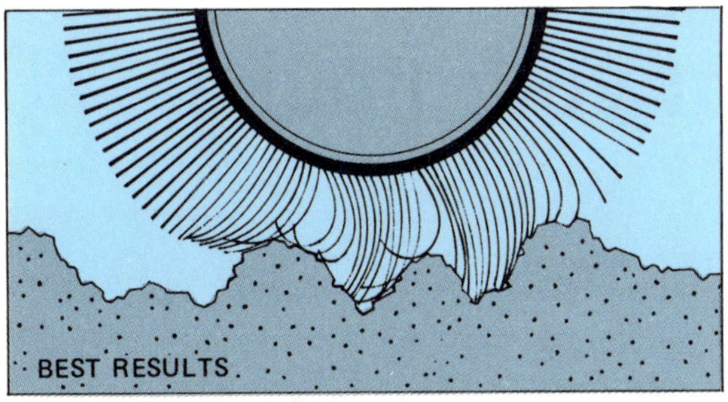

THE ROUGHER THE SURFACE, the longer the nap length of the roller cover should be. When the fiber length is correctly matched to the surface, a smooth, uniform coat without "show-through" is possible. This is the secret of a professional-looking job.

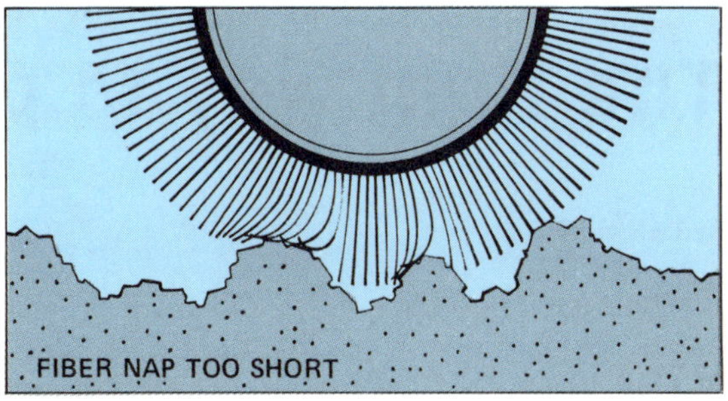

IF THE FIBER length is too short for the surface texture, the roller cover will fail to reach the bottoms of the valleys in a rough surface like stucco. The result: a paint job with show-throughs, commonly called "holidays." The right roller avoids this situation.

SEE ALSO
**House painting . . . Ladders . . .
Painting, exterior . . . Painting tools . . .
Painting, furniture . . . Painting, interior**

GUIDE TO PAINT-ROLLER SELECTION

CODE FOR CHART BELOW

SIZE (Number)	CORE (1st letter)	FABRIC (2nd letter)	NAP LENGTH (3rd letter)
9—9″	J—Jumbo	A—Lamb's wool	S—1/4″
12—12″	F—Fiber Phenolic	C—Carpet	I—1/2″
18—18″		K—Texfab	L—3/4″
		M—Mohair	E—1″
		P—Pronel	X—1 1/4″
			U—1 1/2″

PAINT OR COATING MATERIAL	SMOOTH SURFACE[1]	SEMIROUGH[2]	ROUGH[3]	EXTRA ROUGH[4]
Primers, Metal				
Chlorinated rubber	9FP, 9JP	9FPI, 9JPI		
Epoxy	9FAS	9FA, 9JA		
Oleo-resinous	9FAS	9FA, 9JA		
Red lead or tinner's red	9FP, 9JP, 9FA, 9JA	9FPI, 9JPI, 9FA, 9JA		
Vinyl	9FAS	9FA, 9JA		
Wash coat	9FP, 9JJP	9FPI, 9JPI		
Wetting oil	9FAS	9FA, 9JA		
Zinc chromate	9FP, 9JP, 9FA, 9JA	9FPI, 9JPI, 9FA, 9JA		
Primers, Wood				
Oil and alkyd	9FP, 9FPS	9FPI, 9JPI, 9FA, 9JA		
Enamel undercoat	9FM, 9FPS, 9JM	9FPI, 9JPI		
Primers, Masonry				
Block fillers, oil or latex				9FPX, 9JPX
Silicone water repellent		9FA, 9JA	9FAL, 9JAL	9FAX, 9JAX
Sealer, clear		9FA, 9JA	9FAL, 9JAL	9FAE, 9JAE
Oleo-resinous		9FPI, 9JPI	9FPL, 9JPL	9FPE, 9JPE
Primers, Wallboard				
Emulsion or latex	9FP, 9JP	9FPI, 9JPI		
Oil and alkyd	9FP, 9JP, 9FA, 9JA	9FPI, 9JPI, 9FA, 9JA		
Exterior Wood Finishes				
Oil and alkyd paints	9FPS	9FPI, 9JPI, 9FA, 9JA	9FPL, 9JPL, 9FAL, 9JAL	
Latex house paints	9FPS	9FPI, 9JPI	9FPL, 9JPL	
Oil stains	9FA, 9JA	9FAL, 9JAL	9FAE, 9JAE	9FAX, 9JAX
Wood preservatives	9FA, 9JA	9FAL, 9JAL	9FAE, 9JAE	9FAX, 9JAX
Floor Coatings				
Alkyd	9FM, 9JM, 12JM, 18JM	9FP, 9LP, 12JP, 18JP		
Chlorinated rubber	9FM, 9JM, 12JM, 18JM	9FP, 9LP, 12JP, 18JP		
Epoxy	9FM, 9JM, 12JM, 18JM	9FA, 9JA, 12JA, 18JA		
Latex	9FM, 9JM, 12JM, 18JM	9FP, 9JP, 12JP, 18JP		
Sodium silicate (water glass)	9FM, 9JM, 12JM, 18JM	9FP, 9JP, 12JP, 18JP		
Urethane	9FPS, 9FM, 9JM, 12JM, 18JM	9FA, 9JA, 12JA, 18JA		
Seamless flooring system	9FPL for base, chip coats 9FPS for glaze coats			
Interior Flat Finishes				
Oil and alkyd flat	9FP, 9JP, 9FA, 9JA	9FPI, 9JPI, 9FA, 9JA	9FPL, 9JPL, 9FAL, 9JAL	9FPE, 9JPE, 9FAE, 9JAE
Latex	9FP, 9JP	9FPI, 9JPI	9FPL, 9JPL	9FPE, 9JPE
Masonry Paints				
Alkyd	9FP, 9JP, 9FA, 9JA	9FPI, 9JPI, 9FA, 9JA	9FPL, 9JPL, 9FAL, 9JAL	9FPE, 9JPE, 9FAE, 9JAE
Latex	9FP, 9JP	9FPI, 9JPI	9FPL, 9JPL	9FPE, 9JPE
Styrene-butadiene	9FP, 9JP	9FPI, 9JPI	9FPL, 9JPL	9FPX, 9JPX
Stipple Paint	9FC	9FC		
Texture Paint	9FK	9FK		
Varnishes				
Alkyd	9FPS, 9FM			
Phenolic	9FPS, 9FM			
Urethane	9FPS, 9FM			
Wire-Fence Paints		9FAL, 9JAL	9FAE, 9JAE	9JAU

Footnotes: 1—smooth wallboard, putty coat plaster, sanded wood, smooth metal; 2—sand-finished plaster or drywall, metal, poured concrete; 3—textured plaster, light stucco, wood shakes, filled block; 4—raw block, brick, heavy stucco.

The right way to paint your house

By LEN HILTS

■ THE PROS WILL TELL YOU, the real secret in painting a house is in the preparation. Take the time to do a good job of preparing the place and you can be assured of a fine finished product.

The first step is to wash the house. A good hosing is sufficient for big, well-exposed walls. Be sure to rinse away all the chalky residue of the present coat of paint. Look for areas with special problems, such as mildew, and give these an extra treatment. Wash them down with a solution of trisodium phosphate and water. (See the TSP package for mixing instructions.) Use the same solution on walls which haven't been exposed to the weather—such as the walls of porches, the undersides of eaves, etc. Because these haven't weathered much, they are probably covered with strange substances—pollutants—deposited by the air. Rain washes the exposed walls, but not these, and the pollutants may cause the new paint to quickly peel and flake away.

Now get out the scraping equipment and go over the entire house. Use a scraper and a wire brush and scrape all loose, flaked and broken paint. Try to work over all areas where the present paint is not well bonded to the surface. After scraping cracked paint, use the wire brush or sand paper to feather the edges of the remaining paint, so that you don't end up with unsightly ridges and marks in the new paint.

Use a good primer, most of which are fairly fast drying, to seal every place you scrape. Don't apply new final-coat paint over bare wood.

Go over all of the windows and the door frames, scraping them where necessary. Examine the caulking around their edges, and dig out any which is loose or cracked. Use a caulking gun and a good grade of caulking compound to repair these now, before you apply the final coat. Look especially at the top of window

SEE ALSO

**House painting . . . Ladders . . .
Masonry, painting . . . Paint rollers . . .
Scaffolding . . . Siding**

Selecting primers and top coats

The charts below show primers and top coats appropriate for exterior surfaces. Find the primer or the choice of primers for the surface, then the top coat—or work backward from the desired top coat to find the primer and make sure that coatings are right for the surface to be painted

OUTSIDE PRIMERS / SURFACES	SMOOTH WOOD SIDING	ROUGH-SAWN SIDING	SHINGLES AND SHAKES	PLYWOOD	WOOD TRIM	CONCRETE, BLOCK, STUCCO	BRICK, STONE, CINDER BLOCK	IRON AND STEEL	GALVANIZED STEEL	ALUMINUM	ALUMINUM SIDING	COPPER, BRASS, BRONZE	ASPHALT ROOFING	SHINGLE AND SHAKE ROOFING	METAL ROOFING	TERNE PLATE ROOFING
OIL PRIMER (1)	●	●	●													
ALKYD PRIMER (2)					●											
LATEX PRIMER (3)	●	●	●		●											
STAIN-BLOCKING PRIMER (4)	●	●	●	●	●											
ALKYD-BASE METAL PRIMER (5)								●	●	●	●	●			●	
OIL-BASE METAL PRIMER (6)								●	●	●	●	●			●	
LATEX METAL PRIMER (7)								●	●			●			●	
PORTLAND CEMENT PAINT (8) (FOR METAL)								●	●							
MASONRY SURFACE CONDITIONER (9)						●	●									
PORTLAND CEMENT PAINT (FOR MASONRY) (10)						●	●									
ALKALI-RESISTANT COATINGS (11)						●	●									
IRON OXIDE PRIMER (12)																●
NO PRIMER NECESSARY (13)														●		
TOPCOAT MATERIAL USED FOR PRIMER (14)						●	●									

OUTSIDE TOPCOATS / OUTSIDE PRIMERS	1	2	3	4	5	6	7	8	9	10	11	12	13	14
OIL-BASE GLOSS HOUSE PAINT	●			●		●			●			●		
OIL-BASE FLAT, EGGSHELL HOUSE PAINT	●			●		●			●			●		
BARN PAINT	●			●		●			●			●		
ALKYD HOUSE PAINT		●		●	●				●			●		
ALKYD TRIM ENAMEL		●		●	●				●			●		
LATEX FLAT HOUSE PAINT			●	●			●		●			●		
LATEX TRIM ENAMEL			●	●			●		●			●		
CLEAR FINISHES													●	●
SEMITRANSPARENT STAIN													●	
SOLID COLOR STAIN													●	
ALKYD-BASE MASONRY PAINT									●					●
LATEX MASONRY PAINT									●					●
ALKALI-RESISTANT COATINGS									●		●			
PORTLAND CEMENT PAINT (FOR MASONRY)										●				
SILICONE WATER-REPELLENT COATING													●	
OIL-BASE EXTERIOR METAL PAINT						●						●		
ALKYD-BASE EXTERIOR METAL ENAMEL					●							●		
ALUMINUM PAINT					●									
PORTLAND CEMENT PAINT (FOR METAL)								●						
BITUMINOUS ROOF COATING													●	
COLORED ALUMINUM ROOF COATING													●	
LATEX PAINT (FOR ROOF COATING)													●	

and door frames—spots often neglected but very important—to see that the caulking there is sound.

Make one final trip around the house, looking for loose or popped nails, and for nails which have rusted and bled under the present paint. Drive in loose nails, and drive new nails near them as reinforcement. Use the wire brush to scrape clean areas where rust has bled through the paint, and prime the area to seal against further bleeding.

Now, with all of this done, you are ready to begin painting. The first question is: What kind of paint to use? The basic choice is between latex and oil-based paints. You can find advocates of both kinds, and there is no doubt that quality brands in both kinds are good.

Latex-based paints spread easily, can be applied on damp surfaces, dry faster, have little smell, and offer quick and easy cleanup using only a detergent and water. You can stop painting anywhere today and start up again tomorrow with no problems.

Oil-based paints have exceptionally good hiding power, adhere better than latex to chalked surfaces, and level better as you brush. They provide a tough and long-lasting coat. However, cleanup is more difficult, and you must use solvents.

How about using a latex now over an old oil paint—or an oil now over latex? Experts say that present-day latex formulations have a good ability to penetrate the present coat, which means that they can now be used over an old oil-base paint. That wasn't true a few years ago. Since that is the case, there seems to be no reason that you can't apply a latex over oil.

Incidentally, one reason for washing the house before you begin painting is to get rid of excess chalk on the surface. The inability to properly penetrate this chalk has been one reason the latex paints didn't work well over oil-based products. By washing, however, you give the latex an excellent opportunity to bond to the existing surface.

Having made your selection and purchased the paint, you can go to work. The fastest and easiest application is done by using both a paint roller (one with a long handle which can be attached when needed is best) and a good, 4-in. or wider brush. Use the roller to coat large flat areas. Use the brush near the edges and to coat small areas and the undersides of siding. You can also brush over the area you rolled, to assure even coating and to fill in any areas not well coated.

Use a sash-and-trim brush, which has its bristles cut on an angle, for painting windows and other trim. You'll find it easiest to begin the job by doing the windows, doorframes, and other trim.

Don't attempt to extend any exterior paint too much. Remember that you are not just coloring the wood; you are putting a protective coating on it. Therefore, apply enough paint to make a coating. If you brush it out too much, you don't leave enough paint to weather in the next couple of years, and your wall will show signs of wear and erosion rather quickly.

At the same time, don't slosh the paint on too thick. Thick paint tends to crack and peel, especially when moisture gets under it. If you believe a heavy coating is necessary, then give the house two thin coats rather than one heavy coat.

Preparing surfaces

Use this checklist:

- ☐ **Sound existing paint:** Remove loose dirt with dusting brush, smooth rough areas with sandpaper.
- ☐ **Checked, alligatored, blistered, wrinkled or peeling paint:** Scrape, wire-brush and sand down to bare wood. Chemical paint remover may be required for large areas; do *not* use a blowtorch.
- ☐ **Mildew** (looks like gray dirt): Scrub with solution of household bleach, laundry detergent and trisodium phosphate (wear rubber gloves and eye protection); rinse; use primer and paint containing mildewcide.
- ☐ **Excess chalking:** Remove with a wire brush.
- ☐ **Loose, rotted or damaged boards:** Replace badly damaged or rotted boards; renail loose boards that are sound, set and fill nailheads. Small cracks can be filled with wood putty.
- ☐ **Glossy areas of existing paint:** Sand to provide "tooth" for new paint to adhere to or apply deglossing surface conditioner.
- ☐ **Openings and joints:** Fill with caulking compound.
- ☐ **Old caulking, window putty:** Replace if dry or brittle.
- ☐ **Nailhead staining:** Sand area to bare wood, bare metal of nail; set nailhead, prime before filling hole.
- ☐ **Bleeding** (stains caused by seeping of colored matter in wood): Use stain-blocking primer.
- ☐ **Masonry:** Remove dirt and loose material with wire brush.
- ☐ **Gutters and leaders:** Remove all rust and corrosion with wire brush and sandpaper; patch any holes.

GOOD PREPARATION is the key to a good exterior painting job. The first step is to wash the surface of the old paint with a TSP (trisodium phosphate) solution to remove accumulated dirt and other deposits. Areas which have been protected, such as the walls or porches and the undersides of eaves should be scrubbed with the solution. Next, go over the entire surface and scrape away all loose, peeling or flaking paint.

A GOOD TECHNIQUE for painting the outside of a house is to use both a brush and a paint roller. The brush can be used for painting the bottom edges of siding and for edging.

THEN THE ROLLER is used for covering large flat areas. Finally, the brush can be used a second time, to brush out areas previously covered by the roller. This technique is fast.

PAINTING WINDOWS and trim takes time, but the final appearance depends on doing the job well. Use a trim brush with angled bristles. After scraping, apply a coat of primer to cover the scraped areas, then apply the final coat of house paint.

One problem occurs when homeowners thin out the paint before applying it. Most house-paints today have been designed to be used as is, right from the can. Don't thin out latex paints with water, and only thin out an oil-based paint when the directions tell you to. And even then, be sure to use the specified thinner (absolutely no substitutes) in the recommended proportions.

Generally speaking, you should expect about 400 sq. ft. of coverage per gallon of paint. However, the coverage differs somewhat according to the formulation, so check the label of each brand as you shop for your paint.

Also, the coverage will depend on the overall condition of the existing coat. If it has weathered to the point that there is little of the original coat left, then the wall will act like a sponge. In cases like this, you may get as little as 200 sq. ft. of coverage from a gallon. If, on the other hand, the present surface is good, smooth, and well-covered, you may get considerably more than 400 sq. ft. from a gallon.

ROLLERS AND BRUSHES will last a long time if you clean them properly after each use. Always scrape the excess paint from a roller before washing it. Then wash it in clear water, working the paint from the nap of the cover with your fingers. Keep washing until the paint is out of the nap, then shake or spin excess moisture from it. Finally, stand it upright for drying.

TO CLEAN A BRUSH, first rinse the paint out of the bristles in a solvent (water if the paint is latex), then use a brush comb to clean hardened paint from the area around the ferrule. When all signs of the old paint are gone, spin out the excess moisture by rotating the brush between your hands. Then wrap it for storage.

Give unpainted furniture a custom look

By PENELOPE ANGELL

turn page for full instructions

BEFORE our decorating job, the "Pennsylvania Dutch" pieces looked dull.

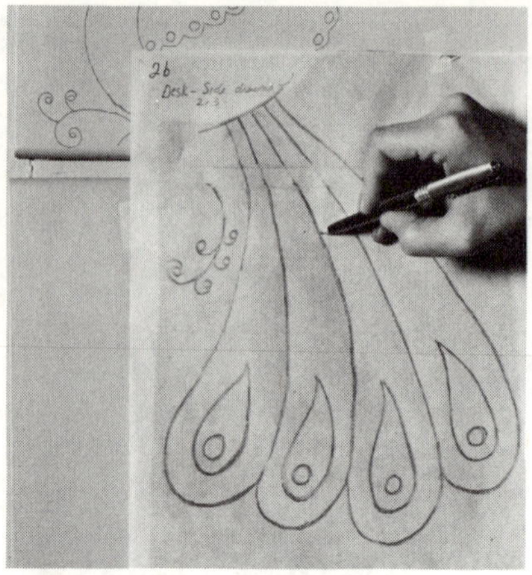

TAPE the pattern in place over graphite paper. Trace with a ballpoint pen.

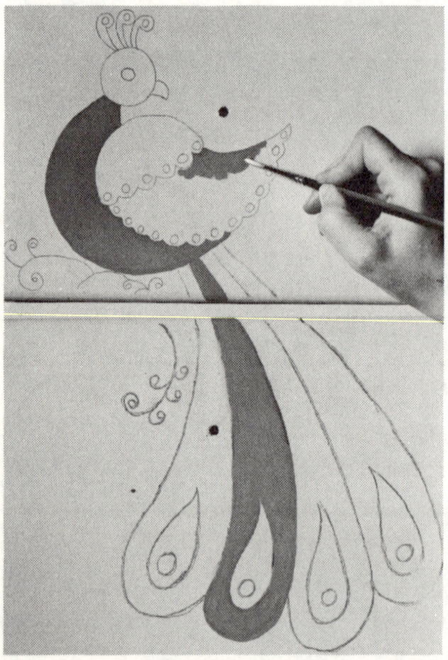

BEGIN painting largest area of color (blue). Finish before starting next color.

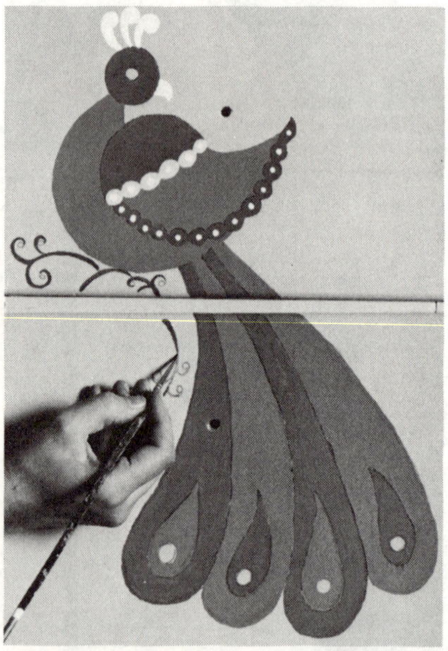

LAST, apply the detail colors, the white decorative dots and the greenery.

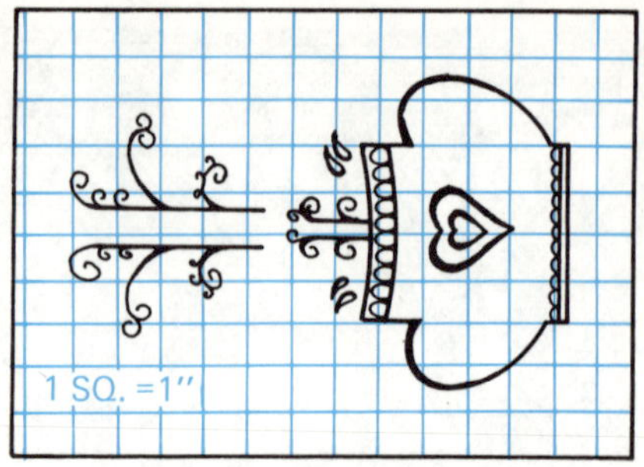

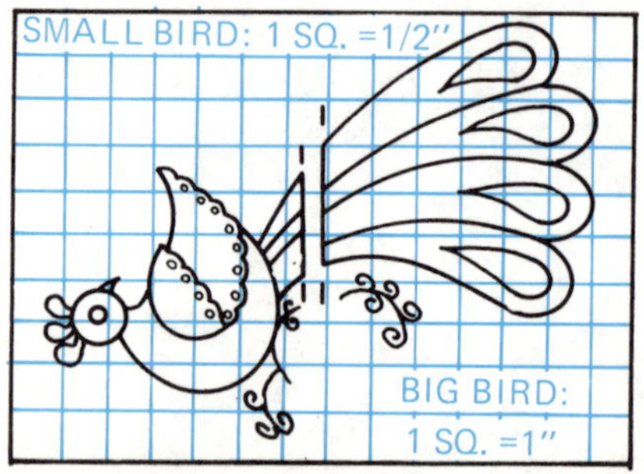

■ THERE ARE TWO important reasons why so many people these days are lugging home unpainted furniture: Economy, of course, is the primary motive. Careful examination reveals that some manufacturers and retailers now offer well-made furniture at reasonable prices.

The second reason is the waiting time for finished furniture; it isn't uncommon to wait six months for a chair, as an example. Most unfinished furniture, on the other hand, can be carried home the day that you buy it.

We commissioned three top-notch designer-artists to develop three distinctly different "looks" for furniture-in-the-raw. The successful results are shown on these pages. And full instructions and plans for all the designs are given, so that you can duplicate what you see.

We've supplied the patterns in two forms: You can use the art and grids that follow to make enlarged tracing or cutting patterns. Or you can cut out the patterns on page 2080, treat them as described and use a projector to enlarge them to the size you want.

Prime-paint all exposed surfaces with an undercoater, or thinned finish coat, to provide a smooth, nonporous surface for good top-coat adhesion. Since the primer or undercoater is white, and tends to lighten the final color, try mixing in some of the colored enamel, or use artists' pigment from the tube to tint the undercoat.

Next, apply the first coat of enamel paint. Begin by submerging the bristles of your brush halfway into the paint and applying the enamel evenly on a small area of the wood, moving in the

SUPPLIES—PENNSYLVANIA DUTCH

Furniture: Ladderback chair, Sears, Roebuck and Co.; desk, three-drawer chest, Montgomery Ward.

Paint: Fuller O'Brien alkyd semigloss enamel undercoating, Golden Field, Liberty Blue, Ultra Red, Ultra Green, White Wing.

Accessories: Calico Cat, Fiddlestix, New City, NY 10956; violin player soft sculpture, Pamela Arrand, East Ryegate, VT through Fiddlestix.

Misc: Tracing paper, graphite paper (it wipes off more easily than carbon), turpentine, cellulose tape, fine ballpoint pen, cotton swabs, Nos. 00, 1 and 4 artists' brushes.

WOULD YOU BELIEVE that the elegant oriental ensemble (right) started life as low-cost, ready-to-finish furniture? Flowers on the screen, as well as the decorative motifs on cabinet front and cube top (above), were created using carefully cut stencils and spray paint.

direction of the grain.

Apply more paint evenly across the grain so that the paint fills the wood pores. Tip off finish with the grain to smooth the surface.

Let the first coat dry. Then sand, dust and apply the final coat.

Pennsylvania Dutch theme

The Pennsylvania Dutch designs are traced directly on the furniture, then hand painted. First prepare and paint the furniture following the general finishing instructions, using the finishing materials listed.

Use the photo on page 2039 to identify pattern placement and color. Enlarge patterns to full size by using grid or slide-projector.

Tape the graphite paper and pattern in place on the furniture. Trace the pattern with a fine-point pen.

Remove the pattern and graphite paper and begin painting the largest color area, blue or red, with a No. 4 brush. After this paint dries, paint the next largest color area. Use a No. 1 brush to paint medium-size areas. Paint the white decorative dots with a No. 00 brush. Paint the greenery with a No. 1 brush.

oriental motif

Designs on the oriental furniture are stenciled and spray-painted. You'll need to add tops to the table/storage cube and the cabinet and also apply a design made of lattice to the screen, to duplicate the finished pieces that appear in the photo.

Table/storage cube: Cut a plywood or particleboard top for the storage cube. Nail two cleats inside the cube, centered on opposite sides, so the top is flush with the sides. Bore four finger holes carefully positioned as shown in the color photo. Then paint cube and add the stencil design.

Cabinet: The cabinet is topped with plywood or particleboard. Nail the top to the cabinet with 1½ in. (4d) finishing nails after the cabinet has been painted. Then glue protective vinyl to the top (see list of supplies). After the glue sets, trim excess vinyl with a razor knife.

LATTICE was applied to screen; tops were added to cube and cabinet.

SHARP knife cuts kraft-paper stencil for black areas of cabinet.

SPRAY-PAINT after rubber-cementing and burnishing stencil to work.

The paint dries quickly. Almost immediately, you can remove the stencil.

REPEAT STENCIL procedure with orange pattern. Apply spray paint.

STENCIL is removed and project is complete. If needed, touch up with brush.

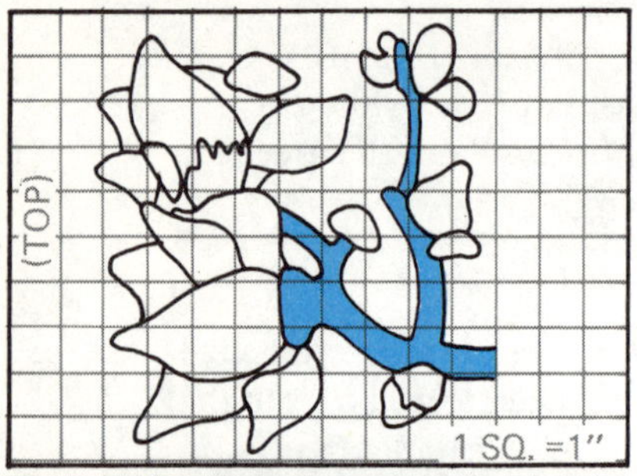

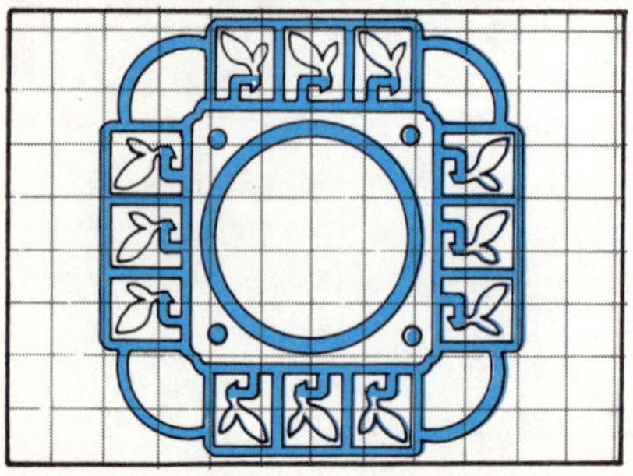

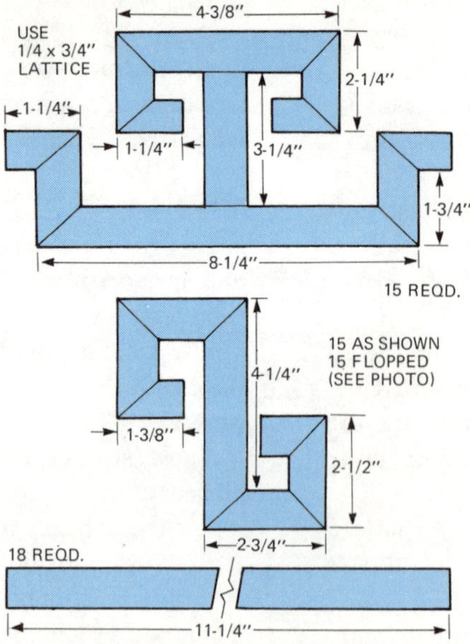

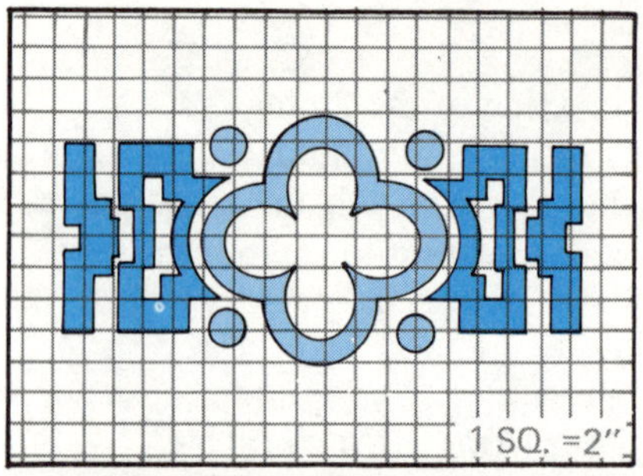

SUPPLIES—ORIENTAL MOTIF

Furniture: table/storage cube, J.C. Penney; cabinet, Sears, Roebuck and Co.; folding screen, Montgomery Ward.

Construction materials:

Table/storage cube: ½x14¼x14¼″ plywood or particleboard, 2, ¾x¾x7″ cleats; ⅞″ 4d finishing nails.

Cabinet: ½x13½x37½″ plywood or particleboard; 1″ 4d finishing nails; 1½″ 4d finishing nails; Goodyear Evergleam All-Purpose Vinyl; Goodyear 200 adhesive; 1⅛x1⅛″ corner guard molding.

Folding screen: ¼x¾″x108″ lattice, white glue.

Paint: Krylon Crystal Clear Acrylic sealant and All-Purpose White primer, plus the following Krylon spray enamel paints: For *table/storage cube,* Mandarin Orange, gloss black, antique white; for *cabinet,* antique white, gloss black, Mandarin Orange, Sunset Orange; for *folding screen,* gloss black, beige, Spanish Brown, antique white, plus small jars of bright yellow, black and turquoise.

Misc.: lacquer thinner, carbon paper, tracing paper, brown kraft paper, rubber cement, plywood or textured work surface, sharp hobby knife and small paint brush.

Seal, prime and spray-paint the corner guard (molding) a Sunset Orange color, sanding and dusting between steps. Miter-cut the molding and attach it in place with 1-in. finishing nails. Set the nails; fill the holes and retouch the paint.

After the design has been stenciled on, the cabinet doors can be fitted with oriental-style pulls.

Folding screen: Seal, prime and spray-paint the lattice strips gloss black to make the designs on the screen; sand and dust between steps. Then cut the pieces following the art. Spray-paint the entire screen beige and the edging gloss black. Next, cut the lattice pieces and arrange them on the screen. Be sure you make the angle cuts so the pieces can be properly positioned painted-side up and glue them in place. You may want to retouch the ends. Finally, paint the stencil design.

making oriental stencils

Draw patterns full size onto tracing paper. Use carbon paper to transfer the patterns to kraft paper to cut the stencils. First, apply rubber cement on the back of the kraft paper to adhere to a plywood work surface.

Cut out the stencil using the color photo as a guide. Make sure you cut out only the area that you want to color on each stencil. All pieces of furniture require two stencils: black and white for the table/storage cube, black and orange for the cabinet, brown and white for flowers on the folding screen.

Carefully remove the cut stencil from the plywood. When you reuse a stencil, apply another coat of rubber cement, let it get tacky, and then burnish the edges securely in place on the painted furniture so paint won't seep under it.

Apply two light coats of paint, preferably with the workpiece in a horizontal attitude, to keep the paint from seeping under the edge of the stencil. Since spray paint dries quickly, you can remove the stencil immediately after spraying. Apply finishing touches of yellow, black outlining and

THE DESK, chest and bed below were changed into a cosmic habitat suitable for today's space-age kids. It's a fail-safe project they can do themselves by cutting designs out of self-adhering plastic.

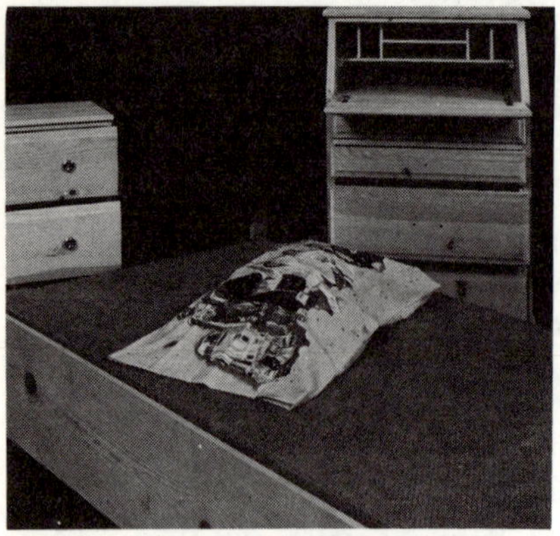

ADDING cosmic designs of stick-on plastic is an easy, no-mess project.

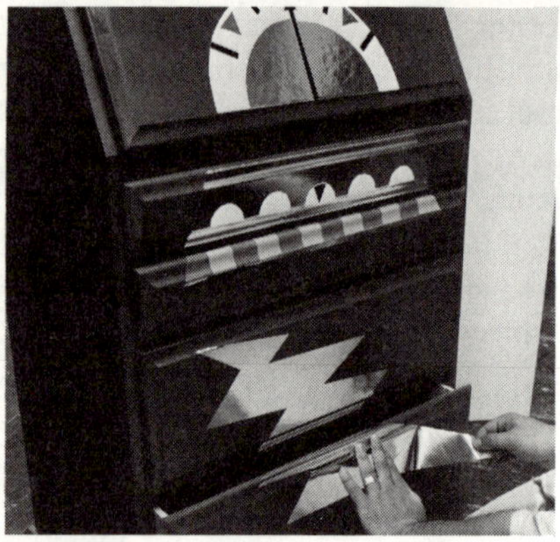

PLASTIC is smoothed in place after it is cut with a knife and straightedge.

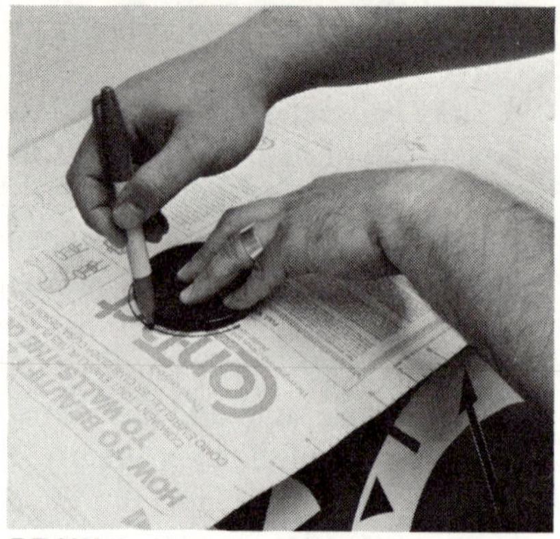

DRAW the figures on the back of the plastic. Then cut them out.

REMOVE the backing and smooth pieces in place. Overlap colors as needed.

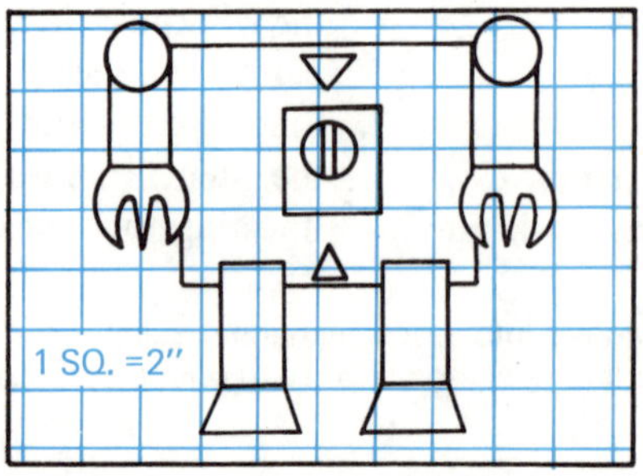

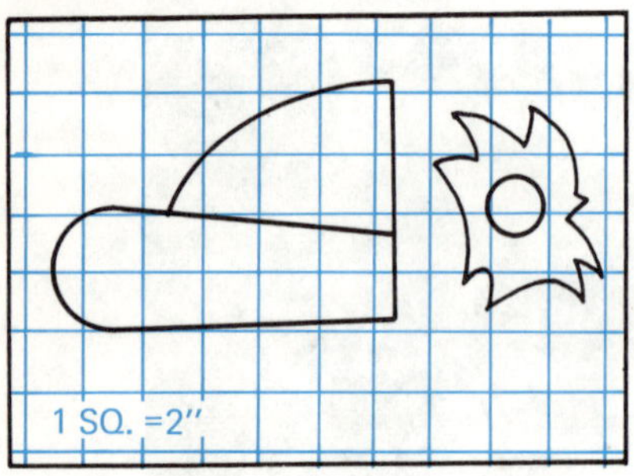

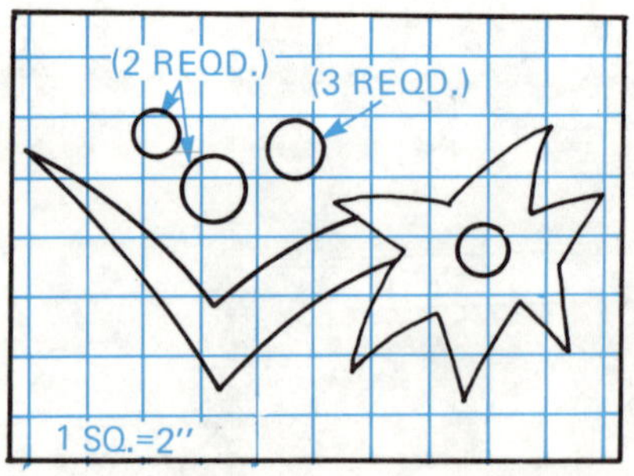

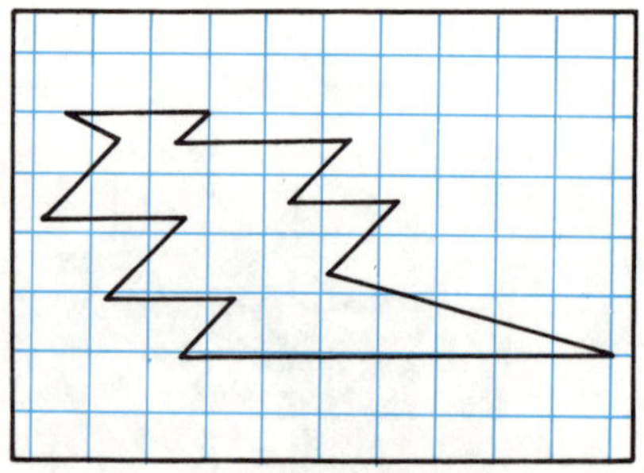

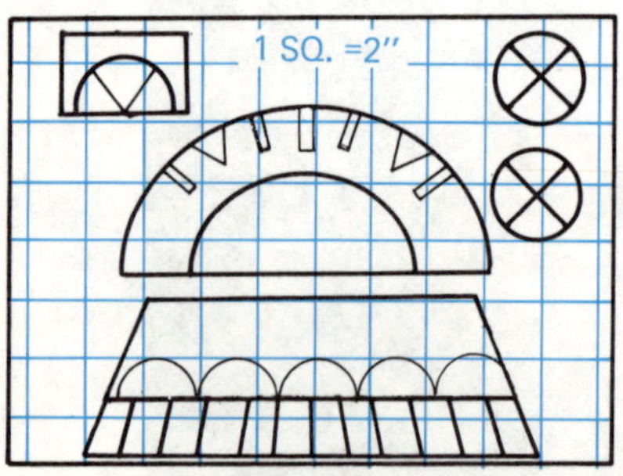

SUPPLIES—COSMIC HABITAT

Furniture: platform bed, Sears, Roebuck and Co.; secretary desk, chest of drawers, J.C. Penney.
Decorations: Con-Tact self-adhesive plastic in white, lemon, brass, chrome, red, lime and black.
Accessories: Philip's Chart of the Stars (over bed), $4.50 postpaid, Jupiter's Great Red Spot poster (over desk), $2 postpaid, from Planetarium Shop, The American Museum-Hayden Planetarium, 81st St. and Central Park West, New York, NY 10024.
Misc.: tracing paper, graphite or carbon paper, ballpoint pen, scissors, hobby knife, metal straightedge.

FINISHING MATERIALS—ALL PROJECTS

Sandpaper: 120- and 180-grit aluminum oxide or garnet; opencoat 220- and 280-grit garnet: 360-grit silicon carbide, wet/dry.
Tools: dropcloth, tack cloth, sanding block, good-quality flat brush.
Misc.: 3-lb. cut shellac, denatured alcohol, undercoating (same make as paint), paint (as needed), Elmer's or other wood filler.

turquoise to the flower on the folding screen.

cosmic habitat

The furniture in the cosmic room is decorated with brightly colored, self-adhesive plastic which you can purchase by the half yard. After the furniture has been prepared and painted as described in the general finishing instructions, draw the decorative patterns to size.

Turn the tracing paper over, top side facing *down* on the back side of the self-adhesive plastic. Using graphite or carbon paper, trace the shapes and cut them out. It helps to use a hobby knife and straightedge to make clean cuts on straight pieces. Peel off the backing—a little at a time on large shapes—and smooth plastic in place. Puncture small air pockets with a pin.

PAINTING WINDOW SASH goes much quicker if you first apply masking tape to the glass to protect it from paint. It takes only minutes to do.

The right way to paint a room

By LEN HILTS

The right way doesn't take much longer than the wrong way when painting a room, but there is a big difference in the final result

PAINTING A ROOM these days is a relatively quick and easy job. Latex paints, rollers, and a myriad of helpful accessories such as edgers and plastic drop cloths have eliminated much of the labor and cut the time needed. You can actually begin painting in the morning and have a party in the room that evening. That's how far we have progressed.

But, as usual, there is still a right way and a wrong way to do the job. The right way takes a little more time—but not much—and the job will look better and last longer. Here are the steps to follow to do it right:

1. Move as much furniture from the room as you can. Move the rest to the center of the room.

2. Cover the furniture and carpeting with a thin, plastic drop cloth. No matter how careful you are, paint rollers throw off tiny splatters.

3. Examine the wall for cracks, holes and other damage. Using patching plaster and a putty knife, fill these, allow them to dry, then sand the surface smooth. If the cracks are large, dig out loose plaster first. Be sure, when the patching is finished, that it is level, so it will be invisible under the new paint. Patching plasters may shrink a little as they dry, so a final top coat may be necessary to fill in the shrunken area in order to make a level patch.

4. Wipe the wall free of dust.

5. Kitchen and bathroom walls should be washed with a wall-washing compound and then rinsed. This gets rid of the thin film of grease that's sure to have built up on them.

6. In other rooms, you need wash only excessively dirty areas. (If the kids have marked the walls with crayons, be sure to wash these off.)

7. Now remove all hardware—wallswitch and outlet plates, for example. Drop the cover plates on ceiling fixtures and remove all window hardware.

8. Now you are ready to paint. Do the tough work first—which is painting the ceiling. You can do this quickly and easily if you buy a roller with a long handle. This enables you to stand on the floor while rolling paint on the ceiling. First, of course, you must edge the ceiling, painting a strip 2 to 4 in. wide all around the room.

9. Roll the ceiling area, overlapping the edge strip.

10. Now do the woodwork and windows. Use a 2-in. angular-cut sash brush for this. Put masking tape on the window panes next to the wood to keep paint off the glass.

11. Next, "cut in" the walls. That is, use a brush to paint the corners and the ceiling-wall junction. Paint 2 to 3 in. out from each corner and away from all woodwork.

12. Finally, apply paint to the open wall areas with a roller. Charge the roller in the paint pan by rolling it back and forth on the corrugated bottom. Carry it to the wall and make a W about a foot high and 18 in. wide. Then roll through the W to spread the coating evenly. Don't attempt to spread the coating too thinly.

13. With the painting done, wash your tools in water, put the hardware back in place, remove the drop cloths, and move the furniture back where it belongs. The job is done.

SEE ALSO
Home improvement . . . Paint rollers . . . Painting tools . . . Painting, exterior

How to make cracks disappear

SEE ALSO

Basement waterproofing . . . Hardboard . . . Paint rollers . . . Painting tools . . . Plasterboard . . . Remodeling

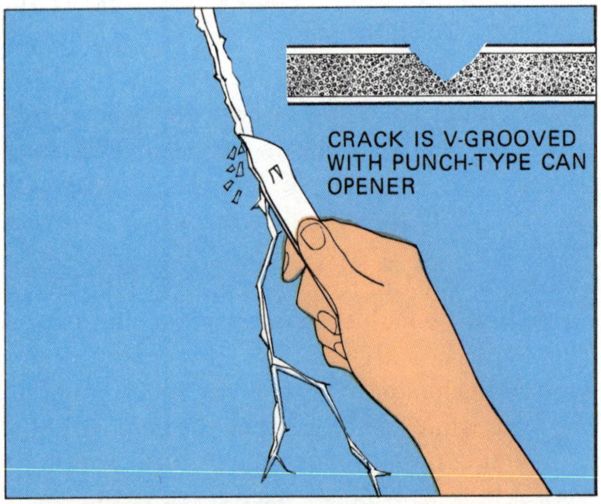

1 FIRST PATCHING STEP is to clean out the entire crack, making certain no loose particles remain. (Patching compound must be applied to a solid surface to be permanent.) Paint stores sell tools for gouging out cracks, but a punch-type can opener does the same job. If you're repairing plasterboard, you may have to cut away some paper on the surface. Dust off the crack with a dry brush before proceeding.

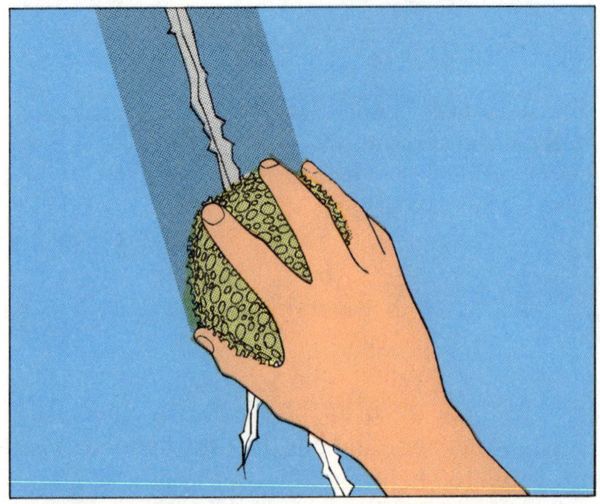

2 SOAK A LARGE SPONGE in water and squeeze out the excess. Then thoroughly dampen the surface to which the joint compound will applied. The idea is to slow down moisture absorption and thus achieve a better bond between new material and old. To keep floor or carpeting underfoot free of damage during repairs, spread layers of newspaper to catch the scrapings, water and compound that will fall.

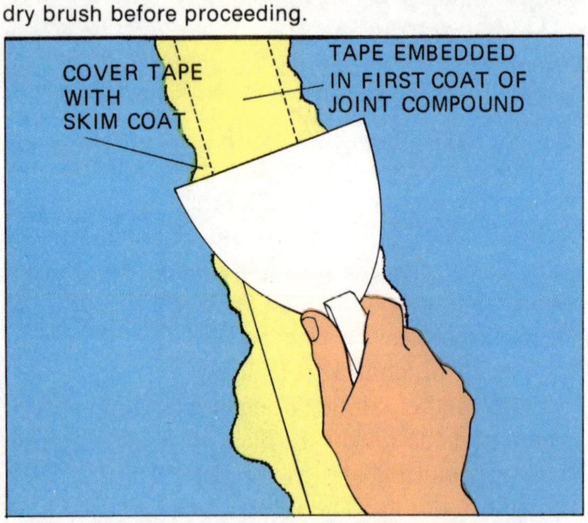

5 WHEN THE ENTIRE CRACK has been covered with tape, take your wallboard knife and firmly press the tape into the bedding compound with knife held at a 45° angle. You'll know that the pressure is correct if you squeeze out some compound from under the tape—*but enough must be left for a good bond.* When it's dry, if air pockets (bubbles) have formed under the tape, cut them out with a sharp razor blade.

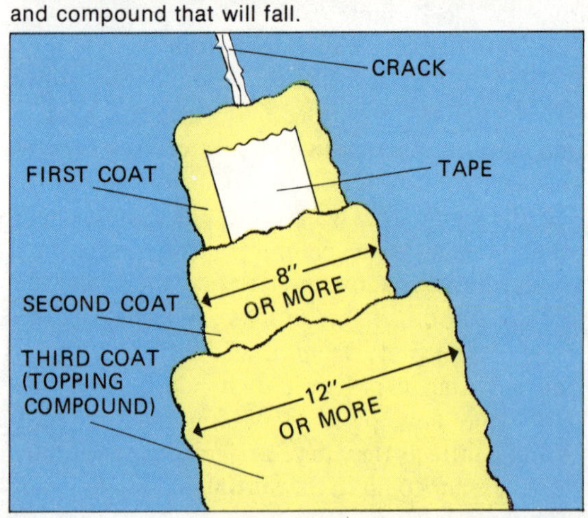

6 A MINIMUM OF THREE COATS is recommended for all patches—the embedding coat and two coats over the tape. The last coat can be a topping compound; it's extra smooth. Successive coats are progressively wider. Allow each to dry thoroughly before applying the next. Check between coats and sand off any high spots. If you are patching plasterboard, be careful that you *don't oversand* the adjacent paper surfaces.

ANY PAINT JOB is only as good as the surface preparation that went into it. In most cases—on inside jobs—this is not much more than a thorough surface cleaning before applying paint. But as a new home settles with age, cracks are sure to appear on the walls, especially if they're plaster. And cracks can show up in plasterboard walls too. Regardless of how they got there in the first place, the chore is to eliminate them for good before you dip your brush or roller in the paint. As you'll see on these pages, you can. Some of the tricks have been around awhile; others are those used by professionals. Now, you can add them to your bag.

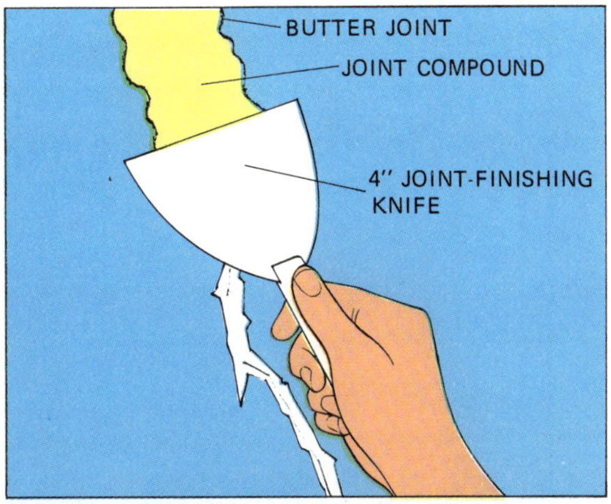

3 WHILE THE GOUGED SURFACE is still moist, apply the joint compound, forcing it into the cracks. You can use a dry compound that requires mixing with water, but to save time, a premixed compound is recommended. It comes in quart, gallon and 5-gallon sizes and, if kept covered and protected from freezing, lasts indefinitely. After buttering the cracks with the compound, carefully smooth off the surface with the knife.

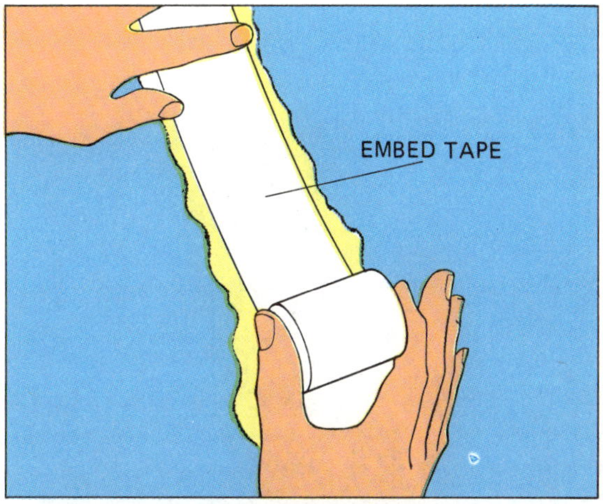

4 APPLY WALLBOARD TAPE to the buttered crack. Using your fingers, loosely press the tape in place. Basically, there are three types of tape you can use: heavy paper (one with perforations and one without) and a gauzelike material that is available at many paint stores. All do the job, but if you are patching plaster, gauze is the best. If desired, paper tape can be moistened slightly before it is applied.

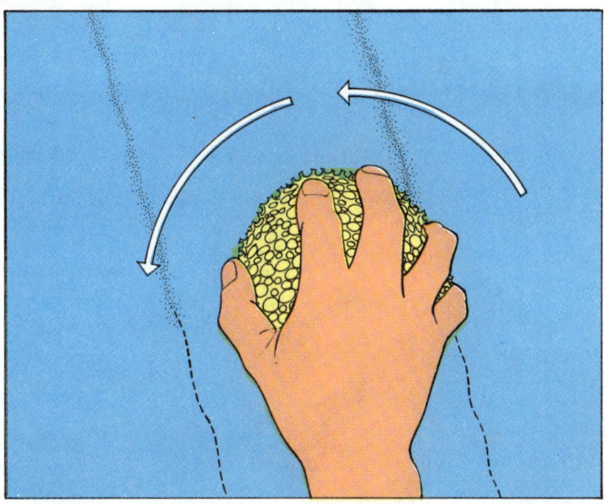

7 WHEN DRY—at least 24 hours after applying a topping coat—the surface can be sanded to feather into the adjacent surfaces. One good way is to "sand" with a damp sponge. Since the joint compound is water soluble, don't get the sponge too wet and don't rub continuously in one spot. This method of "sanding" prevents your breathing fine sandpaper and dust and eliminates most dusting and cleanup afterward.

8 AFTER THE PATCHED AREA has been sanded, the compound and the wall surface should be primed with a suitable sealer (vinyl or oil base primer/sealer, or shellac) to equalize the (paint) absorption difference between the existing wall and the joint compound in the old crack. You should now have a uniform surface texture ready for final decoration. Just follow the instructions supplied by the paint maker.

Pick the right painting tools

By JOSEPH R. PROVEY

PAINT TOOL design continues to evolve. Roller systems (right) include snap-on, birdcage, and end-cap-frames. Foam corner and shielded rollers eliminate paint misting (see text).

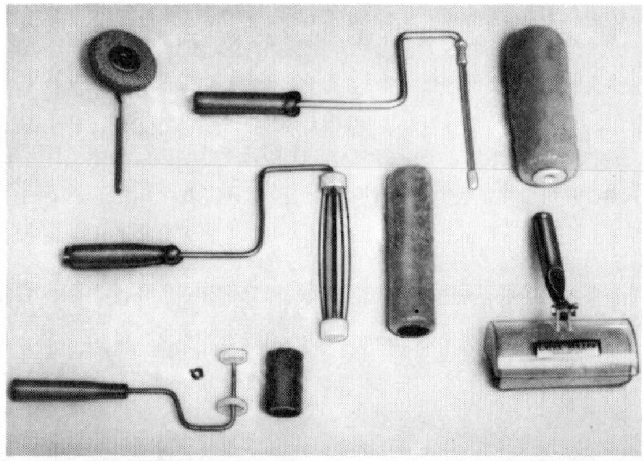

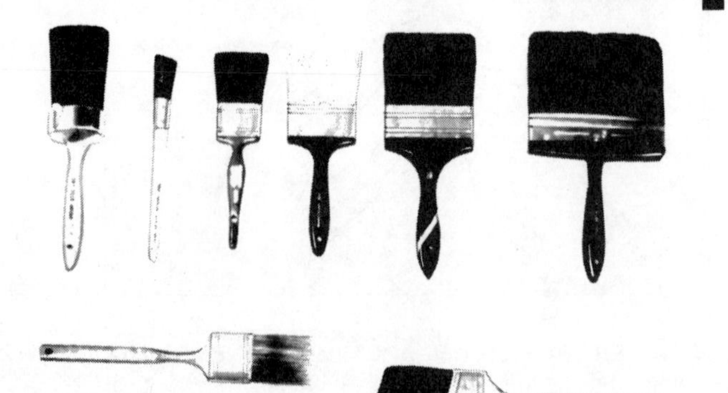

BRUSHES (left to right): oval varnish, oval sash, enamel, varnish/wall, wall, wall-coating; (bottom) flat and angular sash.

PAD FAMILY includes minipad, sash painters (right); edgers (center); replacement pads (on pan) and 9-in. applicator.

■ WHEN IT COMES to a paint job that isn't just a whitewash, quality painting tools in the hands of a person who knows how to use them are just as important as the quality of the paint used. Yet, when it comes to cutting costs, the first item most people skimp on is the paint applicator.

Well-chosen tools, even if initial cost is significantly higher, are a wise investment. Unfortunately, it is not always easy to recognize a quality product. Superficial features and useless gimmicks can mislead. Study the notes, drawings and photos on each of the three basic applicator types—and the next time you're pondering an addition to your painting tools, you'll know exactly what to get.

The primary job of any painting tool is to apply paint quickly and easily, leaving no unwanted marks, dust, lint or filaments. Rapid coverage will depend on three things: (1) how much paint a tool can pick up and hold; (2) how much can be transferred to the surface and (3) uniformity of the flow or discharge rate.

A well-designed paint tool is also comfortable to use. Check for balanced weight. The correct handle on a brush, for example, counterbalances paint-loaded bristles and makes the tool easy to control, less tiring to use.

Look for innovations which make life simpler. Some pad applicators, for instance, have knob-type grips which pivot freely or float to permit strokes that don't have to be interrupted often for grip changes.

Always choose tools suited to you. A jumbo, 9-in.-long roller or 6-in. wall-coating brush might be too heavy for you to manipulate effectively—while it might help someone else get the job done faster.

Finally, a good applicator is easy to clean and, when properly cared for, can be used over and over. Disposable applicators may or may not work well, but in the long run cost more.

Brushes, pads, and rollers each have definite advantages—and disadvantages. Choosing one over another depends on how large the job is, how quickly you want to get it done, and personal preference.

Brushes are well suited to all surfaces. They pick up paint well and are neat, easy to use and come in a variety of shapes for every purpose—and with proper care last indefinitely.

Rollers for all surfaces also get large jobs done rapidly but they often leave a texture on either painted or stained surfaces. They tend to shed and they create a fine mist of paint which can be tedious to clean off unprotected floors. Minimize misting by using a slow rolling rate and not applying too much pressure. Padco's shielded No-Spray roller or Arsco's Rapid Roller with spin-retarding, snap-on roller cartridges also help to solve the misting problem. A roller cover should be replaced when its pile loses resiliency or when its core weakens.

A paint pad does not pick up as much paint per dip as either brush or roller—but does let you get the paint on quickly with relatively little expertise. The correct pad is particularly effective on smooth interior surfaces and for applying stain to shakes and siding. Textured surfaces, however, will often separate pad laminations.

THREE KINDS OF PAINTING TOOLS IN ACTION

OVAL sash brush is great for painting window trim, mullions, scrollwork, moldings or any irregular surface.

FOAM ROLLER is shaped for painting inside corners. Use it to start job; then do trim with 3-in. roller.

PAD-TYPE EDGER is kept off stained molding by plastic wheels. You get sharp edge without using tape.

WHAT TO LOOK FOR IN A BRUSH

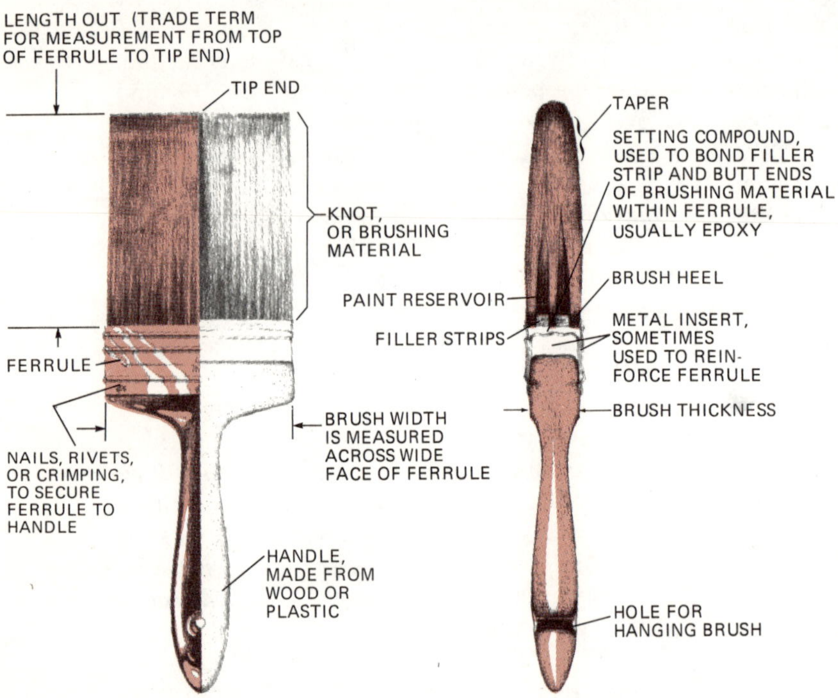

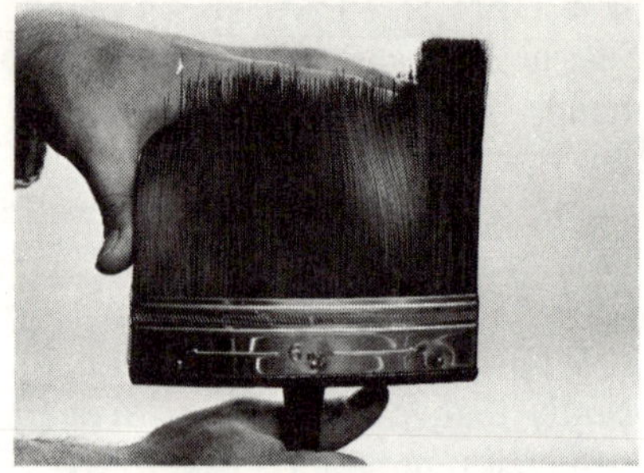

A BRUSH with varied bristle lengths picks up and releases paint better. Examine brush for shorter lengths.

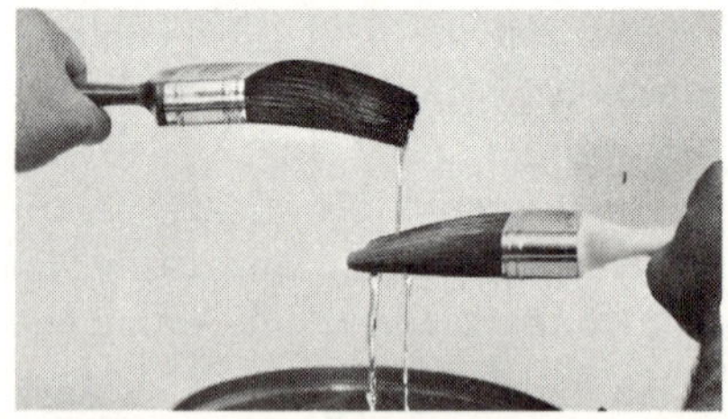

NATURAL bristles (top) lose shape and stiffness after soaking in water. Stiffer synthetic filaments (bottom) will not swell or weaken in waterbased paints.

TO AVOID rust stains, stainless-steel ferrule is best, brass, nickel plate next, tin for throwaways.

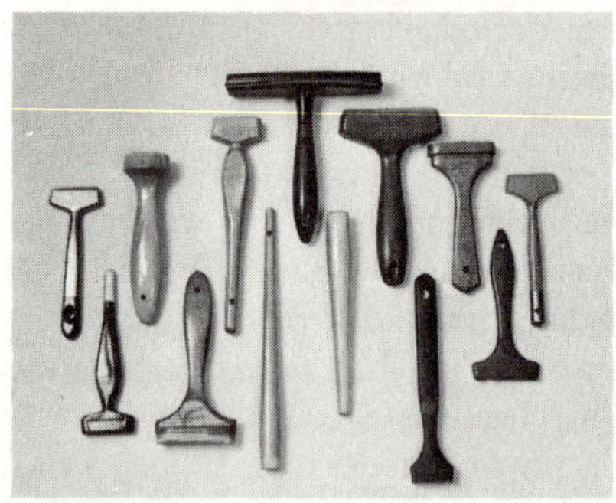

GOOD BRUSH handles are made of beech, birch, hard maple or solid plastic. Length, weight, neck diameter and shape are suited to recommended use.

If you decide on a brush, first check it for fullness. It shouldn't feel skimpy. Filler strips, which create reservoirs for paint, should not be too large. Second, the knot should be tapered, to make the brush thinner and more flexible at its tip. This means fewer brush marks and a brush edge which releases paint gradually, with less effort. Flags (the split ends) also help to pick up, hold and release paint more evenly. Be sure at least 50 percent of the brushing material is flagged.

Finally, choose a brush shaped to suit your task. Wall-type brushes are for large, flat areas; oval brushes for irregular or contoured surfaces and smaller trim and sash brushes are for close work around windows, doors, molding and on furniture. Use natural bristle for varnish, enamel, shellac—and polyester or nylon for almost any coating. Note: nylon is not recommended for use with shellac.

PAINT PAD, OR FLAT APPLICATOR

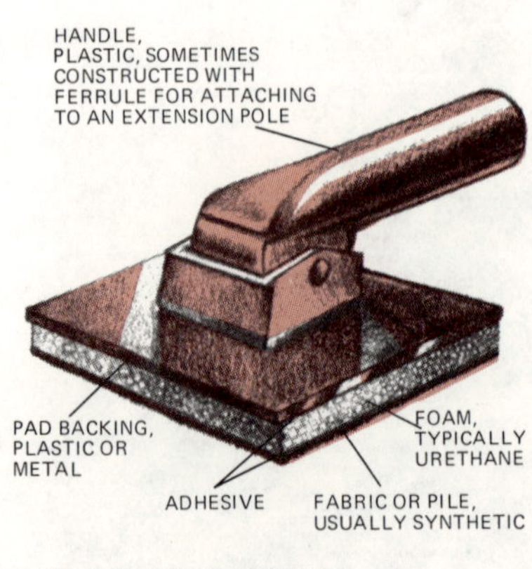

REPLACEABLE PAD NORMALLY LOCKS INTO POSITION

CHOOSING THE RIGHT ROLLER

CAGE-TYPE ROLLER FRAME

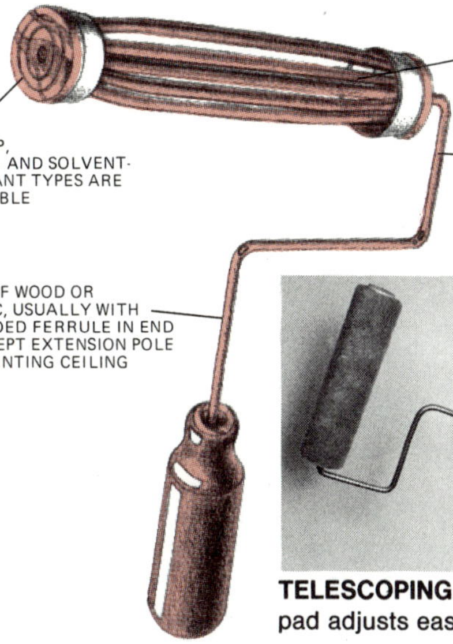

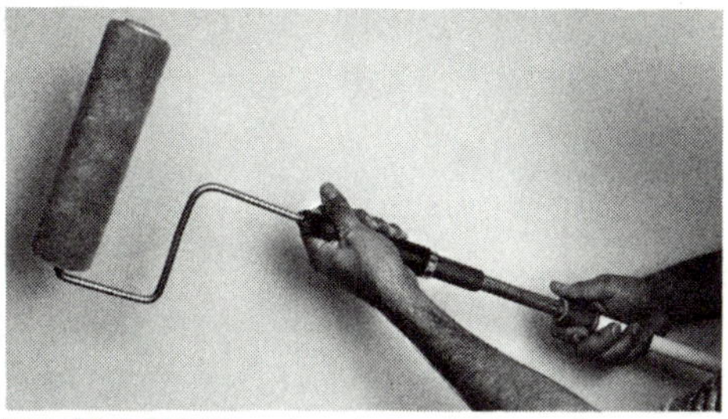

TELESCOPING extension pole for roller or pad adjusts easily as required.

ROLLER COVER REPLACEMENT

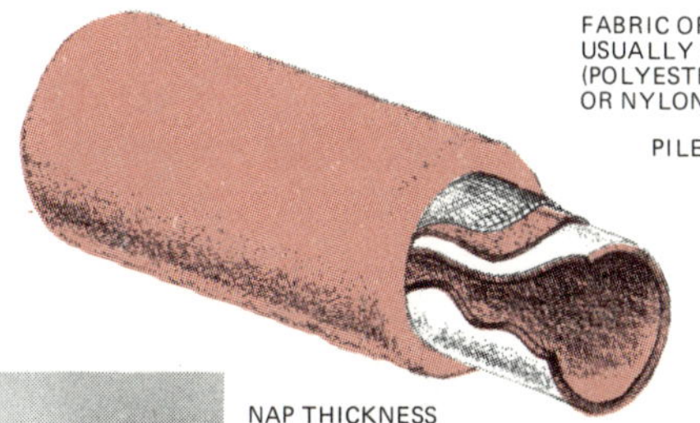

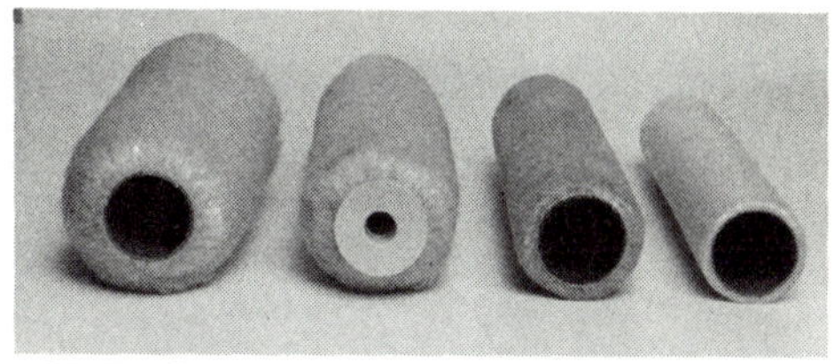

USE THICK-NAP cover on rough surfaces; shorter naps are for smooth and gloss finishes.

Most roller covers today are synthetic—and do a good job with both latex and oil-based paints. Nap thicknesses of ⅛ to ⅜ in. are for smooth surfaces, ⅜ to ¾ in. are for semi-rough surfaces like sand finishes and cement block, while ¾ to 1¼ in. are for rough surfaces like cinder block, stucco, brick, and chain fence. Use special 3/16-in. nap to apply all textured wall coatings.

A good roller cover sheds little lint, has beveled ends and smooth, even seams. The best cores are of phenolic-treated fiberboard or plastic.

GENERAL RULES FOR PAINT TOOL CARE

■ When using latex, rinse tool every few hours to keep free of hardened deposits.

■ Wrap tools in plastic or foil to keep them from hardening during work breaks.

■ Use only cleaning solvent, and solutions recommended by the paint maker.

■ Tools used with latex paints that contain alkyd resin or emulsified oil need to be cleaned with paint thinner between water and soap rinses.

■ Don't let brush, roller or pad rest on bristles or nap while drying or storing.

■ Wrap pads and rollers in foil or plastic after cleaning.

■ Keep two sets of tools—one for oil-based paints, the other for latex.

Preventive brush maintenance

Brushes can represent a sizable investment and are particularly susceptible to damage in use. Never dip more than ½ to ⅓ of total length out. Always *tap* a brush to remove excess paint—wiping it on the can's edge may cause flaring. Your stroke should be compatible with the brush shape—don't, for instance, poke into corners with a wall brush. When finished, clean the brush as soon as possible. Don't soak overnight or the handle may swell.

ROLLER/PAD SCRAPER

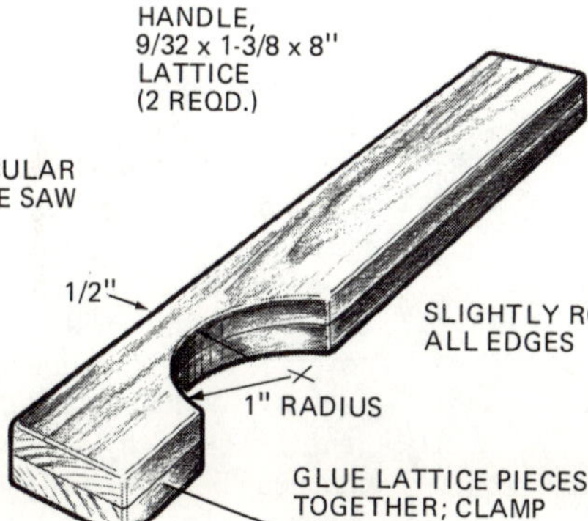

BRUSH COMB

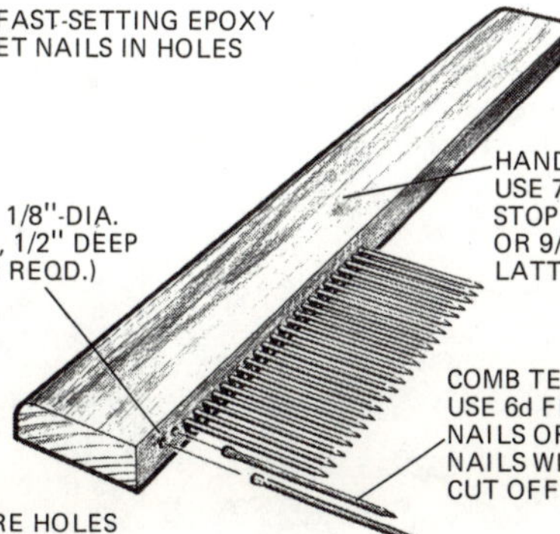

How to paint with spray cans

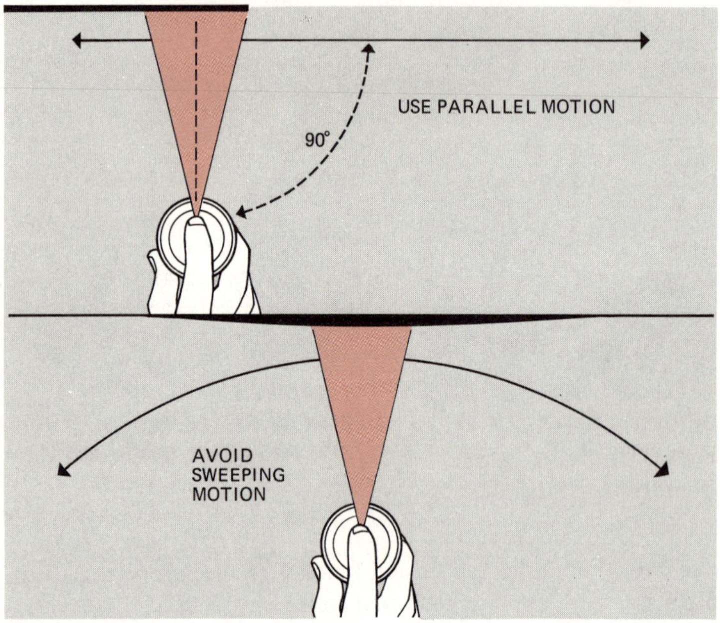

There's a knack to it

While the pressurized spray can has made painting a lot simpler than it used to be, there's a knack to handling these self-contained spray guns beyond just pressing a button. One of the secrets of a perfect paint job is to keep the can moving at all times. Another thing to remember is that the paint goes on in a uniform layer when the distance between the spray head and the surface is the same throughout a parallel sweep, as shown in the upper diagram, on the left. When applied with a sweeping motion as shown in the lower diagram, the paint film is heavy at the center of the arc and thin at each end, producing a coating which is not uniform

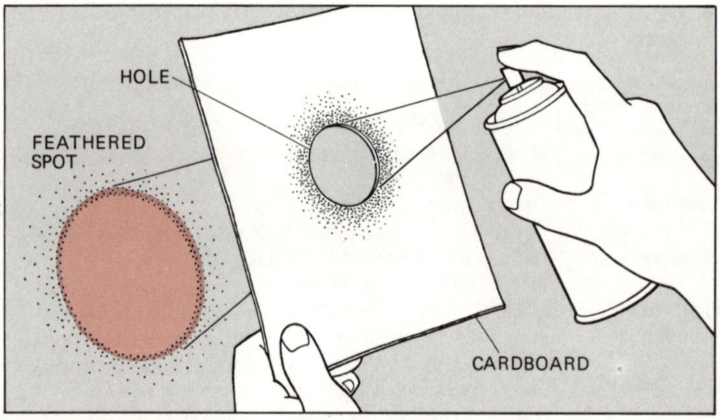

Control touch-up feathering

A neat trick to remember when doing touch-up work, such as refinishing a fender scratch, is to aim the nozzle through a hole in a piece of cardboard held 10 in. or so from the surface. This feathers the edges so the paint will blend into the surrounding area rather than concentrate in a single spot

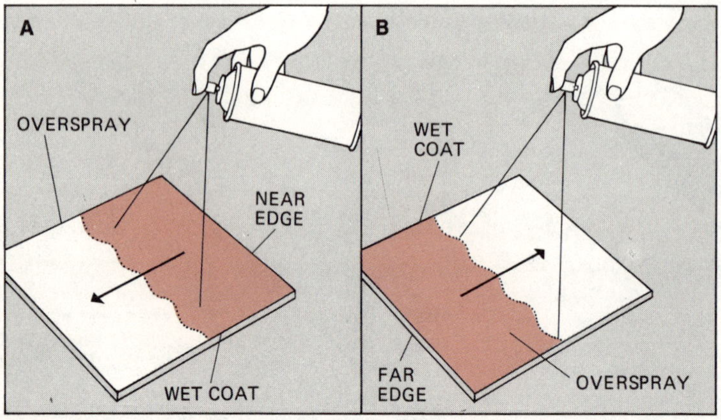

Always work from the near edge

When painting a horizontal surface such as the top of a table, start at the near edge and work away (A). This lets the overspray (mist) settle ahead of the full wet coat following. Working from the far edge (B) allows the mist to fall on top of the wet coat, producing a less smooth, "pitted" finish. Several thin coats will produce better coverage and hiding quality than one thick coat. Since aerosol paints are generally quick-drying, succeeding coats can be applied as litle as five minutes apart

Wait until paint is warm

To dry properly, paint in aerosol cans should be at a temperature between 60° and 90° F. If cans are stored in a garage or other unheated place during cold weather, the paint will be too cold to use immediately. To warm it, place the can in a pan of lukewarm water (*not* over a fire) for a few minutes

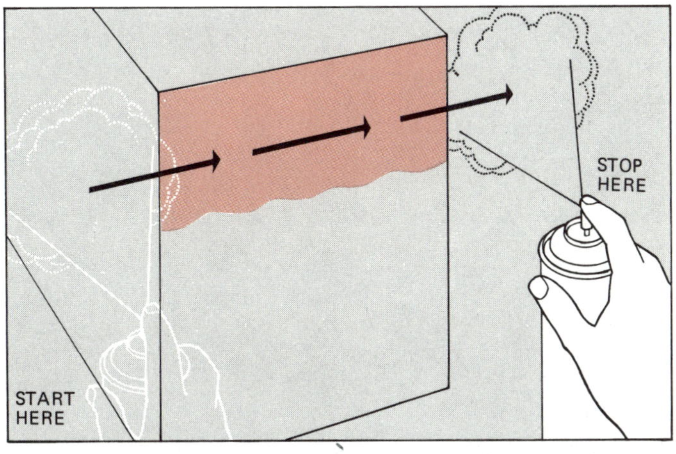

Start spraying before you paint

When spraying flat vertical surfaces, learn to trigger the spray so you start and stop the spray stroke off the work. This results in an even coating. Stay parallel to the surface and move back and forth across the full width of the work with each pass. Hold the spray head 10 to 12 in. from the surface and use a firmly rapid stroke. If applied too slowly, the spray concentration becomes too great and the paint will run and sag on vertical surfaces. Shake the can to keep the paint well mixed

SEE ALSO
Paint rollers . . . Painting, furniture . . . Painting tools

Good to the last drop

When a can is nearly empty and fails to spray when it's tilted, chances are that the siphon tube is above the paint level as shown in cutaway A. The remaining contents can be reached in most cases by turning the spray head 180° or until the siphon tube is in the lowest part of the can and below the paint level, as in B

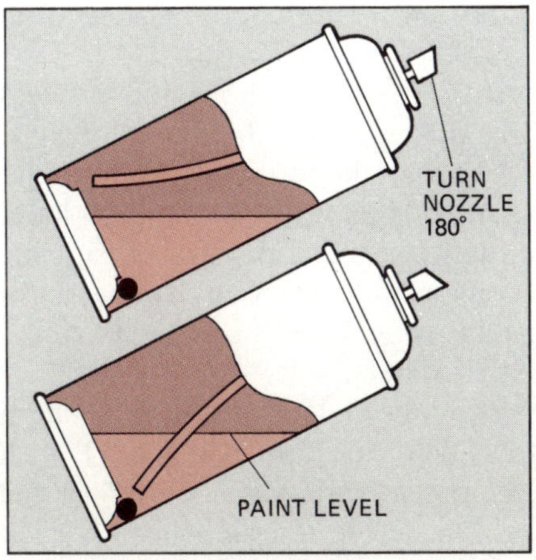

Keep it clean when job is done

After each job, be sure to clear the spray head of the paint so it won't be clogged for the next use. To do so, turn the can upside down and give the spray a few bursts to blow out the pinhole orifice. Aim the nozzle at a dropcloth or newspaper as some remnants of paint will be forced out along with the gas. Even when emptied of paint, enough pressure is left to be a hazard. Before disposing of any aerosol can, hold down the spray head (release valve) until the remaining gas is completely exhausted

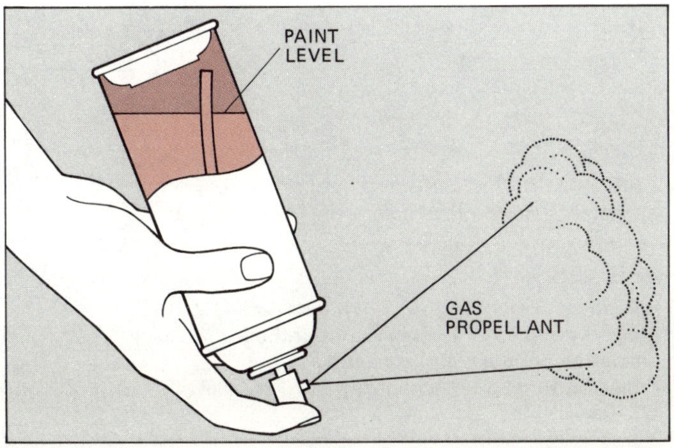

TWO TYPES of decorative hardboard paneling were used in this room, including the stucco over the fireplace.

Hardboard wall paneling

By LEN HILTS

HARDBOARD PANELING now duplicates the natural appearance, texture and color veining of clinker brick.

SEE ALSO
Basement remodeling . . . Brick, simulated . . . Family rooms . . . Fasteners . . . Hardboard . . . Insulation . . . Paneling, plywood . . . Paneling, wood . . . Remodeling . . . Tile, wall . . . Wallpaper

■ ABOUT THREE DECADES AGO, the manufacturers of hardboard developed a photographic method of reproducing the look of any wood—a look so natural that new possibilities of paneling in rare and exotic woods became available.

A few years later, an embossing process brought three dimensions to hardboard panels. The embossing reproduces the feel and texture of the wood to accompany the natural color look. Since then, new types and designs of paneling have been coming out every year. Today, hardboard panelings offer a real opportunity to develop "theme" rooms.

Want the rough-hewn look of a ranch house of the old West? Or the rich, formal look of a British clubroom, complete with panel insets? Or the cool feeling of the inside of a sunbaked Mexican cantina? Or perhaps you want to decorate in French Provincial, or you are reproducing the charm of old Spain and need a Mediterranean wall.

Whatever theme you have in mind, there is a hardboard decorative paneling to help you reproduce your vision.

Hardboard decorative paneling comes in all the standard hardwoods—mahogany, walnut, cherry and oak—and in beautiful, rare exotics, ranging from pecky cypress to teak and Brazilian rosewood. You'll also find it simulating brick, stone, tile and marble, and in woods tinted in the attractive deep reds and greens of the colonial period.

The paneling is tough. It resists dents, scratches and nicks, so it looks good for a long time on your wall. You don't have to baby it.

In rooms above ground, it is wonderfully easy to put up yourself, using a vinyl adhesive applied with a caulking gun. In most applications you don't have to nail, set the nails or fill the nail holes. In the basement or on masonry walls, you must first put up furring strips—but these, too, go up quickly with vinyl adhesive, and no nailing is required.

Giving the wall a professional finished look is no problem, either. You'll find a complete assortment of base, cove and corner moldings, as well as casings and stops for finishing around doors and windows. These are all prefinished, in colors and designs to fit every type of paneling. If you choose to mount your wall with nails, color-coordinated nails are available, too.

The standard panel is ¼-in. thick and 4 x 8 ft. in size. You'll also find some paneling in ⅛-in. thicknesses. The marble designs for use in bathrooms are ⅛-in. thick, and you'll find special moldings made for use with this thickness. You can even buy kits with moldings designed for installation around bathtubs.

The new designs put one new burden on the homeowner: You must plan and measure your installation with care. Those panelings with regular repeat designs, such as panel insets, must go up so that the pattern occurs correctly on the wall. You don't want half an inset panel occurring somewhere in the middle of a wall. The planning isn't tricky, but it does take some thought about each wall.

Study the paneling before you buy, and measure the pattern, so you know where the panel can be cut. Then make a few sketches of your wall, in scale, to see how many panels you need, and how the design will fill each wall.

HAND-TROWELED STUCCO hardboard panels offer a dimensional texture that is hard to tell from real stucco.

THIS ROUGH-HEWN CEDAR paneling has everything the original old western boards had except the splinters.

How to work with plywood paneling

One of the surest ways to succeed in remodeling or redecorating is to recover your walls with wood. Paneled walls provide a surface that is compatible with every decorating style. New products are available to suit nearly any taste. And here are detailed tips to steer you right

1

2

By HARRY WICKS

THE HOW-TO INFORMATION given on these pages applies to all prefinished paneling whether it is plywood or hardboard (the latter is shown in the photo above). The only difference is that hardboard usually requires more patient handling because of its density. But it's that very density that gives this paneling a marproof resistance to bumps and bangs; hardboard is a good choice when you anticipate covering a wall that will receive rough treatment.

sizes and thickness

Prefinished panels come in ¼-in. thickness and 4x8-ft. sheets. In some woods, 7, 10 and 12-ft. sheets are available by special order. In recent years, many manufacturers have attempted to hold the price line by shaving the panel thickness—in some cases to a scant ⅛ in. You should know, however, that high-quality paneling in full ¼-in. thickness is still available from top manufacturers. Don't settle for less if you want a first-rate job.

Since each 4x8 panel covers 32 sq. ft. of wall area, you'll find that the work of paneling a room will go surprisingly fast.

3 **PANELING** comes in smooth finishes or textures, in wood tones and colors. Prefinished panels in the rooms on these two pages illustrate the wide variety that is available. On the opposite page are Masonite's Coach House White (top) and U.S. Plywood's Weldwood Gothic Oak. Above on this page is Weldwood Country Place; below are Weldwood Ticonderoga (left) and the finish that Georgia-Pacific has named Portsmouth Hemp.

SEE ALSO

Basement remodeling . . . Family rooms . . . Fasteners . . . Hardboard . . . Moldings . . . Paneling, hardboard . . . Paneling, wood . . . Plasterboard . . . Plywood . . . Remodeling

4

5

Preparing, fitting and cutting panels

STACK panels for 48 hours before installation to acclimate them to local conditions. Be sure to use spacers.

STAND panels around the room for the best grain match in artificial and natural light, then number the panels.

MARK ALL stud locations on floor and ceiling before applying any panels. Use a lumber crayon or chalk.

MEASURE from a corner to the center of the farthest stud the panel reaches, then cut the panel an inch wider.

A GOOD setup for panel work with a portable saw is a pair of sawhorses and three lengths of 2x3 or 2x4.

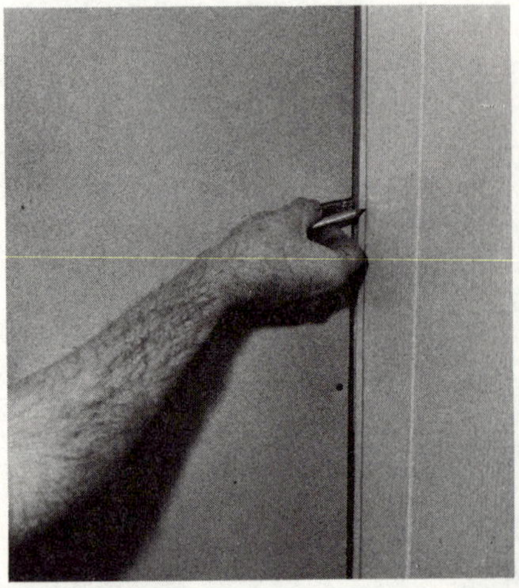

PLUMB the first panel and temporarily tack it. With scriber at 1 in., transfer the corner's outline to the panel.

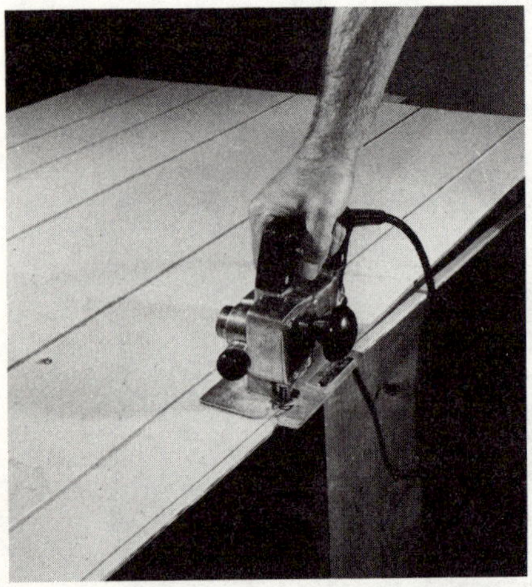

CUT the scribed edge with a plywood blade in a sabre saw or an 8-pt. crosscut saw having little or no tooth set.

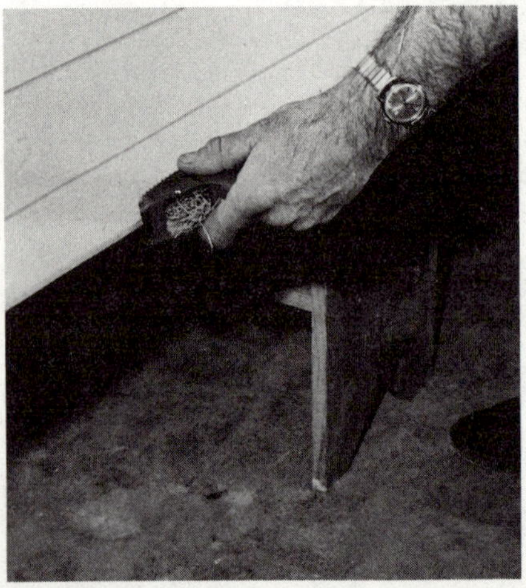

LEAVE the line in cutting the scribed side, then trim carefully up to the line with a block plane or Surform Shaver.

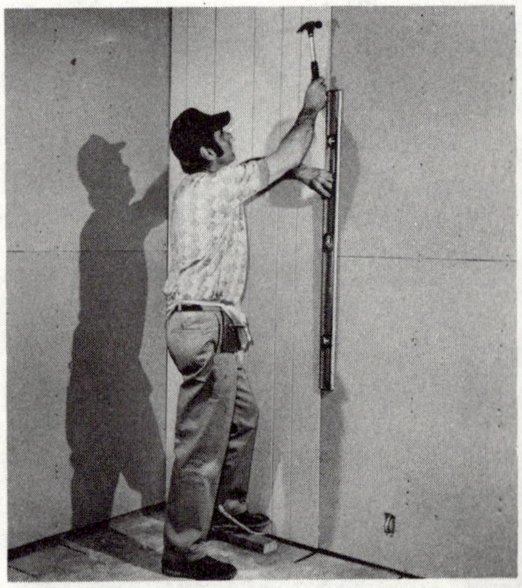

RE-PLUMB the panel, tack it again, check the corner fit, and pencil the wall to show the limit for adhesive.

estimating your needs

Carefully measure the room you plan to remodel and be sure that your figures for windows and door openings are accurate. The easiest way to figure your needs is to add up the lengths of your walls in feet and then to divide this total by 4 (panel width). For example, if the room measures 12x16 ft., add 12 + 12 + 16 + 16 to get 56. Divide this by 4 and you find that 14 panels are needed.

If there are a number of door and window cutouts, you may be able to use those leftover scraps to panel above and below windows and in other less-than-full-height areas. You can estimate this by planning to position a full panel *along the edge* of a large opening. To be safe, bring along a scaled floor plan of the room you want to panel and let your dealer doublecheck your figures.

preparing the walls

If the paneling is to be applied over bare studs, use a straightedge—a long 2x4 without any twist—to determine if any of the 2x4 studs aren't perfectly straight. If you find high spots, whittle them down with a hatchet or plane; low spots can be filled by shimming studs with shingles or folded 15-lb. felt. On new construction, you should staple a vapor barrier (6-mil polyethylene sheet) over exterior wall studs before putting up the panels.

In an existing room, start by removing all casings, moldings and other trim. If the walls are of plaster, it will be necessary to shim out the stud faces where baseboard has been removed. If any plaster is falling, remove it and patch the holes with plasterboard.

Remove plate covers from all electrical boxes and, if possible, free the boxes. These will have to be moved forward at least 1 in. if furring strips are used. They can be reinstalled using clips.

If plaster is in good shape—walls are sound and there is little variance in surface plane—install paneling directly over the plaster. Use plenty of adhesive and don't spare the nails either. Contrary to popular belief, it is a good idea to use a goodly number of nails—in the center of the panels as well as along their edges—even though panel adhesive is also used.

Furring strips are nailed horizontally to the wall and spaced 16 in. on center (o.c.). Use 1x2 furring strips—they're an inexpensive grade of pine—and fasten them by nailing directly into studs. To support vertical edges of the panels, position a vertical strip every 48 in. (or to suit panel width) from floor to ceiling. Apply furring around doors and windows as shown in the sketch at top of page 2060. Where necessary, shim out the furring so that the faces of all strips are in the same plane.

The best way to get a smooth, good-looking wall is with your eye, not a spirit level. Put up all strips without driving the nails home, check the planes of strips using a straightedge and when satisfied, drive home all nails. Low spots can be shimmed (to the straightedge) using undercourse shingles; high spots are reduced either by chopping away plaster from behind a strip or planing down the furring.

putting up panels

Start the job at a corner as shown on page 2058. You'll find most corners are not perfectly true. Thus, you will have to scribe the first panel to the

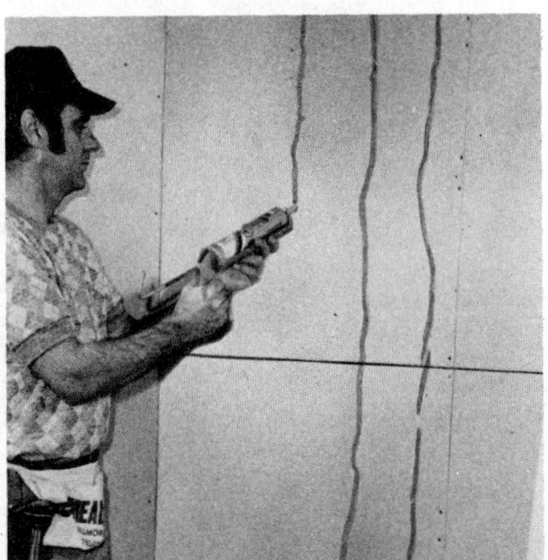

APPLY adhesive generously. Makers say a cartridge handles five panels, but pros get only two per cartridge.

LET THE PANEL touch adhesive, tack it along the top, then back the bottom away to let the solvent flash off.

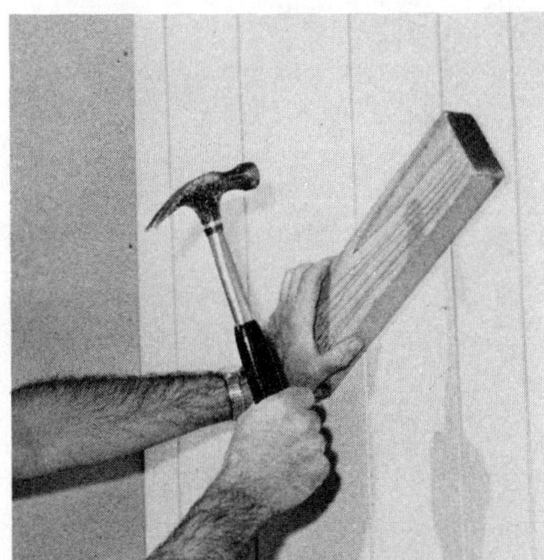

FINALLY, spread the adhesive by sliding a hardwood block over the surface while you rap the block with a hammer.

Working with furring strips

APPLY FURRING STRIPS at the top and bottom of the wall (right), then use a straightedge and level to make certain that they are in a plane with each other

RUN VERTICAL FURRING strips to support the panel edges (far right). The horizontal strips are held in place by 6d common nails driven into the studs.

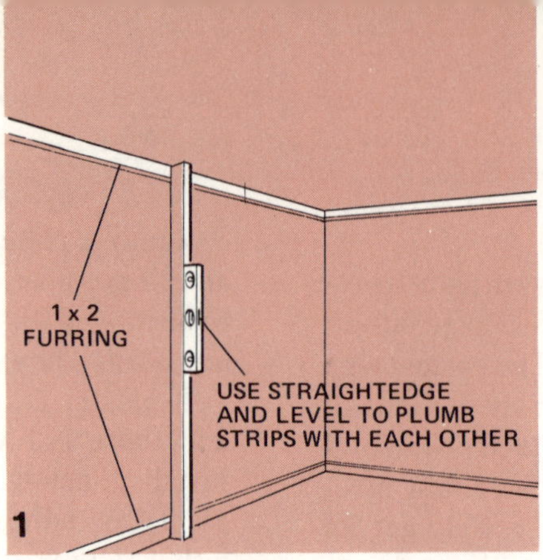

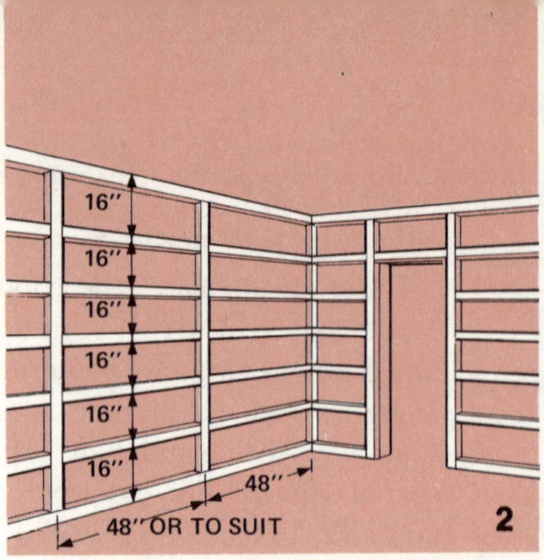

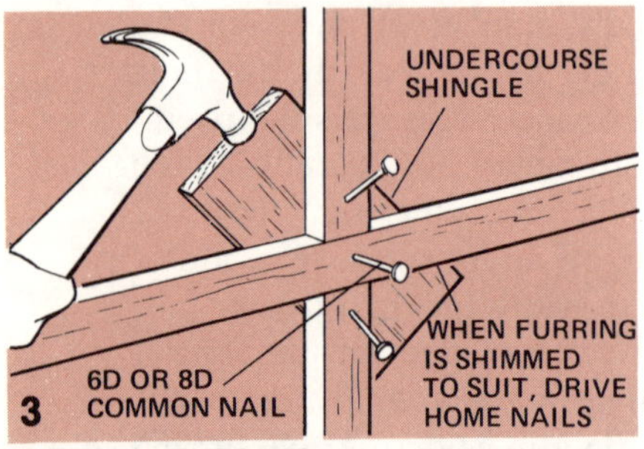

PUT ALL FURRING up without driving home the nails. Then use a straightedge to locate and shim out the low spots.

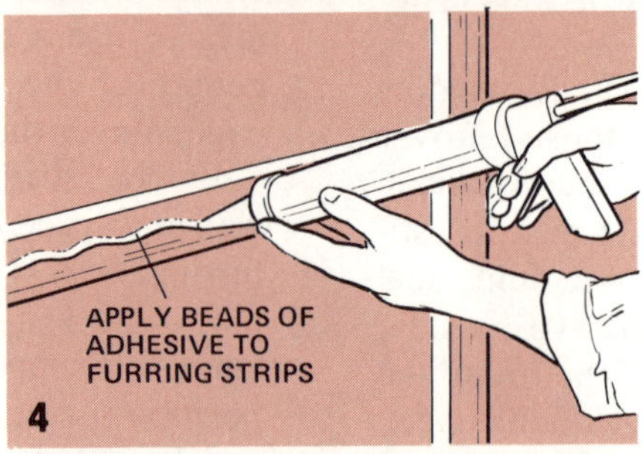

LAY adhesive beads along furring strips. Install panels over the strips with the same technique as on walls.

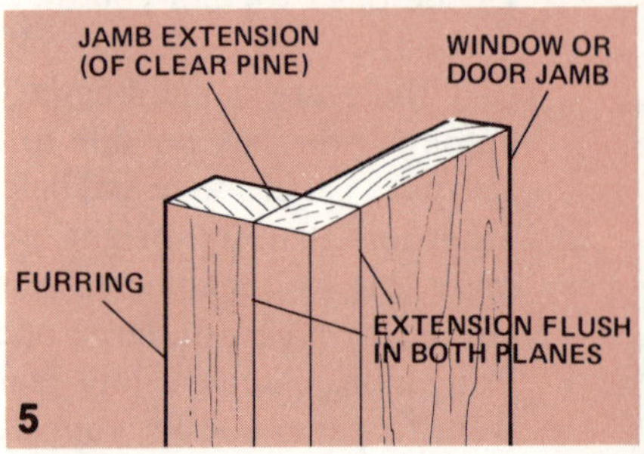

FURRING out existing walls means window and door jambs must be extended. Use clear pine for this work.

Fitting around windows

WITH a helper butting a new panel against its predecessor, mark the edges above and below the window.

CHECK for height irregularities under a window by measuring from floor to jamb at each side of a 48-in. panel.

TRANSFER measurements to sheet back. Cut pieces to go over and under a window from the same panel for a good match.

CONNECT measurement marks across a panel's full width with a 4-ft. T-square. Then mark the saw shoe's offset.

CLAMP a T-square to the paneling so it can guide the saw. The saw's blade should barely clear ¼-in. paneling.

NAILS that are used along the top and bottom edges are located so they'll be hidden by moldings to follow.

Two ways to make box cutouts

A POPULAR but uncertain method is to rub chalk on the face of the box.

THEN bang the panel's face and hope a clear box outline is transferred.

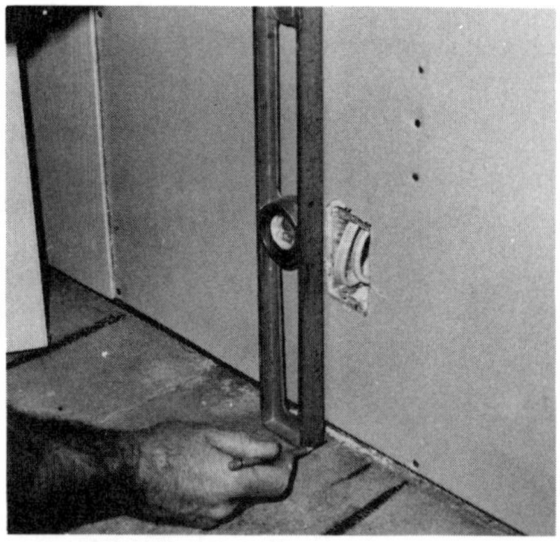

INSTEAD, use a level to locate box edges on the floor just below.

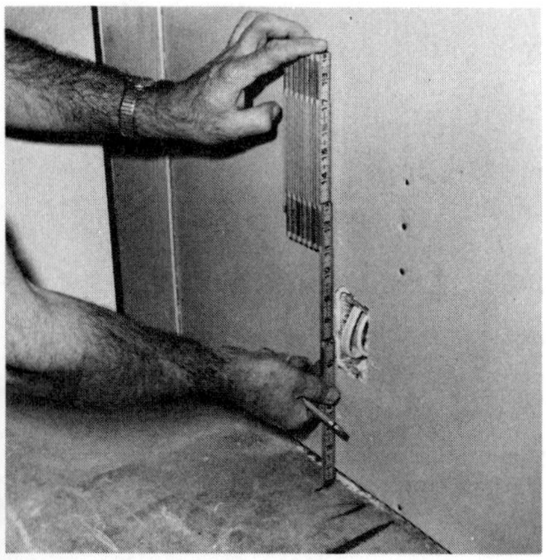

MEASURE and record distances from the floor to box top and bottom.

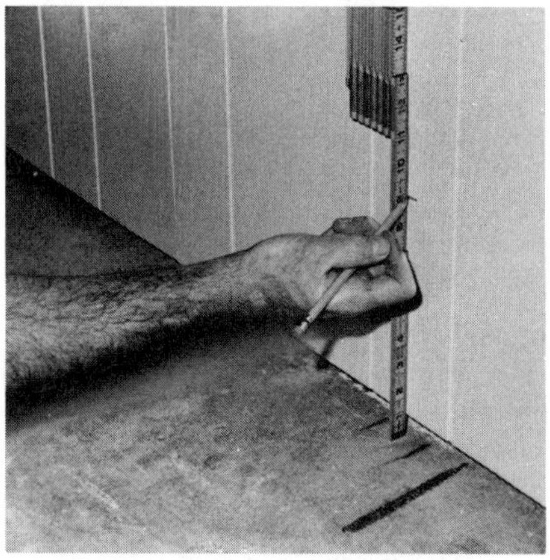

WITH the panel tacked in place, mark vertical dimensions on its face.

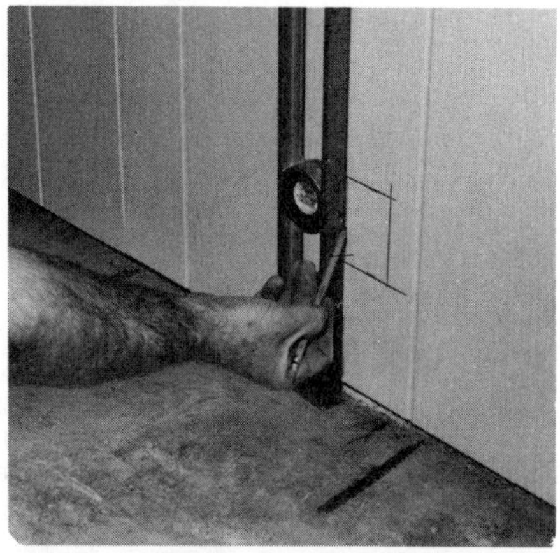

LEVEL guides the edge marks from the floor back to the panel's face.

LAY the panel face up and drive a small marking hole at each corner.

FLOP the panel, locate a gem box at the holes, and trace the opening to cut.

SABRE saw's plunge cut begins the cutout. Or start with a ¾-in. hole.

corner. To do it, measure the distance from corner to the *center* of the farthest stud that a full panel will reach. On the job shown, that measurement was 39 in. Next, you add 1 in. of this measurement and cut the first panel to width; in this case, that made it 40 in. Then you hold the panel in place, plumb it with a spirit level and temporarily tack it. Now, with your scriber (a compass works just fine) opened 1 in., transfer the outline of the abutting wall.

Take down the panel and with your sabre saw make the cut, *leaving the line*. Finish by dressing the edge exactly to the line with a sharp block plane or rasp plane.

About moldings

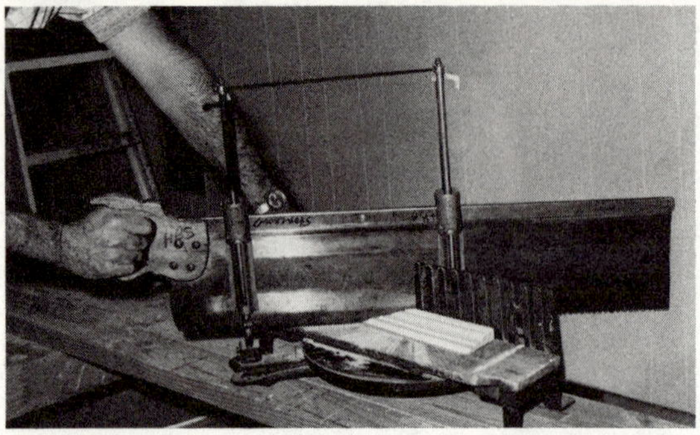

MOLDINGS go on after all paneling is up. For a neat, accurate job, use a miterbox to make all the molding cuts. The precision is built in.

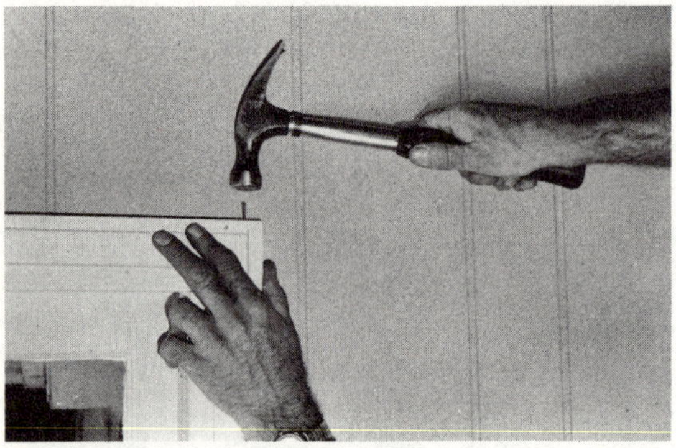

TO COMBAT joints' tendency to gap open, put white glue into molding joints. Then drive 4d finishing nails in from each side for extra insurance.

Butt each succeeding panel tightly against the previously installed panel. (Except when installing hardboard; here you should leave a slight space at the joints. To avoid butting hardboards, tack a couple of thin nails next to the edge of each previously installed panel; pull tacks after the following panel is installed.)

nails and adhesive

When you're nailing to studs, furring strips or sheathing, use either 3d finishing nails or 1-in. brads. Nails should be used every 6 in. along edges and 12 in. on intermediate furring. Generally, it is best to drive nails at a slight angle (toenail) through bevels and grooves. Set nailheads and hide them with a matching putty stick.

Adhesive speeds up the job because it cuts down on the number of nails needed. Don't apply adhesive to the wall until you're satisfied with the panel fit; then mark the panel edge on the wall so you will know the limit for adhesive application.

Squeeze on adhesive liberally and stand the panel in position. Drive in five or six nails *along the top edge*. Then, to permit adhesive solvent to escape (flash off), prop the panel open for six to eight minutes. Remove the block, return the panel to the wall and finish installing it with nails spaced 12 in. along edges, 24 in. in the center.

Pick the right molding for the job

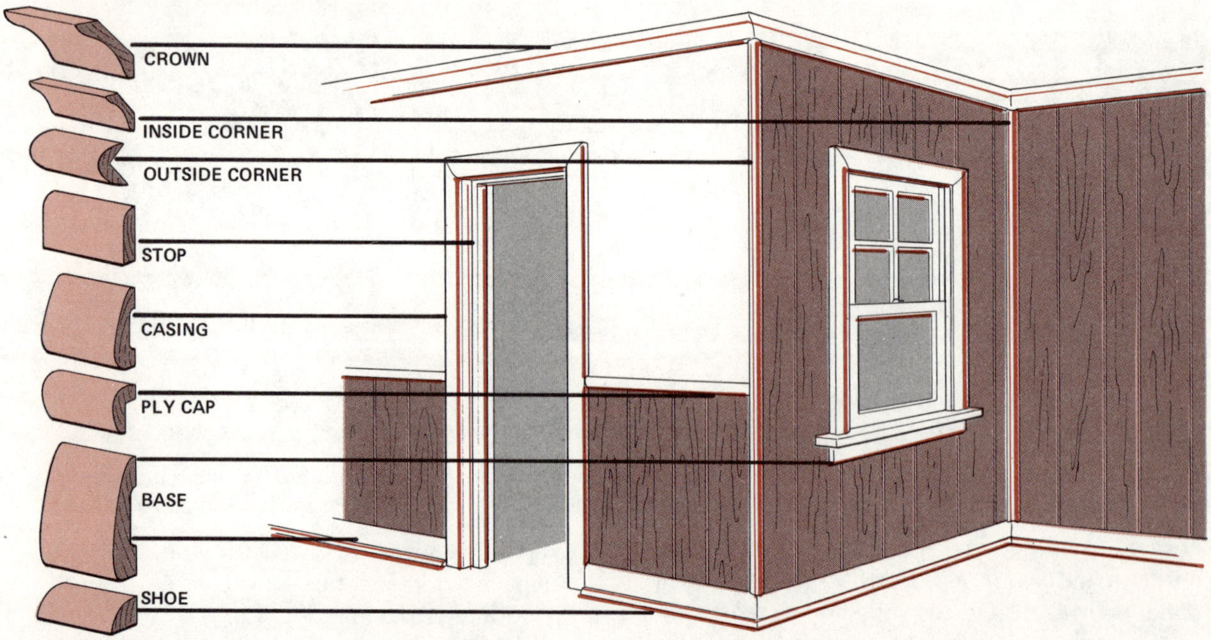

PREFINISHED moldings are offered by paneling makers to match their panel finishes. To keep costs down, you can consider using pine moldings and staining or painting them to match. If you choose this course, install the moldings temporarily for an accurate fit. Remove and mark the installation order of the trim. Then apply the finish to them while they are down. Wait until finish is dry for the final installation.

The easiest and most accurate method of making a cutout is that where a ruler and spirit level is used as shown on page 2061. If you haven't used this stunt before, try a practice run with scrap. The trick here is to make sure that the panel is temporarily tacked in the *exact position* it will occupy when permanently installed so that marks transferred to its face are accurate.

After you mark the panel, place it on your worktable and punch holes with a finishing nail at the cutout's four corners. Flop the panel and connect the holes to mark the cutout on the back side. The easiest way to make the cutout is with a sabre saw. Lacking this tool, you can cut the panel face-side up using a keyhole saw after boring a starter hole with a ¾-in. bit.

There are other methods of marking cutouts—transferring chalk or grease pencil as shown on page 2061, for example. In my opinion, this method is inaccurate because the transferred mark is always too wide for accuracy. Which side of the line do you cut? Or do you cut down the middle? For best results, stick with the first-described method.

carpentry tricks

Worktable. Easy to set up, the worktable shown provides a rigid table for ripping, crosscutting or for making cutouts in paneling. You can make it of a height that's comfortable for you by altering sawhorse-leg lengths; generally, it is best to work over a table no higher than 26 to 28 in. from the floor.

Use at least three 2x3s across the sawhorses. When ripping, make certain a pair of these supports are beneath that portion of the paneling on which the circular saw is riding. The cutoff portion rests on a single 2x3 so it will fall away as the cut is completed and not bind the saw.

Cutting panels. You can use either hand or power saws, depending on your work preference. With either, cutting edges must be razor sharp for you to turn out a craftsmanlike job.

Some use the gimmick of putting masking tape along a line to be cut, believing this to be the only way to avoid splintering a plywood edge. But a sharp tool used properly guarantees the same results.

For hand cutting, use a sharp, crosscut saw with little or no set. Cut with the panel face up, and make certain you support the cutoff piece as each cut nears completion.

With a power saw, use either a plywood-veneer blade or hollow-ground combination blade (no set on either). Cut paneling this way:

- Table saw: Cut with face side up.
- Radial arm saw: Cut with panel face down.
- Portable circular saw: Cut with face down.
- Sabre saw: Cut with face side down. Use a fine-tooth plywood blade, and use the shoe insert if one is provided by the saw's manufacturer.

Moldings. Though it's often tempting to rely on moldings to hide a multitude of sins—in this case that means a sloppy job—every effort should be made to cut and install paneling accurately so you can use the narrowest-possible moldings.

Prefinished moldings, though considerably more expensive than conventional pine moldings, have exacting contours and finishes that perfectly match the panels they are mated to.

Use a miterbox to make all molding cuts—both straight and angled. All inside joints should be coped with a coping saw—to assure a non-opening joint. To do this, first make the 45° cut in the miterbox; next, follow the molding profile with a coping saw. For the tightest fit, hold your coping saw at an angle so that the cut is made with a slight back cut—that is, the front edge should come to a feather edge.

All outside corners should be mitered. To prevent them from opening, apply white glue and install 4d finishing nails through the edges and into the mating molding.

Molding can be applied with appropriate-sized finishing nails or with construction adhesive and (fewer) nails. It's a matter of personal preference.

Moldings are available in a great number of sizes and shapes; you can choose what you need from charts or sample boards that your lumberyard dealer will have on display.

Finishing details. It is not necessary to set and fill every nail on every panel in the room. Professional carpenters locate those that must be set by shining a harsh light along the walls and watching for nailhead reflections from both sitting and standing positions. Nails easily spotted can then be punched in with a nailset and filled by rubbing with a putty stick colored to suit paneling.

To use filler sticks, rub them briskly across the indent to be filled; friction more or less melts the substance into the hole. You can then rub off the excess filler with a clean, soft rag.

If you cannot match your paneling with a single filler stick, mix several sticks until you obtain the perfect match.

Wood paneling—the aristocrat of walls

By RICHARD NUNN

Solid hardwood paneling comes in woods from ash to willow. It complements rooms of contemporary design as well as traditional. And it radiates luxury. Here's the inside story of what's involved in applying this magnificent material

SEE ALSO
Fasteners . . . Hardboard . . . Moldings . . . Paneling, hardboard . . . Paneling, plywood . . . Plasterboard . . . Remodeling

SOLID HARDWOOD PANELING can be called the aristocrat of wall coverings. Much of its charm lies in the fact that it's "solid all the way through," and it will complement rooms of contemporary as well as traditional design.

There are many different solid woods from which to choose. Those readily available include pecky cypress, willow, cherry, maple, pine, ash, cottonwood, red oak and walnut. The panels range in thickness from ½-in. to 1-in. (25/32-in. dressed). Widths vary from 4 in. to 8 in. in 1-in. increments. Lengths are random, although "packaged" solid hardwood paneling such as sold by Townsend, Inc., of Stuttgart, Ark., is put up in cartons that contain an appropriate assortment of random widths and lengths. The pieces are end-matched and packed in random lengths which total 8 ft.

Some panels are tongue-and-groove-matched

and they are installed in random widths. Other boards are especially cut in various patterns for use on walls and ceilings. They usually have a V-notch or a bead down the center of the board to add to the decorative effect. You can buy the paneling prefinished with a baked-on acrylic that contains no pigmentation. This makes the surface virtually impervious to damage from children and stains. The material can also be purchased unfinished and rough-sawn.

If you plan to use the paneling to build a wall, you will have to frame the wall first (Fig. 4). With new construction, the panels are nailed with 3d or 4d finishing nails on the stripped studs or additional fire blocks spaced between the studs on 18- to 24-in. centers.

On existing walls, you nail furring strips not more than 24 in. apart (Fig. 5). The panels are then nailed with 3d or 4d finishing nails (Fig. 1) and the nails are countersunk with a nailset. Nailing strips can be applied directly to the studs in new construction, of course. It is not necessary to include nailing strips or blocks behind each end match (horizontal joint); the tongue-and-groove system will provide ample strength (Fig. 6). Fig. 2 shows inside and outside corner details.

If the paneling you buy is unfinished, don't store it in any spot where it will be exposed to the weather or excessive moisture. New construction should be closed in and dry before application. Be sure all plaster, gypsum wallboard and masonry work is complete and dry before the paneling is installed. The backs of the panels should be sealed before they go up, and the first coat of finish should be applied immediately after installation. Moldings are made to match the paneling (Fig. 3).

Another tip: If you run the boards horizontally, frame the wall with studs on 16-in. centers. Horizontal applications will make the room appear larger, and the ceiling lower. Vertical applications will make the ceiling appear higher.

Before you plan to finish a room in solid hardwood paneling, figure not only the price of the paneling but also the framing materials. The cost of framing materials is a substantial part of the cost of the finished wall.

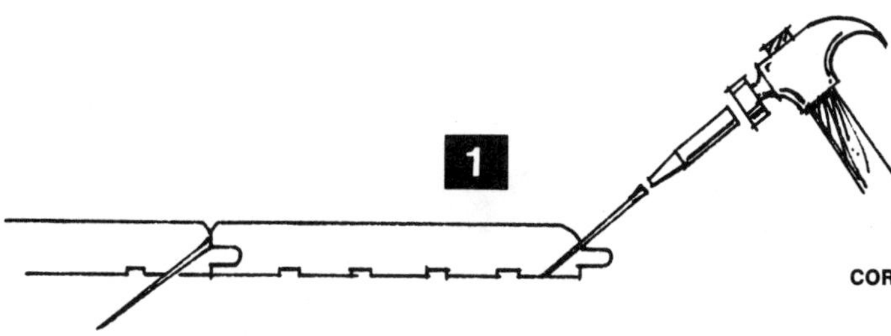
1

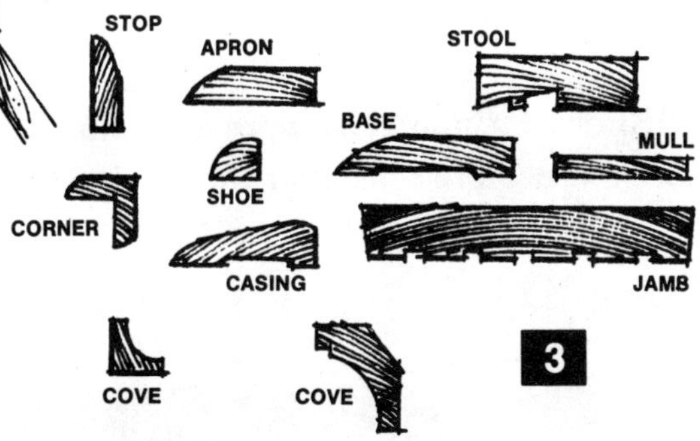

3

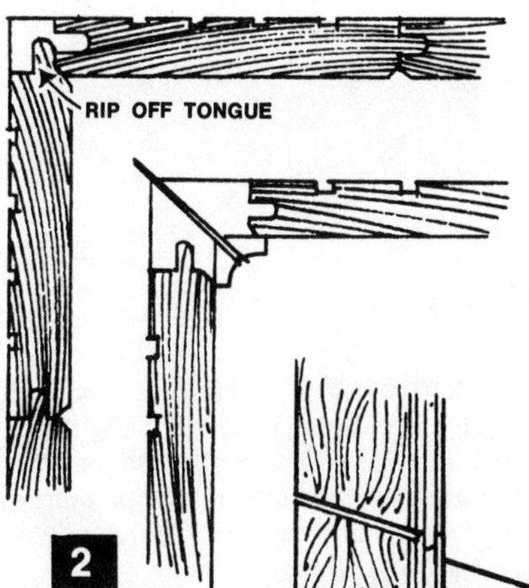

2

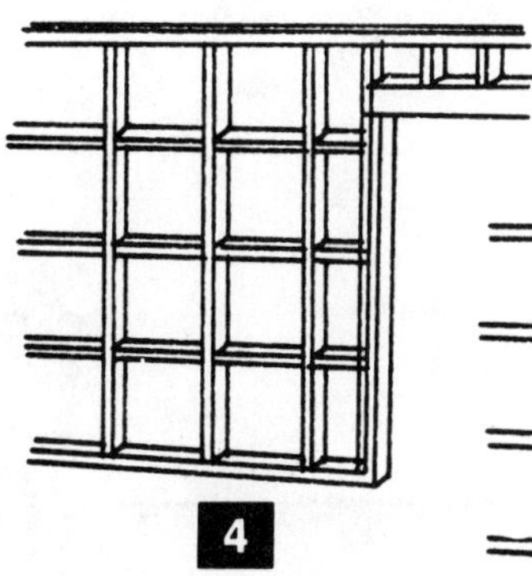
4

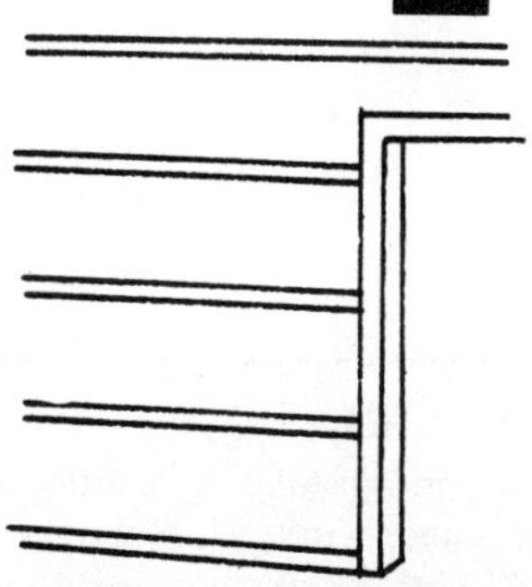
5

6

Big panoramas from little pictures

By GORDON SMITH

When you want to capture a beautiful view that's too wide for your camera lens, just shoot it in several parts and piece them together. You don't even need a tripod

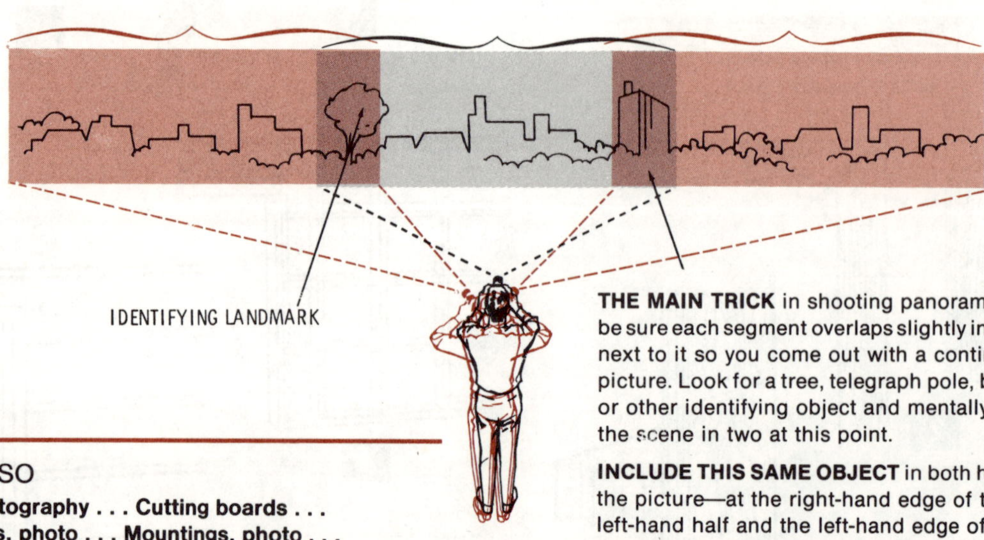

THE MAIN TRICK in shooting panoramas is to be sure each segment overlaps slightly into those next to it so you come out with a continuous picture. Look for a tree, telegraph pole, building or other identifying object and mentally divide the scene in two at this point.

INCLUDE THIS SAME OBJECT in both halves of the picture—at the right-hand edge of the left-hand half and the left-hand edge of the right-hand half. Then you can use the object as a guide to join the two parts of the scene perfectly, as shown on page **2068**.

SEE ALSO

Boat photography . . . Cutting boards . . . Montages, photo . . . Mountings, photo . . . Night photography . . . Outdoor photography . . . Photography . . . Prints, photo

■ HOW WOULD YOU LIKE to make a photograph two or three feet wide capturing the sweeping grandeur of a mountain view, a shimmering seascape or a far-flung city skyline? Such scenes are too big to put on one piece of film. But you can put them on several pieces of film and join the pictures side by side.

Shooting panoramas is often considered a job for a pro, but it's actually a simple process. If you can take one picture, you can take three in a row. The only thing you need to be sure of is that the segments will join together properly to form a continuous picture. Since you can't judge exactly where one scene will end and the next one begin, you deliberately overlap your segments slightly, then trim them later. The drawing on the opposite page shows how you can use a tree, pole, building or other identifying object to help guide you in matching scenes.

MATERIALS FOR SPLICING are simple—some tape and a razor knife. A paper cutter is handy but not essential. The three prints shown here are those from which the panorama at the top of the page was made.

As you swing the camera to take in different views, pivot your body from the waist up without moving your feet. This will keep the camera in the same relative position and minimize distortion. Try to hold the camera at the same level for each view, but don't worry if the alignment isn't perfect. Slight mismatches between views are simply trimmed off later. As a rule of thumb, locate the horizon line about a third of the way down from the top of the viewfinder and this will automatically keep the views aligned. If there is no horizon, use your identifying object to guide your positioning.

Wherever possible, make all shots at the same exposure. Minor differences in negative density can be adjusted in printing to keep the background areas close in tone so the seams won't show.

THIS SPRAWLING GOLF COURSE panorama was shot in two parts, requiring only a single splice.

1 **THE FIRST STEP** is to trim the side edge off one print. Make this cut through or near your identifying object. Now slide the trimmed edge over the adjacent print until you have a match. At this point, cut a slit at top and bottom, using the trimmed edge as a guide.

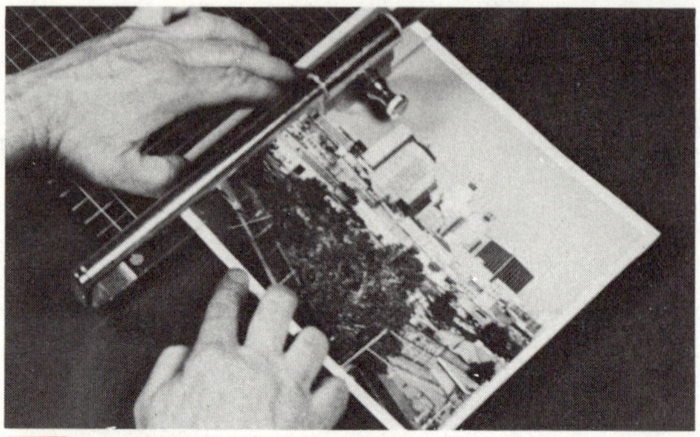

2 **TRIM THE SECOND PRINT** on a paper cutter, using the slit marks on the top and bottom to line it up. This will give you a perfect match with the trimmed edge on the first print. If no paper cutter is available, lay a straightedge over the print and trim off excess.

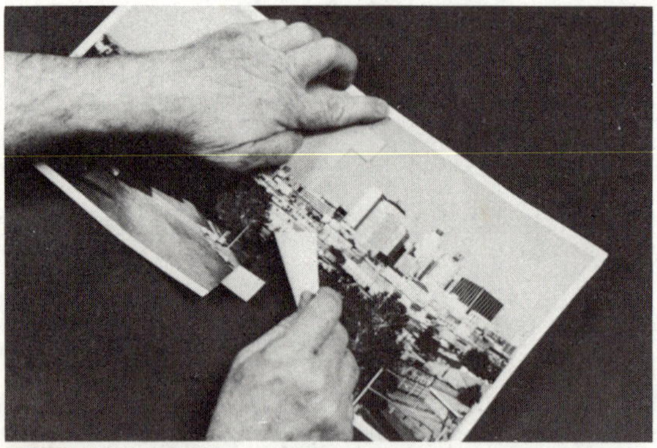

3 **STICK SMALL TABS** of tape to the back of one print so the ends protrude slightly. Let these tabs slide over the adjacent print while you're adjusting the alignment. When the match is perfect, lift the corners of the second print so the tabs slip underneath, then press firmly down.

4 **AFTER THE PRINTS** have been temporarily joined with the tabs of tape, reinforce the seam with a strip of wide paper tape. This can be the brown gummed kind used in stores to seal packages, or you can cut a strip of stiff regular paper and fasten it with print-mounting cement.

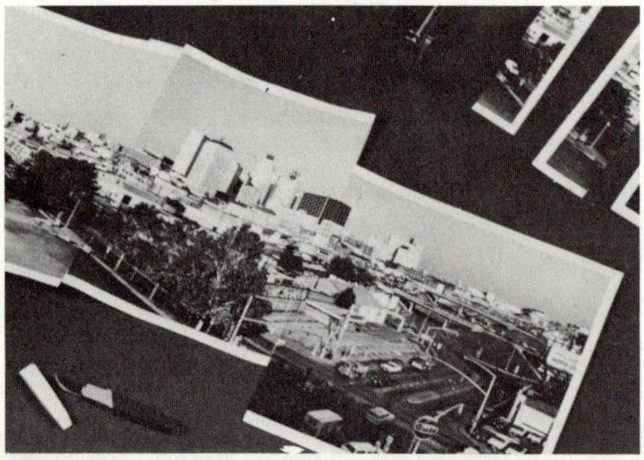

5 **JOINED AT THE SIDES,** the prints are now ready for trimming at the top and bottom. Note that the views do not have to be shot at exactly the same level. The discrepancy shown here was deliberately exaggerated to show that the effect isn't harmful.

6 **FINAL TRIMMING** eliminates ragged edges at the top and bottom and gives the appearance of a single photograph. Be careful to keep the horizon level. Lay a straightedge across the top of the picture and measure up from the horizon line at each end so trim will be parallel.

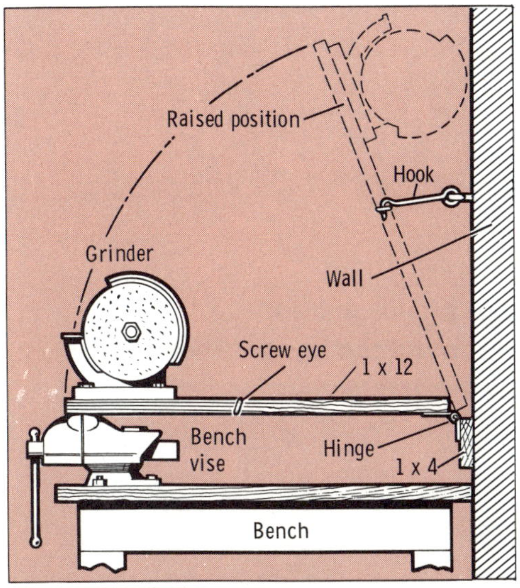

IF A MACHINIST'S VISE is already taking up valuable workbench space, you can hardly afford to have a grinder permanently bolted to it also. Since a grinder is used far less frequently than a vise, here's a way you can mount it to swing up out of the way when not in use. Bolt it to a 1x12 board and hinge it to a 1x4 block screwed to the wall. Mount the block to a height to bring the grinder level with the top of the vise. A 3 or 4-in. vise will hold the grinder at a nice working height. A couple of sturdy hooks and eyes will stow the grinder against the wall.

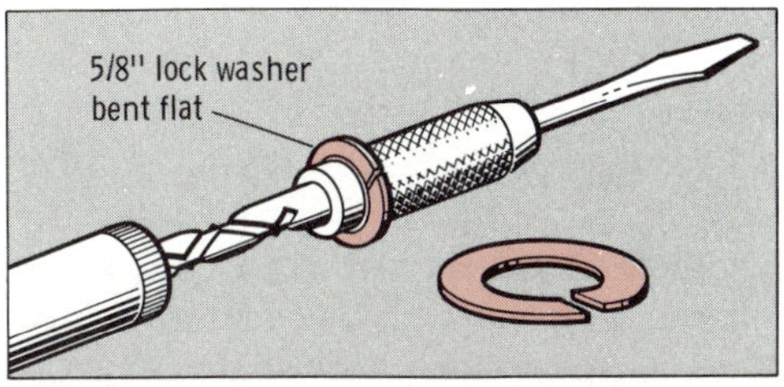

SOONER OR LATER you're going to pinch your fingers when using a spiral ratchet screwdriver. You can avoid this by placing a collar over the chuck as shown. A split lock washer, annealed, flattened, spread apart and forced over the knurled grip, will do the trick nicely. To anneal the washer, heat it to a dull red, then let it cool slowly.

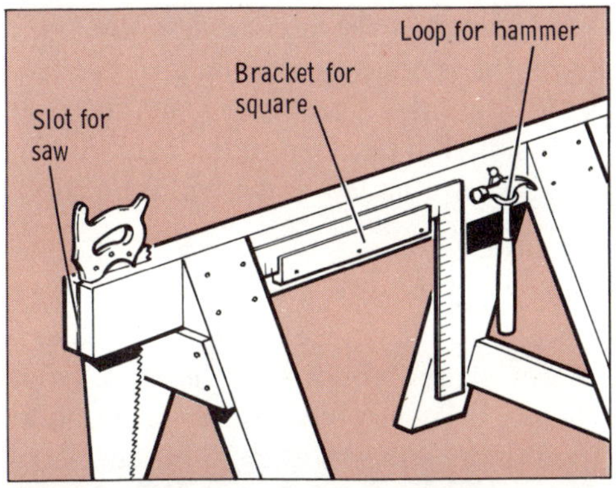

THERE ARE THREE THINGS you can do to make a wooden sawhorse handier when it comes to keeping track of your tools. Cut a slot in one end for the saw, tack a piece of flooring (groove side up) to hold a framing square and attach a loop for your hammer. You'll know right where these tools are when you're looking for them.

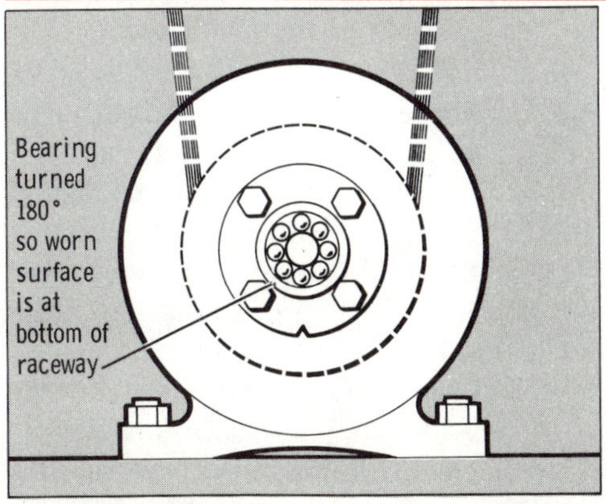

THE BEARING next to the pulley on your lathe motor may start to run noisily at some point. Constant belt tension causes the outer raceway of the bearing to wear. Simply rotate the bearing housing 180°. This brings a new surface to the top to resist belt pull and stops the noise.

WHEN CUTTING corrugated aluminum roofing, you may find that the regular skip-tooth blade of an electric saw will cut across the "hills and valleys" much faster if the blade is put on backward. It also will make a smoother cut.

Nesting party tables

Whether they are for a child's birthday party or just for chairside use, these handy tables will always be handy around the house. They can be mass-produced and are covered with bright decorative laminate

By WAYNE C. LECKEY

■ WHEN IT COMES to storing, these individual serving tables are no problem. They all nest neatly within a lamp table to become part of it.

You'll find them handy whenever a small chairside table is needed to hold a drink, ashtray or TV sandwich. They're perfect, of course, for a children's party.

The best way to wind up with four identical nesting tables is to mass-produce them. For example, the four top shelves can be bandsawed at one time, likewise the four center shelves and the four bottom shelves. Stock for the eight backs can be ripped 11 13/16 in. wide, then crosscut into 19½-in. lengths. Stock for the fluted aprons is grooved, kerfed on the back and then ripped crosswise into four strips 2 in. wide.

Run the miters on the eight backs before you cut back the front edges. To cut the latter, run your table-saw blade as high as it will go and set the fence for a ¾-in. cut. Then rip four of the backs for a distance of 8 in. Do the same with the other four after resetting the fence to the left side of the blade. This will produce four right and four left-hand members. Finish the cuts by sawing in from the edge on a ¾-in. radius, then round off the top corner.

cover with laminate

The tops and front edges of all 12 shelves are covered with decorative laminate in whatever color you prefer. We used J-M's Melamite (gypsy red) to contrast with white painted tables. The edges are banded first, then the surfaces, except the four top shelves. Wait until these shelves are nailed in place.

You can save a lot of masking if you paint the inside surfaces of the backs before installing the shelves. Glue and nail the mitered edges, keeping the assemblies square, sink and putty the nailheads and spray with two coats of white semigloss lacquer.

Any void found in the plywood at the front edges should be puttied beforehand, of course, and sanded smooth. The center and bottom shelves are nailed in place from the back, while the top shelves are nailed down from the top.

making the flutes

This leaves the fluted aprons. Two pieces of ¾-in. pine, 8¼ in. wide, are edge-glued to make a board 16½ in. wide. Notice that the grain must run vertically. Twenty-two flutes are made across the board, either with a ¾-in. core-box router bit or a molding head on your table saw. If you make them on your saw, use a ¾-in. scrap for a spacer. Set the fence to make the first cove and make the cut. Then with the work brought back against the fence and held intact, back the fence away and drop in the ¾-in. scrap. This is done each time as you work across the board. The last cove cut should arrive at the very edge of the board.

Now a series of ½-in.-deep, closely-spaced saw cuts (kerfs) is made on the back of the board, with the grain, and completely across its width, after which the board is ripped crosswise into 2-in.-wide strips. The kerfing permits bending the strips so they can be glued to the curved cleats which are screwed to the underside of the bottom shelves. Notice that the cleats are set in

SEE ALSO
Coffee tables . . . Family rooms . . . Game tables . . . Occasional tables

BIRtHDa HaPPY
HaPPY BIRtHD
IRtHDaY HaPPY
HaPPY BIRtHDa

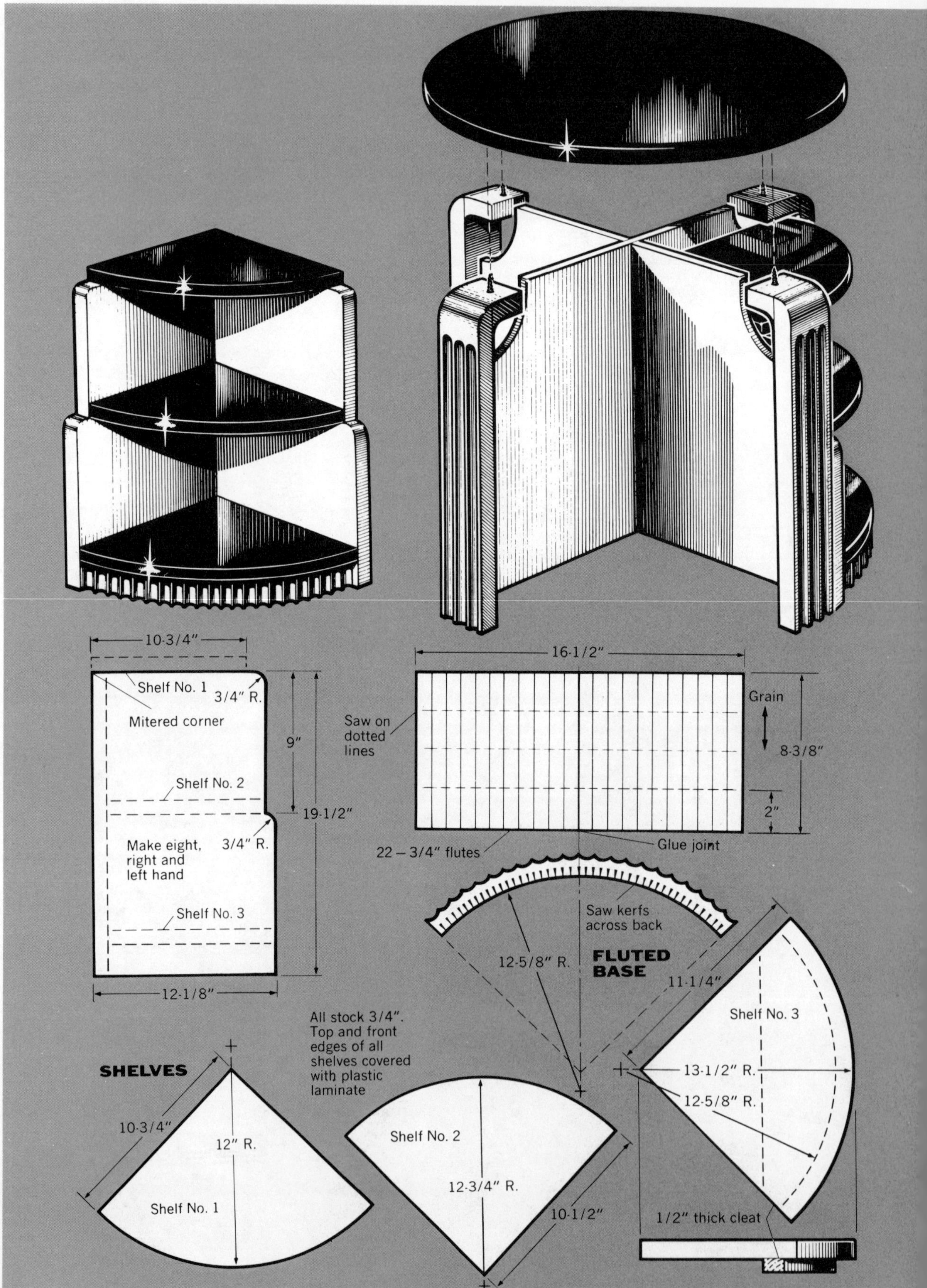
10-3/4"
Shelf No. 1
3/4" R.
Mitered corner
9"
Shelf No. 2
19-1/2"
Make eight, right and left hand
3/4" R.
Shelf No. 3
12-1/8"
16-1/2"
Saw on dotted lines
Grain
8-3/8"
2"
22 – 3/4" flutes
Glue joint
Saw kerfs across back
12-5/8" R.
FLUTED BASE
11-1/4"
Shelf No. 3
All stock 3/4". Top and front edges of all shelves covered with plastic laminate
13-1/2" R.
12-5/8" R.
SHELVES
10-3/4"
12" R.
Shelf No. 1
Shelf No. 2
12-3/4" R.
10-1/2"
1/2" thick cleat

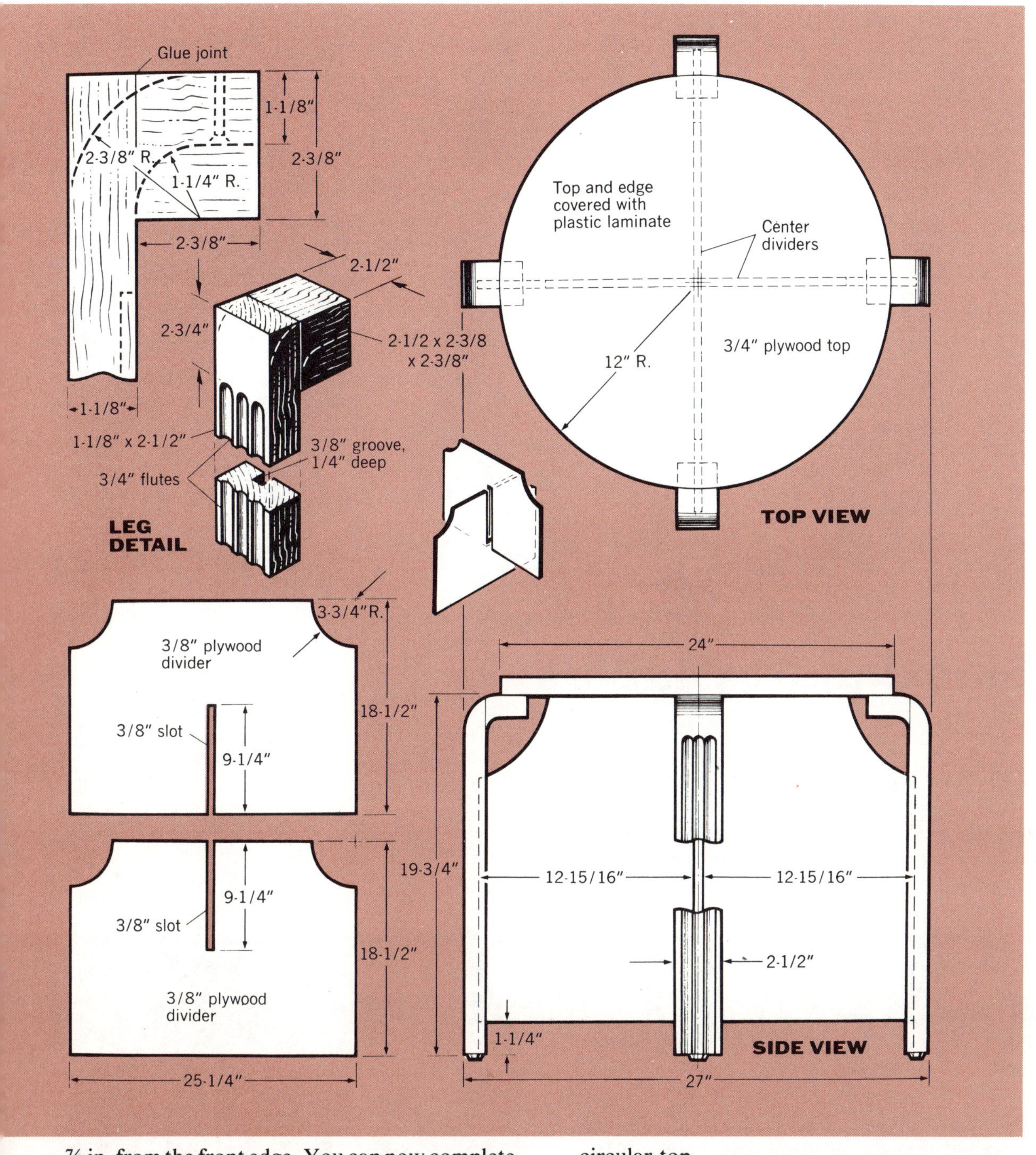

⅞ in. from the front edge. You can now complete painting to suit your tastes.

To build the circular parent table, start with the legs. These are cut to size from 1⅛-in.-thick pine and grooved down the center on the inside for a distance of 16 in. to accommodate the two plywood dividers. Blocks are then glued to the upper ends of the legs, scribed with a compass, bandsawed and sanded. Three ¾-in. flutes are run in the face of all four legs and stopped 2¾ in. from the top. Then holes are drilled for flatheaded screws for attaching the legs to the circular top.

The dividers are made alike except one is slotted down from the top. Add a little glue to the slots and slide them together, then add glue to the grooves in the legs and insert the dividers. They should be flush with the tops of the legs.

This leaves the circular top which is cut from ¾-in. plywood and covered with matching decorative laminate. Complete the painting before attaching the top, and finally hammer metal furniture glides into the ends of the legs. Your tables are ready for use.

Stacking tray tables

This one small unit holds five attractive and functional tables

By ROSARIO CAPOTOSTO

■ THIS HANDSOME serving table will prove to be a conversation piece at a party as well as a very functional piece of furniture when it comes time for snacks. Five good-sized triangular tables store conveniently to add to the striking design, as do the legs, which are contained along the sides of the table. The construction is sturdy—¾-in. plywood surfaced with Conolite flexible plastic laminate in a smart white, leather-textured pattern.

The legs are simply 1-in. dowels cut to length and sanded smooth. Sixteen dowels are used in the interest of symmetry; only 15 are required for the 5 tables. The tables are set up by simply inserting three legs borrowed from the main table.

Make the brackets for the legs by drilling three 1-in.-dia. holes at a 65° angle in triangles of plywood and glue them to the underside of the

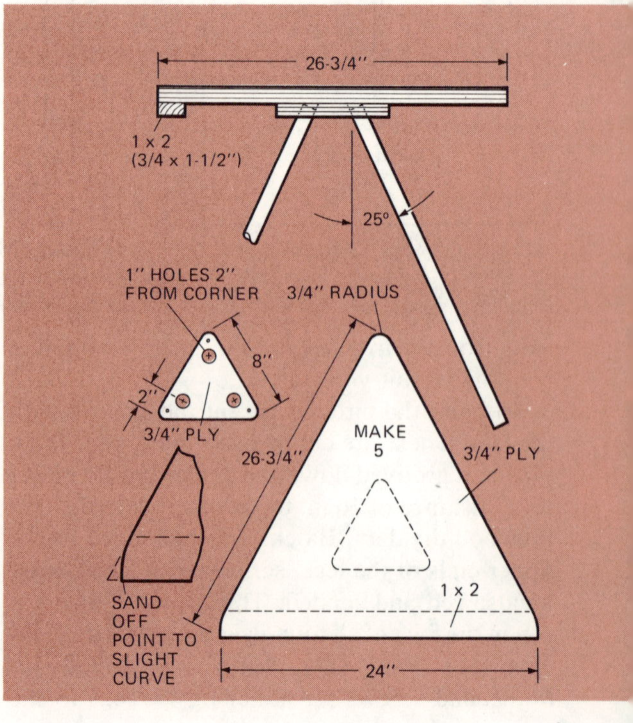

SEE ALSO
Butler's tables . . . Game tables . . .
Laminates, plastic . . . Occasional tables

tables in the center. Add five pairs of cleats to the inside and three swivel casters on the bottom.

Use a plywood blade to cut the five triangular tabletops to minimize sanding of the side edges, which will be left exposed and simply painted. Double up the table fronts by adding ¾ x 1½-in. strips after jointing the front edges smooth. Cut the laminate (with knife or scratch awl) about ¼ in. oversize. Apply contact cement to both surfaces; apply the laminate.

The top and base of the main table are built up to double thickness around the edges to provide a "thick look." You can rough-cut the top and bottom panels, glue on the extra strips, and then cut to the required dimensions. A bandsaw is best for this, but you can do it with a sabre saw. In either case, the edges must be trued up with a stationary disc or belt sander. Since the edges are curved, it will be easier to apply the edge trim in two or even three sections, rather than work with one continuous strip.

After the edge trim is applied to the top and base, proceed to add the laminate to the outer portions of the base top surface. Do *not* laminate the tabletop until after the unit is completely assembled. Mark off the positions of the dowel holes and bore small pilot holes through both base and top at the same time to guarantee alignment. Then bore 1⅛-in. holes for the dowels; ⅝ in. deep in the base, and all the way

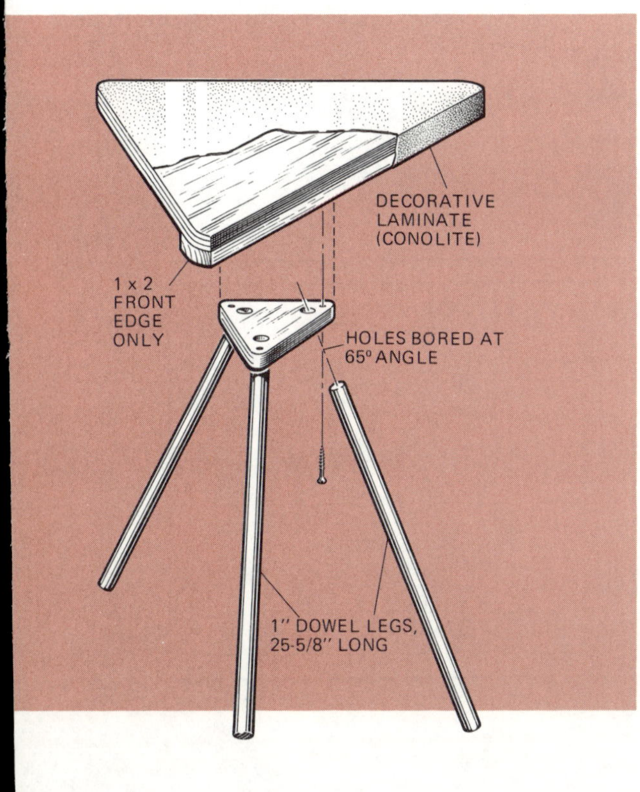

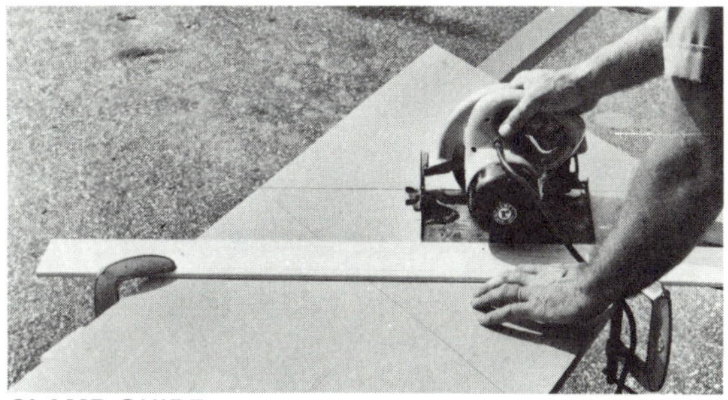

CLAMP GUIDE to work and use a smooth-cutting plywood blade. You can get two tops from a 2x4-ft. panel.

LAY OUT triangular patterns on laminate; allow at least ¼ in. waste all around for final trimming.

WHILE CONOLITE is tough, it can be cut with a sharp utility knife or scored with an awl and snapped off.

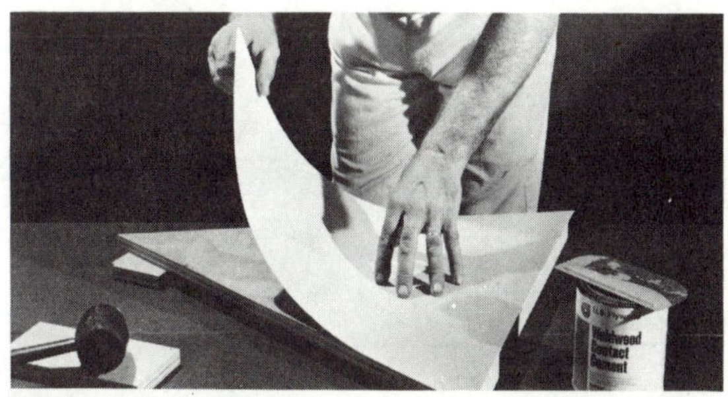

APPLY CONTACT cement with notched spreader, let set 30 minutes. Tap laminate with a block for good bond.

FINISH OFF the edges with a router and a bevel cutter set for very slight cut. (Can also be done with file.)

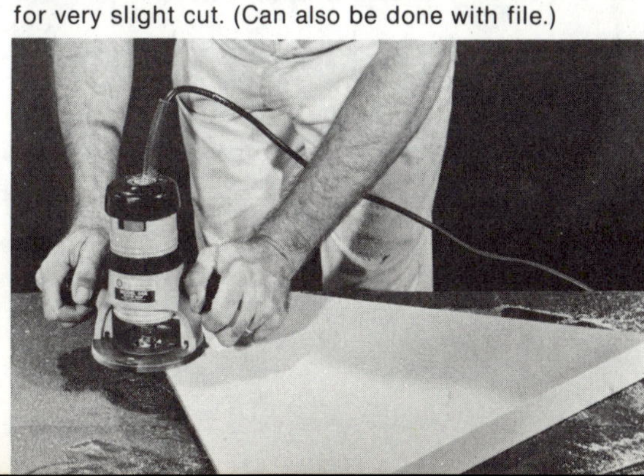

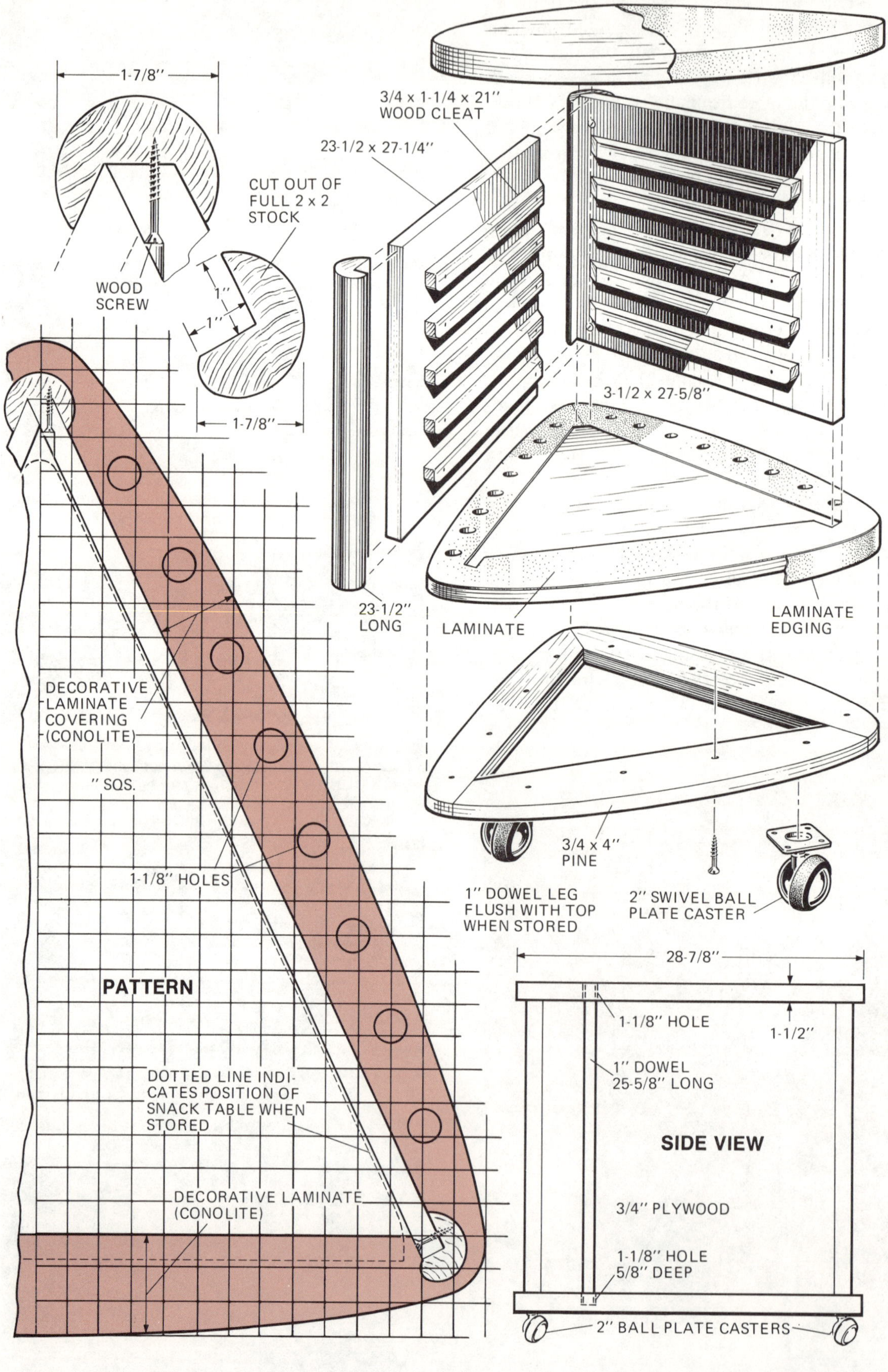
1-7/8"
WOOD SCREW
CUT OUT OF FULL 2 x 2 STOCK
1"
1"
1-7/8"
3/4 x 1-1/4 x 21" WOOD CLEAT
23-1/2 x 27-1/4"
3-1/2 x 27-5/8"
23-1/2" LONG
LAMINATE
LAMINATE EDGING
3/4 x 4" PINE
1" DOWEL LEG FLUSH WITH TOP WHEN STORED
2" SWIVEL BALL PLATE CASTER
DECORATIVE LAMINATE COVERING (CONOLITE)
" SQS.
1-1/8" HOLES
PATTERN
DOTTED LINE INDICATES POSITION OF SNACK TABLE WHEN STORED
DECORATIVE LAMINATE (CONOLITE)
28-7/8"
1-1/8" HOLE
1-1/2"
1" DOWEL 25-5/8" LONG
SIDE VIEW
3/4" PLYWOOD
1-1/8" HOLE 5/8" DEEP
2" BALL PLATE CASTERS

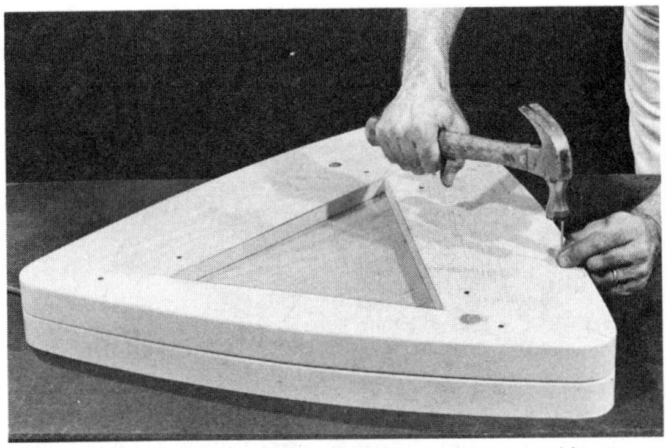

MARK OFF and drill pilot holes through top and bottom at the same time to align dowel holes in the base.

HOLD OFF laminating plywood top until it's glued and nailed to the sides with 2½-in. finishing nails.

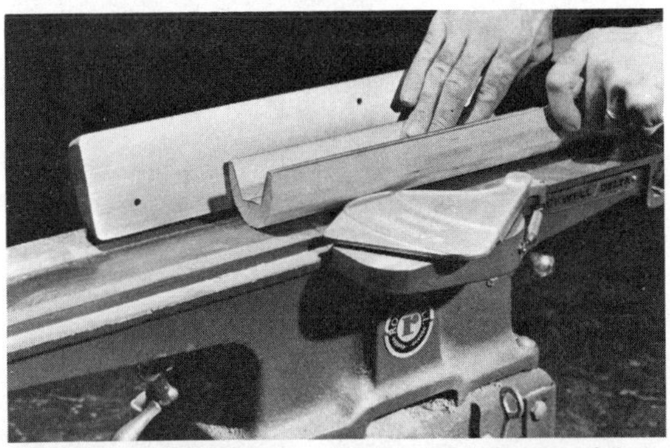

FORM THE TRIM pieces on the jointer, being careful not to trim fingers. Complete shaping with a sander.

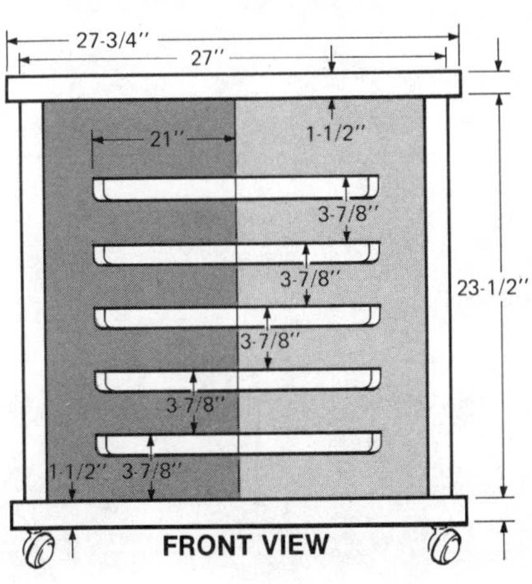

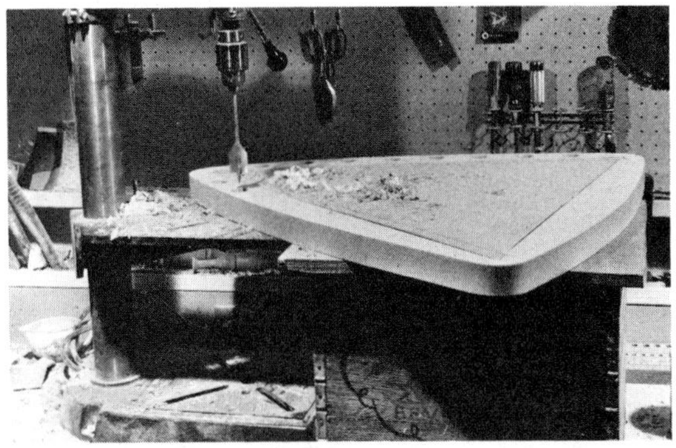

SUPPORT THE HEAVY pieces on drill press for a neat drilling job. Holes in the base are only ⅝ in. deep.

BORE UNDERSIZE holes in plastic covering 1-in. holes, then rout to conform to the diameter of holes below.

through the top. Add the laminate to the side panels.

The reason the plastic is not applied to the top until after final assembly is to permit nailing the top into the sides. Use glue and 2-in. finishing nails. Although the dowel holes are already bored in the top panel, the laminate is applied in a solid piece without attempting to predrill and align the holes. When the top is laminated, simply bore holes just large enough to allow the router bit to penetrate; then rout them to size.

Make the vertical wood trim for the front and back corners by first doing the required inside cuts, followed by a few angled cuts on the table saw. You can further shape them close to size on the jointer by continually changing the angle of the fence. But watch your fingers.

Some tips on painting: Tack lengths of wire to the bottoms of the dowels and hang them on a line for easy spraying semigloss black. Give edges of individual tables a coat of wood sealer before you paint them with a brushing lacquer.

TO HOLD small tools for heat-treating, I add removable extensions to my spring clamps. The holder shown comprises two $^1/_{16}$ x ¾ x 4½-in. steel strips bent to fit the clamp jaws at one end and the workpiece at the other. Drill and tap jaws receive 6-32 screws to hold the "tongs" securely.—*Walter E. Burton, Akron, OH.*

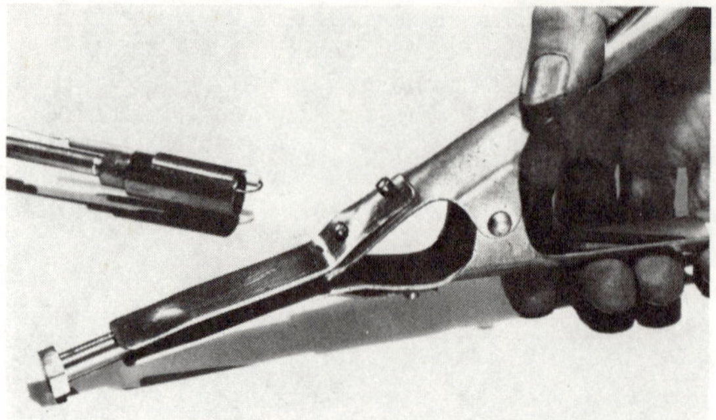

IF YOU'VE EVER forgotten which abrasive grade is on your power sander, you know that the paper has to be removed to check the number. But, by marking the face of the paper with a felt-tip pen, you'll always know grit size and other data such as bond type. I've found the markings usually last the life of the paper.—*John R. Pilznienski, Dearborn Heights, MI.*

YOU CAN PUT a retired felt hat back to use (partially at least) by cutting it into pads, washers and gaskets for home use. At right, a gasket cutter was used to make a neat ring which was then glued to the bottom of a jug to save furniture from scratches. Make certain that glue used works for both porous and nonporous surfaces.—*B.W. Ervin, Kent, OH.*

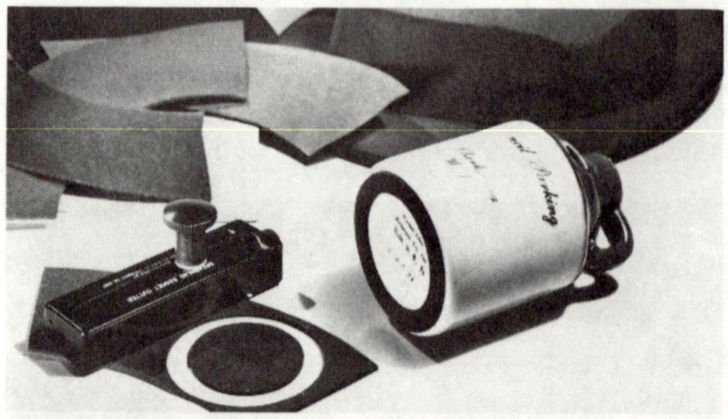

WHEN MAKING irregular cuts in plastic tile, a jeweler's saw often works better than a larger saw with a coarser blade. At left, starter holes were drilled, then the cut was completed with a 4/0 blade. Jeweler's saws and blades are available from sources such as William Dixon, Inc., Carlstadt, N.J. The saw shown is similar to model No. S-1806.—*Walter E. Burton, Akron, OH.*

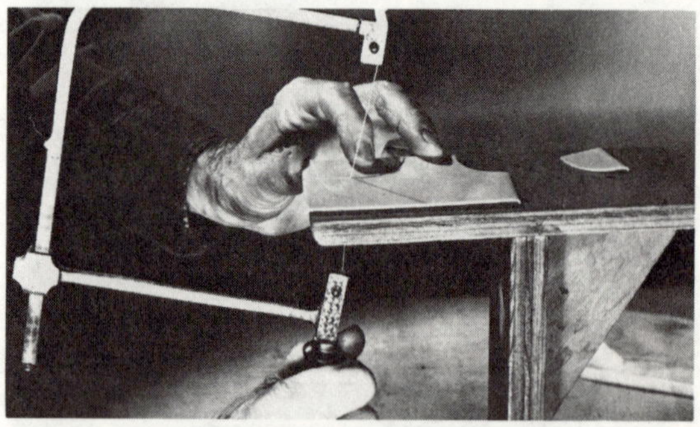

AN EASY-TO-MAKE desk pen and pencil holder can be quickly fashioned from perforated hardboard. Resembling a twistdrill stand, the base is of finished hardboard. Holes drilled at the four corners receive the four $^3/_{16}$x3-in. bolts that hold the setup together. If necessary, ream and enlarge holes for specific items to be parked.—*W.B. May, Oak Park, IL.*

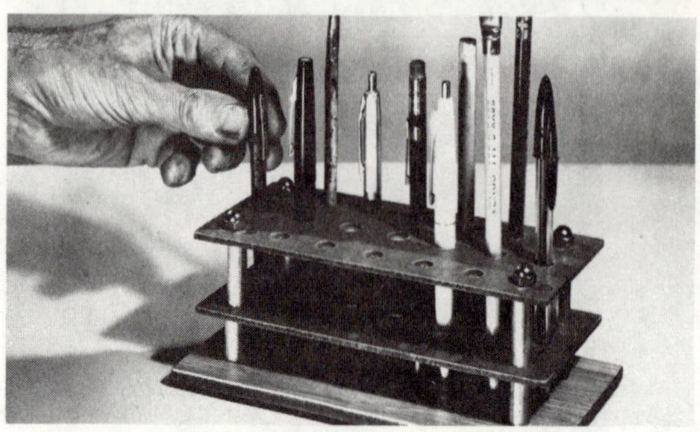

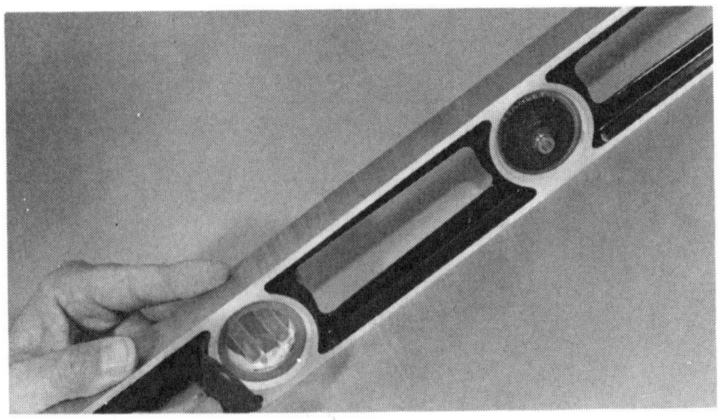

IF YOU CARRY a carpenter's level in your toolbox as most do-it-yourselfers do, there's a good chance a tool will bump it and break the glass over the vials. To protect this glass, which may be irreplaceable, just press a small suction cup to each of the glass surfaces.

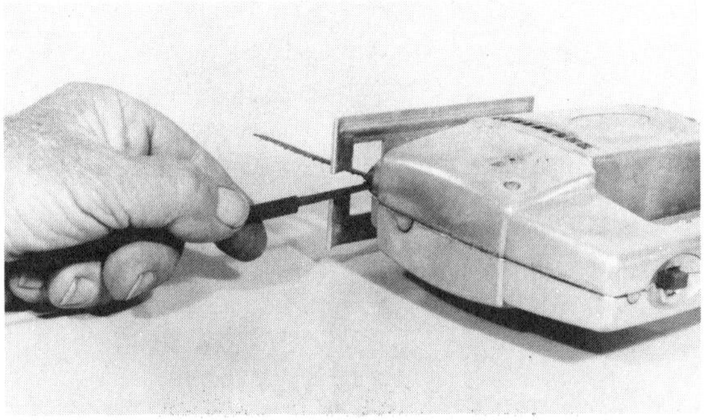

IN A PINCH you can use a three-cornered file as a wrench to tighten or remove a recessed (Allen-head) setscrew. Grind the tang until it fits the setscrew. The handle removed from the tang can be used on the other end of the file. If necessary for a good fit, you can drill a larger hole in the handle.

USING TWO COATHANGERS and a couple of pieces of scrap wood, you can fashion a bird feeder, as shown above. For your own enjoyment, hang the feeder from a clothesline, tree or other support so that feeding birds may be observed from a window. Squeeze ends of the coathangers so that wind won't blow the feeder off.

SEE FOLLOWING PAGE FOR PROJECT-A-PLANS

Project-a-plan

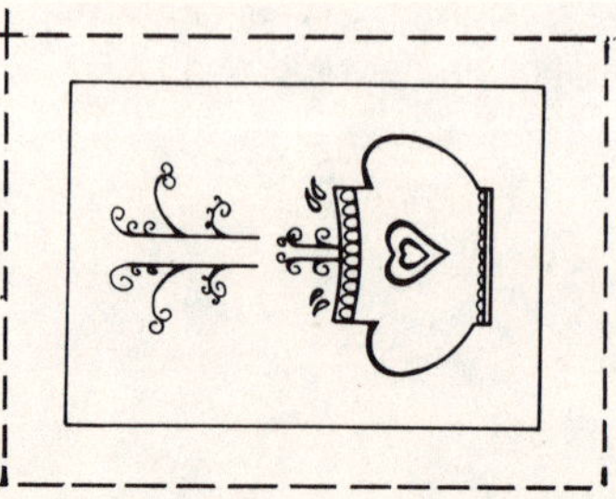

HOW TO USE PROJECT -A-PLAN

1 CUT OUT PROJECT-A-PLAN AND COAT IT WITH VEGETABLE OIL.

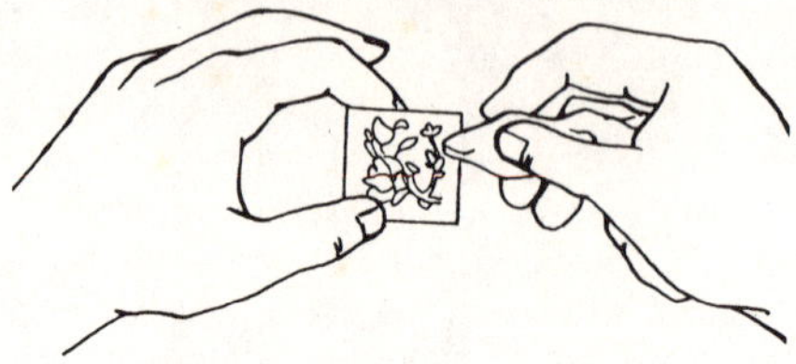

2 INSERT IT INTO A STANDARD 35-MM CARDBOARD SLIDE MOUNT.

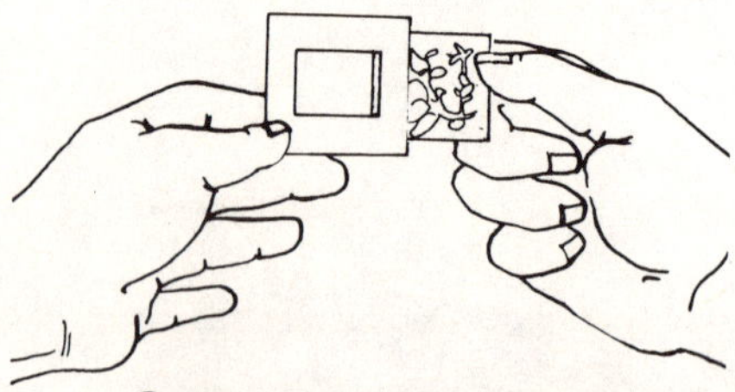

3 PROJECT THE SLIDE ONTO A WALL TO ENLARGE IT FOR TRACING.

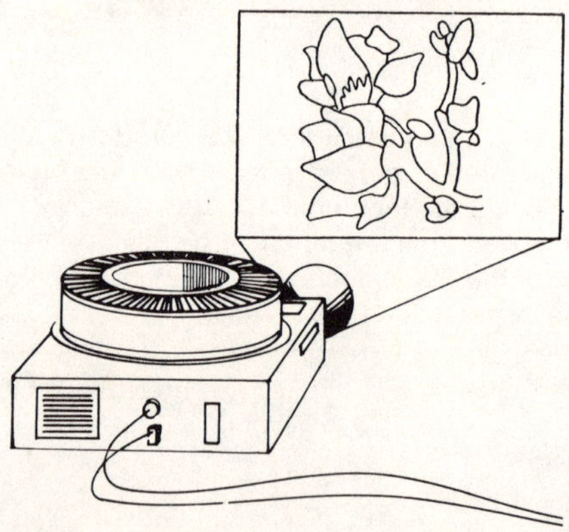

THE PROJECT-A-PLAN method of enlarging a pattern to any size you need is a simple, three-step exercise. First, clip drawings from the page. Coat them with vegetable oil to make the plan 'transparent.' Second, insert the paper "film" into a 35-mm cardboard slide mount available at camera shops. Third, place the slide in a projector and position it the proper distance to get the size plan you want. Trace the plan onto paper fastened to the wall, or directly onto the painted piece.

METRIC CONVERSION

Conversion factors can be carried so far they become impractical. In cases below where an entry is exact it is followed by an asterisk (*). Where considerable rounding off has taken place, the entry is followed by a + or a - sign.

CUSTOMARY TO METRIC

Linear Measure

inches	millimeters
1/16	1.5875*
1/8	3.2
3/16	4.8
1/4	6.35*
5/16	7.9
3/8	9.5
7/16	11.1
1/2	12.7*
9/16	14.3
5/8	15.9
11/16	17.5
3/4	19.05*
13/16	20.6
7/8	22.2
15/16	23.8
1	25.4*

inches	centimeters
1	2.54*
2	5.1
3	7.6
4	10.2
5	12.7*
6	15.2
7	17.8
8	20.3
9	22.9
10	25.4*
11	27.9
12	30.5

feet	centimeters	meters
1	30.48*	.3048*
2	61	.61
3	91	.91
4	122	1.22
5	152	1.52
6	183	1.83
7	213	2.13
8	244	2.44
9	274	2.74
10	305	3.05
50	1524*	15.24*
100	3048*	30.48*

1 yard =
.9144* meters
1 rod =
5.0292* meters
1 mile =
1.6 kilometers
1 nautical mile =
1.852* kilometers

Fluid Measure

(Milliliters [ml] and cubic centimeters [cc or cu cm] are equivalent, but it is customary to use milliliters for liquids.)

1 cu in = 16.39 ml
1 fl oz = 29.6 ml
1 cup = 237 ml
1 pint = 473 ml
1 quart = 946 ml
= .946 liters
1 gallon = 3785 ml
= 3.785 liters
Formula (exact):
fluid ounces × 29.573 529 562 5*
= milliliters

Weights

ounces	grams
1	28.3
2	56.7
3	85
4	113
5	142
6	170
7	198
8	227
9	255
10	283
11	312
12	340
13	369
14	397
15	425
16	454

Formula (exact):
ounces × 28.349 523 125* = grams

pounds	kilograms
1	.45
2	.9
3	1.4
4	1.8
5	2.3
6	2.7
7	3.2
8	3.6
9	4.1
10	4.5

1 short ton (2000 lbs) =
907 kilograms (kg)
Formula (exact):
pounds × .453 592 37* = kilograms

Volume

1 cu in = 16.39 cubic centimeters (cc)
1 cu ft = 28 316.7 cc
1 bushel = 35 239.1 cc
1 peck = 8 809.8 cc

Area

1 sq in = 6.45 sq cm
1 sq ft = 929 sq cm
= .093 sq meters
1 sq yd = .84 sq meters
1 acre = 4 046.9 sq meters
= .404 7 hectares
1 sq mile = 2 589 988 sq meters
= 259 hectares
= 2.589 9 sq kilometers

Kitchen Measure

1 teaspoon = 4.93 milliliters (ml)
1 Tablespoon = 14.79 milliliters (ml)

Miscellaneous

1 British thermal unit (Btu) (mean)
= 1 055.9 joules
1 calorie (mean) = 4.19 joules
1 horsepower = 745.7 watts
= .75 kilowatts
caliber (diameter of a firearm's bore in hundredths of an inch)
= .254 millimeters (mm)
1 atmosphere pressure = 101 325* pascals (newtons per sq meter)
1 pound per square inch (psi) =
6 895 pascals
1 pound per square foot =
47.9 pascals
1 knot = 1.85 kilometers per hour
25 miles per hour = 40.2 kilometers per hour
50 miles per hour = 80.5 kilometers per hour
75 miles per hour = 120.7 kilometers per hour